HICAGO PUBLIC LIBRARY
JSINESS / SCIENCE / TECHNOLOGY
0 S. STATE ST.   60605

W9-APU-249

CHICAGO PUBLIC LIBRARY
HAROLD WASHINGTON LIBRARY CENTER

R0021767489

Too Many

Also by GEORG BORGSTROM

The Hungry Planet
Principles of Food Science

GEORG BORGSTROM

Too Many

*A Study of Earth's
Biological Limitations*

THE MACMILLAN COMPANY
COLLIER-MACMILLAN LTD. / *LONDON*

HD
9000.5
.B542

Copyright © 1969 by Georg Borgstrom
Copyright © 1969 by The Macmillan Company

All rights reserved. No part of this book may be reproduced or transmitted
in any form or by any means, electronic or mechanical, including photo-
copying, recording or by any information storage and retrieval system, without permission in writing from the Publisher.

Library of Congress Catalog Card Number: 69-10639

First Printing

The Macmillan Company
Collier-Macmillan Canada Ltd., Toronto, Ontario

Printed in the United States of America

THE CHICAGO PUBLIC LIBRARY

MAR 26 '70 D

R0021767489

CHICAGO PUBLIC LIBRARY
BUSINESS / SCIENCE / TECHNOLOGY
400 S. STATE ST.   60605

Contents

v

Figures

vii

Tables

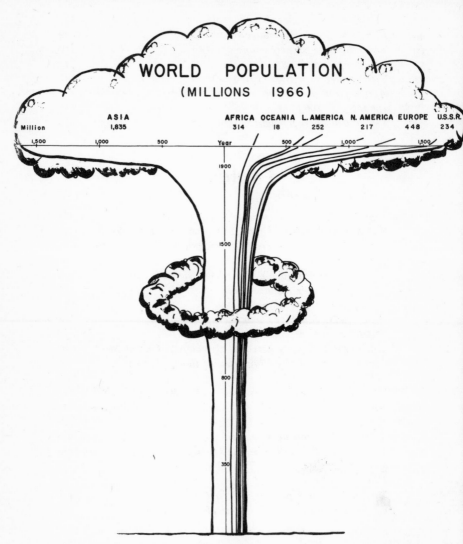

Fig. 1. The growth of world population since the time of Christ from about 250 million to above 3,000 million in the 1960s. The vertical line indicates years, with the base point at the time of Christ, and the horizontal line the number of people in millions. Note the dramatic explosion in the twentieth century and the growing preponderance for Asia.

Preface

Words like *limitless, inexhaustible*, and *boundless* figure prominently in the present debate about the earth and its resources. They are persistently used despite the fact that they would not exist in a Dictionary of Nature. The propagandists utilize them with increasing frequency, as if anxious to prevent the human masses from realizing the truth about Man's own existence and the earth's limitations. But facts are stubborn things. Sooner or later they break into the open and assert themselves, forcing man to make harsh accommodations to reality. The circus acts then get stripped of their luster. The bluff is called and the swindle unveiled. Rather than a rich, well-fed and abundant world, excruciating poverty, widespread hunger, and debilitating diseases emerge.

When the embellishing veils are ripped away, we discern a grim and ugly reality, rapidy encroaching upon the enclaves of the privileged few. Basically there are not many oases left in a vast, almost worldwide network of slums; about 450 million well-fed people living in comparative luxury (the United States, Canada, parts of western Europe, Australia, New Zealand, and the La Plata countries in South America) as against 2,400 million undernourished, malnourished, or in other ways deficiently fed and generally poor (most critical areas are Asia, Africa, and Latin

America, with a total population exceeding two billion). Many living in the rich world, even the United States and Europe, are also hungry. The in-between group of about 650 million (Soviet Union, eastern and southern Europe, and Japan belong here) keep up a running battle to hold their chins over the waterline in a mounting ocean of misery.

In this book are discussed some of the biological limitations that face man, especially in his efforts to secure food for an ever-mounting number of humans. Unfortunately, that era when the task was only catering to the needs of millions belongs to the past. The acceleration in the rate of population growth is, in effect, the most ominous feature of our day. And some of the consequences are inevitable even if a fully efficient and indispensable birth control system can be implemented immediately. All data are affected by this development and constantly change, but practically in every instance for the worse. Therefore, data should not be looked upon as absolute figures but as indications of the order of magnitude involved in each particular happening. It is, for example, an issue of rather academic nature whether China grows by fifteen or twenty million a year, India by ten or fifteen million; it is the order of magnitude that counts, and that is in both cases catastrophic in consequences. However, in order to make my presentation as up-to-date as possible and valid in the present situation, most figures are—when nothing to the contrary is indicated—based upon the latest statistics available.

This book constitutes a sequel to my book *The Hungry Planet* (1965, 1967). In most chapters an effort has been made to report on potentials to improve the food situation for mankind that have so far been little exploited or not put to serve the hungry. It should, however, be kept in mind that none of these alternatives can be the sole remedy; none holds out a promise for miracles. Nor can man expect the biological limitations for his existence to be eliminated or pushed back in any major way.

This book covers man's efforts to exploit more fully the freshwater resources of the globe. The large-scale mobilization of the oceans is only briefly alluded to, since this whole topic was extensively discussed in *The Hungry Planet*. Brief reference is made, however, to current experimentation with transferring fish cultivation to ocean areas. Sea farming is a distant goal, but the initiating phase of what is termed *mariculture* is quite exciting. It constitutes, however, no single remedy to the world's food crisis. Each major achievement on the food front is just one partial contribution to a gigantic challenge.

The immediate gains, which are attainable, are above all a more equitable distribution of the resources of the earth, less squandering by the rich and well-fed nations, improved technical aid, and more appropriate advice to needy and impoverished people. We can certainly not continue our present irresponsible gamble with the world's dwindling resources. Nor can we expect that they shall remain the monopoly of a minor percentage of the human race. The current space adventures and energy playworks on a megaton scale stand out as the acme of irresponsibility to any human who is to the slightest degree concerned about the future of mankind. Such waste of the brain resources and capital assets of the world, as well as our blind and aimless toying, can only be branded large-scale sabotage of the progressive work which must constitute the goal for all human endeavors. A prerequisite for a "New Deal for mankind" is knowledge about the highly tangible limits of our spaceship Earth—the biological limitations for man's existence. The aim of this book is to contribute to man's awareness and knowledge of these facts, so fundamental to human survival and to the future of civilization.

I am greatly indebted to my talented and indefatigable wife, Greta, for help in preparing the manuscript of this treatise. Her concerned interest in the plight of man and her genuine desire to kindle a better recognition of the urgency and nature of his dilemma have been of inestimable value to the wording of the text as well as to the perseverance of the author. My gratitude is also extended to the many faithful typists, in particular Mrs. Sue Janssen, who have struggled through my handwriting and dictations. I am also most anxious to acknowledge the aid and unswerving interest shown by the staff at all divisions of the Michigan State University library.

GEORG BORGSTROM

East Lansing, Michigan, November 1968

Too Many

CHAPTER I

The Forest and
the Field in an Ominous
Confrontation

Soil-protecting Forests

At the end of the Second World War, when the United States occupation authorities were confronted with the feeding of Japan's
burgeoning population, they recommended among other measures
the plowing of additional land at the expense of the forests. Less
than eighty years earlier, in the expansionist ravings of the Meiji
Era, the forests had been ruthlessly taxed to the immediate detriment of forest economy, water balance, and industrial development.
As a direct consequence of that deforestation devastating floods
hit the country. Out of these bitter experiences Japan's model
forest protection laws emerged, against which the occupation power
launched its attack, partly out of despair. It was early recognized
that the West had precious little to teach the Japanese as regards
agricultural growing techniques. The yields per acre from the
small, intensely cultivated plots, called farms, were even higher
than those of western Europe, which in turn far surpass United
States figures.

Natural and commercial fertilizers were applied in quantities
greatly exceeding what was being practiced in the West. The clue
to Japan's high and fairly stable yields was the dependable water
supply, regularly replenished through precipitation. Forests act

not only as catchers and holders of water, but as protectors of the watershed areas, regulating runoff. The forest clearing in Japan started in 1945, but soon had to be stopped, since the ground-water level fell rapidly, and serious erosion set in, not only in the cleared areas, but in a far more devastating way in the growing areas, under the impact of massive water release from the catchment regions. Further clearing had to be canceled, and the provincial forest protection laws were reinstated. These should in effect be a model to the entire world, including North America.

The Crisis of China

The Japanese development provides a telling contrast to the forest crisis of China. The absence of forests in the coreland of this gigantic country has its roots three thousand years back. Already in the famous era of the bronze vases, when the water buffalo was domesticated, China in effect committed its great ecological blunder of cutting down the forest in order to gain agricultural land. The stage was then set for the catastrophic floods which in recurrent sequences wrought havoc upon the country for centuries to come. Heavy downpours were no longer caught and stored in the soil. The rainfall rushed headlong into the nearest riverbed. This created the basic conditions for large scale erosion, which admittedly gave China its rich loess soils and a kind of airborne fertilizing, but on the other side inflicted greater losses by wind and water erosion of the soils. The winds gained greater momentum when not impeded by the forests and their trees. And this is further explanation why droughts became so serious. There were no water reserves. Forests are nowadays recognized as an effective way of ensuring a regulated and more controllable water supply to the catchment areas. Furthermore the silt load of the huge Chinese rivers became excessive—they still carry more silt than all other rivers in the world together. This silt and dirt was deposited on the plains and gradually elevated the riverbeds, increasing the risk of flooding. Some silt was carried by the rivers into the sea, and this still happens. This has a fertilizing effect to the benefit of coastal fisheries, which are exceptionally rich.

Many times in its history China has tried to restore the water balance through large-scale reforestation, but each time the population pressure has defeated the endeavor. It takes an iron will to put millions of acres under forest cover in order to secure the sustenance of future generations when every acre is currently needed to feed those now living. Not even the Chinese, with their deep

THE EARTH

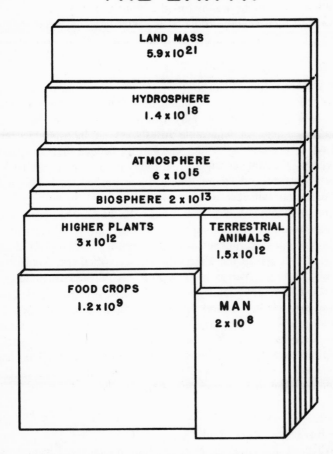

Fig. 2. The weight of the various spheres of the earth as a globe (in metric tons). The biosphere is subdivided into higher plants and animals. Food crops constitute a major portion of the vegetation. Man is naturally part of the animal sphere.

reverence for the sequence of generations, have succeeded too well in these undertakings. At present new efforts are being made along this line. All along the famed Chinese Wall a continuous forest belt is reportedly being created to prevent the dry and chilly highland winds from sweeping across the country into the coreland. The purported aim is to catch and store more precipitation. The main difficulty in these planting operations is finding ways of providing adequate water for the young, newly planted forest trees with their shallow roots. It is easier later on, when the trees are well established and the roots can search deeply to find water.

The Deforestation of Europe

Tacitus, the celebrated Roman historian, depicted—during the first century A.D.—the marshy transalpine European Continent, with its endless, impenetrable forests, as an inhospitable region indeed. A present-day reader can hardly believe that Tacitus was describing the same continent that today is suffering under pressing water shortage and where the forest is pushed back into a few isolated mountain regions covering only a small percentage of the entire continental area. The forests of the British Isles, which aroused so much awe among the conquering armies of the Romans, soon disappeared in subsequent centuries. This deforestation reached its peak in the sixteenth century, when the threat of the Spanish Armada had to be met. For this purpose England's own forests were actually inadequate, and the British were forced to go to western Norway to find timber for shipbuilding purposes. This distant land was then stripped of its fine forests. The soils were lost when they were exposed to eroding winds and rain and the rock laid bare. It still remains so. In a similar way, the karst landscapes on the Adriatic were formed, as a consequence of forest stripping. Iron-making was another forest-devouring force.

The Ravages of the Colonizers

When, in the sixteenth century, Spain implemented what may be called its great plan for the underdeveloped countries of that epoch, it applied the deforestation technique in several regions, among them Mexico. Huge acreages were lost in the process. This laid the foundation for the water crisis which now holds that country in its iron grip. A similar attack upon nature by Western Man was the annihilation through fire and other means of the rich forests which covered the New Zealand islands. Almost fifteen million acres (almost twice the tilled acreage of Michigan or Sweden) were stripped by the Scotch immigrants in order to gain pastures similar to those of the homeland, with the sole purpose of providing the Yorkshire factories back in England with wool. The erosion on the two main islands has nowadays taken on such dimensions that not even the big returns from the present food exports would suffice to reverse the process. The costs for the necessary soil repair would exceed the net gains. The gamble therefore goes on until it will be brought to a halt by reality itself. It is a great pity that Samuel Butler, the antagonist of Darwin, in discussing his New Zealand impressions in the brilliant satire *The Way of All Flesh* (1903), did not lambaste the human vandals instead of the innocent sheep!

A Lost Empire and Other Tragedies

Many an author has described the dense forests that once covered the North American continent. Fiction writers as well as ecologists have depicted man in those forests as if embraced by the ocean, where one cannot see very far and has a feeling of being abandoned, always surrounded by the enormous forests like the fish by the water masses. Conrad Richter in *The Trees*, the second volume of his famous triology about the America of the pioneers, gives an excellent interpretation of this feeling of forlornness. This tremendous forest empire, presumably unique on the globe, now belongs to history. It was doomed not only by the search for arable land but also through sheer profit hunger. Besides, in the eyes of the white settlers, the forest constituted an enemy. They burnt the forests or pulled them down to create open space around the homesteads and townships, and the destruction frequently took on vandalistic proportions. *Burning an Empire* is the title of a book depicting this onslaught. Man in his arrogance believed that the forests were limitless. No other continent was subject to a devastation of such magnitude or over such a brief time span. Truly no less than an empire was lost. Still today, when traveling along the highways of central Michigan, the stubs are discernible as sad evidence of the strip-logging around the turn of the century.

Many more examples could be brought forth to illustrate the ominous large-scale deforestation: on the Roman *campagna,* the Mexican highlands, in Spain, Greece, the Near East, North Africa, and India. Over the centuries the forests were pulled down in all these regions, removed far beyond reasonable limits, and primarily to gain arable land. Even in our own days this devastation continues. Forests, which may take many decades to grow, are pulled

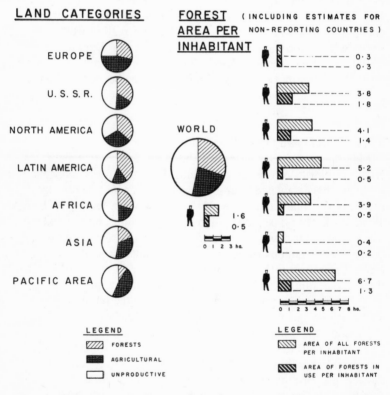

Fig. 3. The forest resources of the continents in hectares (c. 2.5 acres) per individual (approximate figures for 1960). The two overpopulated areas of the world, Asia and Europe, are extremely short. The global potential is seemingly large, but with the exception of the U.S.S.R. little accessible.

down in a few years. Large parts of Brazil, particularly in the northeast, where the energy consumption until very recently was based almost exclusively on wood, were stripped of forest within a single generation. This is part of the explanation for the terrible droughts which recurrently have plagued the Brazilian northeast, the so-called Hump. The tragedy of drought, famine, and suffering in this region was seriously aggravated by man and not the least in this very century. As late as in 1900 the statistics reveal that the Hump was covered with forest as much as 40 to 50 percent; now this figure is down below 5 percent. The present plan is to remedy the situation by building irrigation systems at the cost of two billion dollars, which possibly may give 625,000 acres of irrigated land. It is commendable that such projects are undertaken, but it is not to our credit when we believe that such costly remedial measures are adequate. The ecological balance needs complete redress, and reforestation must be a part of any such program.

A long list could be made of islands around the world where the forests have fallen victim to overpopulation. In eloquent metaphors, poets and prose writers have described such paradises of lush vegetation and many-voiced bird choirs. These oases have in far too many instances been transformed into silent abodes of hell, where the sun shines mercilessly upon ever-growing masses of people. Mauritius, Cape Verde Islands, the Seychelles, Puerto Rico, Jamaica, and Saint Helena are but a few among these lost Edens.

We have taken precious little cognizance of the lessons of history. On the contrary, the pressing population increase has by and large accelerated the deforestation. In vain hope of keeping pace with a population growth already of Malthusian dimensions, *i.e.,* doubling within twenty-five years, man in many parts of the globe is engaged in obliterating the last vestiges of forest.

The Forests Render Farmland

Not only carelessness, profiteering, and ignorance lead to the present situation. In many cases the battle for daily bread forced man to clear the land. At excavations in many parts of central Europe, Scandinavia, and Latin America, charcoal is encountered. This is telling evidence from bygone centuries of the practice of shifting cultivation. The burning of the forest gave rich mineral nutrition to the soil. This was cultivated as long as yields remained satisfactory. The land was then abandoned and new clearings made.

With the mounting population pressure, this type of seminomadic agriculture became impracticable. Transition to permanent settlement became adamant. Thus some of the largest agricultural regions of the globe were created and have repeatedly been enlarged to provide for ever-growing numbers. Only after the major part of accessible and reasonably fertile forest land was taken was intense cultivation of the soil with fertilizing, irrigation, etc., forced upon man.

With considerable justification, the transfer from a primitive nomadic existence to controlled plant production and animal husbandry has been praised as one of man's greatest achievements. At this stage man's attack on the wilderness was initiated. With fire and hatchet the forests were cleared. The immense grasslands of the globe were taken into possession, grazed, and then plowed: the North American prairie, the South American pampa, the South African veld, and the endless Australian grasslands. Through large-scale drainage, central Europe was made habitable for man.

The first stage in this conquest, the cultivation of the huge river deltas of the world, was quite different in character. This was largely achieved in harmony with nature, but the subsequent crusade for man's survival rather resembled a large-scale military operation. The forest, the grass, and the plants of the marshes were visualized as arch enemies and made the subject of ruthless extermination. The modest beginning with shifting cultivation and small-plot farming soon assumed continental dimensions.

Water-regulating Tasks

The large-scale reforestation presently taking place in the U.S.S.R. is sometimes referred to in our newspapers. Chekhov's famous play *The Cherry Orchard* (1904) constitutes a chronicle of the strip-logging epoch in southern Russia, when the forests in that region were considerably reduced. Interestingly enough, the present-day efforts to restore them, at least partly, are basically dictated by a desire to improve the conditions for agriculture. As already mentioned, the forest—though itself an important consumer of water—is a great catcher of snow and rain trickling slowly down the stems and gently seeping into the soil. Soviet studies claim that the water content of the steppe soils is elevated in the soil around tree groves and forest belts to the benefit of bordering farmlands and their productivity.

The forest not only protects the soil on which it grows. Indirectly it also shields adjacent agricultural regions from desiccating winds and their erosive results. The forest catches more driving rain, thereby slowing down the runoff and forcing the soil to absorb more of the water. Forest areas furthermore hold water for gradual release at a slower rate. Admittedly, the forest consumes, for its own production and basically through the transpiration of the trees, large quantities of water, but experience shows that surprisingly enough, the net result is often a positive rather than negative balance. In addition, forests provide windbreaks, and thus prevent the desiccation of plants and protect cattle and other livestock from excessive dehydration. The establishment of shelter belts gave reported yield gains of around 25 percent for oats in the U.S.S.R., for grass pastures in Jylland (Denmark), and for potatoes in Germany.

In many regions trees are needed to stabilize cropping by averting disastrous wind erosion (through reducing wind velocities) and preventing devastating floods (through lowering the rate of runoff) more than they are needed to provide for the local necessities of fuel and timber. The break in the winds also diminishes evaporation. In many parts of the world, therefore, reforestation is a basic prerequisite for dependable agriculture. It makes more likely the attaining of an acceptable nutritional standard for the more than one billion people in different parts of the globe now suffering the consequences of previous deforestations.

The changed ecological conditions also affect crop-attacking insects and fungi, in most instances reducing the hazards of large-scale devastation. The woodlands provide an abode for predators that control the pests of the fields. Some fungous diseases seem, however, to thrive better on the leeside of shelters than in open fields.

The Role of the Forest

The role of the forest may be summed up as follows. In several instances considerable soil acreages are threatened with destruction through sustained cropping. Exhaustion and mineral depletion, together with desiccation, favor erosion. The soils can be saved for future benefit to mankind only by the planting of trees. Many parts of the underdeveloped world are in effect overpopulated and suffer in addition from a scarcity of forests. To these regions, Freedom from Hunger will always remain an empty phrase if the forests are not restored as the chief means of protecting the soil against destructive winds and rain. In addition they regulate the water flow and provide fuel. The forests must be given the care and management now given to sustained crops. Legislation must be universally instituted and knowledge disseminated on how to protect them from fire and ruinous exploitation. Reforestation measures, on a scale never before dreamt of, must be initiated without delay. Forest values must be created on present wastelands in order to restore, gradually, millions of acres of damaged farmland.

The capability of the forest to catch water and regulate its flow is in some parts being looked upon, not as a blessing, but as a luxury one can no longer afford. In several instances man has narrowed down the basis for his existence to such an extent that he can no longer deprive himself of the water that rapidly runs off from stripped areas. For this very reason strong opposition frequently arises even to very moderate plans for reforestation.

A case in point is the prairie states of the western United States, where in many regions forceful criticism has been raised against reforestation projects involving the upper watershed areas of the rivers, due to the simple fact that the agriculture of the plains has become so dependent on the water falling over the Rocky Mountains reaching their lands without undue losses. Every drop of water is desperately needed to sustain production on the farms or ranches. *Nothing* can be sacrificed to restore the forest cover in the watershed area and thus put a halt to the carrying away of soil and sand.

In the same way, Spain cannot afford to allow the forest to regain its hold on the *meseta,* the central high plateau of the Iberian peninsula. The majority of the hydroelectric plants along the rim of the high plateau have been erected on the basis of a calculated runoff from the plateau. Hence water-grabbing and water-robbing forest cannot be allowed to infringe upon the volume of the hydroelectric dams and jeopardize their operations.

Tropical Forests

Much glib talk centers around the gigantic and lush forests of the tropics. But few, even among the experts, seem to realize what a false Eldorado these are, or rather, how genially these forests are adjusted to their ecological environment; how they pump up nutrients to their crowns from deep soil layers and later return them to the surface through the shedding of leaves or through rain-leaching. Every travel book tells about how pleasantly cool the climate is inside these forests. This also contributes to the protection of the soil under the canopy of the large trees, allowing certain crops to grow. Extensive studies have been made of these conditions, the most comprehensive and convincing ones by Belgian scientists in the Congo. Their findings provide an explanation of why so much valuable soil was lost when such forests were ruthlessly pulled down over huge areas and the earth laid bare to the scorching sun. Soil temperatures rose by up to thirty centigrades (94°F), which killed all living organisms, including the many microbes of various kinds without which the soil cannot function properly. Still worse was the fact that the humus, *i.e.,* the organic substances of the soil, rapidly disappeared. Then the soil became an easy victim of heavy rains, or the opposite, extreme desiccation. In both instances the topsoil was carried away on a major scale.

In such regions shifting cultivation is still today highly recommended and seems to offer the best potential for sustaining the soils. The following procedures were employed in the Congo forests: Long, narrow strips of tilled land were created in east-to-west direction for maximum utilization of the sunlight. After three to five years these strips were abandoned and the forest allowed to move in. New strips were cleared and plowed in the "virgin" forests. In any case, one thing is sure: Our type of agriculture is not successful or even feasible under these tropical conditions.

Extensive areas along the Amazon River are, in the rain period, nothing but marshy land. On the whole, drainage is inconceivable due to the minute gradients in the downflow. The chances of using agricultural machinery in these regions are very limited. For the vast expanses watered by the Amazon the idea has therefore been launched to plant oil palms or other commodity-producing tree crops, to be harvested by blimps from the air. Such projects belong entirely in the realm of speculation and have nothing to do with reality.

The Forest Reserve

In the densely inhabited and intensely cultivated parts of the globe, there is no forest left of any significance. Despite improved utilization, North America's forests, including those of the Canadian reserve, have great difficulties filling the enormous needs of the two countries (6½ percent of world population), largely created by modern technological demands. The global situation may be summed up in the following way: Three regions, *viz.,* Europe, the Far East and North America, require more timber than their forests presently are capable of producing through annual growth. One-third of mankind, those living in Europe, the U.S.S.R., North America, and Oceania, use up 83 percent of the world's lumber and 90 percent of its paper pulp. North Africa and the Middle East together have only seventy-five million acres (thirty million hectares) of forest, which is totally inadequate for their present population, rapidly growing in numbers. They must cover their most pressing needs from Europe. This situation is an unfortunate consequence of the forest devastation that began four thousand years ago in North Africa.

Besides Canada and Scandinavia, which still possess some relatively small forest reserves, the U.S.S.R. is for all practical purposes the only country with an important reserve, and this is an era when mankind is growing by hundreds of millions in a few years. Its five billion acres (two million hectares) of registered forest land is, however, located dangerously close to the northern limit for forest growth. The annual increase is very small, and a large portion of the trees is overage and afflicted with diseases.

Asia has hardly any forest left, in any case only a trifle in relation to the needs of its two billion people; the desperate need for food has become the sole dictator in utilizing the soil. The pulling down of the African forests goes on at an accelerated tempo and largely by foreign exploiters. The desiccation of East Africa is largely caused by this gradual disappearance of the forest.

Will the Forest Suffice?

The United States holds the world record in per capita use of forest products. Each American is richly endowed with forest land —about three acres (1.2 hectares)—accessible to economic utilization despite large scale deforestation since the continent was opened up by the pioneering Europeans. But present forest yields are wholly inadequate to support the extravagant consumption of paper and timber. Forest products are therefore imported—primarily from Canada and to some degree from Middle America, Africa, and Scandinavia—corresponding in volume to two acres of forest land per American. Reforestation in the United States is presently not keeping up with the annual outtake, the net loss amounting to approximately one-half acre annually per person. All in all, there are less than 270 million people of the world's 3,500 million who enjoy a luxury of forest land comparable to that of the U.S.S.R. and Scandinavia; Sweden has about 7.5 acres per individual. Most people in the world are limited to one-tenth of that figure or less. More than 1,000 million have only one-fiftieth of 7.5 acres, or 0.15 acre (0.06 hectare). There is simply not enough forest for the majority of the people on the globe.

GLOBAL PAPER PULP CONSUMPTION (1963–64)

Total 80.11 million metric tons

	PULP CONSUMPTION		WORLD POPULATION	
	PERCENT	Σ	PERCENT	Σ
U.S.A.	38.4		5.8	
Europe	27.4	65.8	13.7	19.5
Canada	14.9	80.7	0.7	20.2
Japan	6.6	87.3	3.0	23.2
U.S.S.R.	4.9	92.2	6.9	30.1
Latin America	2.9	95.1	7.1	37.2
Others	4.9	100.0	62.8	100.0

Two-thirds of the world pulp is used by less than one-fifth of the world population.

It is sheer irony to talk about freedom of expression, of libraries, newspapers, and universal literacy without first having secured forest land adequate to provide for these primary needs. Unfortunately, the simple truth is that mankind has already grown far beyond any reasonable boundaries. Priority has long been given to the food needs at the expense of the forest, and this to such a degree that—as I have tried to illustrate above—the production capacity of the tilled lands themselves is being jeopardized. In many climatic regions the soil needs the forest protection of its watersheds. Let us therefore put an end to the fable that the forests in addition are going to take over the feeding burden as such. The tasks of the forest are already overwhelming; it can not in addition be charged with the responsibility of feeding the burgeoning millions. To produce food from wood is a fascinating piece of magic, but it does not constitute a realistic project for conquering world hunger, unless restricted to converting waste such as lignin, etc.

The Forest Gave Food

Aside from the fact that a great deal of forest land has been used as pastures, the forests have in effect throughout the centuries rendered significant contributions to man's food larder. This does not refer to the direct cultivation of such tree crops as oil palms, olive trees, and fruit trees, nor to the gathering of wild mushrooms and berries—which in many countries used to, and in some cases still does, provide supplementary food—but to the forest trees as such.

Experts have even questioned whether, in historical perspective, the human race has not eaten more acorns than wheat grain. To early generations of Europeans acorns were a provider of flour, not to speak of the California Indians for which they were a mainstay of life. As late as 1945, when World War II ended, the schoolchildren of Japan were mobilized to gather more than one million metric tons of acorns for the making of flour. For centuries the beech forests of central Europe served the hog raising, and are still used in this way in marginal areas. Chestnuts constitute a similar food resource, particularly in Spain and Italy. In Siberia the cones of a Siberian cembra pine are still being harvested. The seeds are threshed out and used for food purposes; even "milk" is produced from the edible nuts.[1] American Indians of the arid Southwest still collect seeds of certain small pine trees. They were for long their staple diet. Today such cone seeds are marketed as piñole nuts. Peoples of the northern latitudes, both in America and Eurasia, often resorted to the nutritional reserves of the tree cortex, from which they made a powder as an extender in the flour for bread-making. But all this belongs to an era when human needs were still reasonably limited. To feed the needy billions of today and tomorrow, such makeshift solutions are no longer applicable, even as emergency measures.

The Limitations of the Forest

Man's conquest of forest land has been partly a necessity. To create agriculture was on the whole possible only by taking forest and grassland. The criticism cannot therefore be directed against these measures as such, but against the permanent denudation and massive topsoil destruction that in many instances have accompanied these operations throughout the history of man. It is important that man becomes fully aware of the causal forces involved as described above. Only in this way can the precarious nature of man's present dilemma as related to the forests be grasped. Otherwise it is very hard to understand why the multifarious world of living beings, having been deprived of their natural domicile and habitat, attack man's conquered domains. These hostile forces regroup and launch their attacks against crops and livestock. Man is, however, not only the intruder—he also offers new feeding opportunities for these marauders. No wonder that nature strikes back and mankind is living under a permanent threat, which rather than diminishing in force, seems to be growing in intensity as man pushes his domain further. This line of thought is further expounded in Chapter V, "Man's Competitors for Food," which presents several examples of this process.

A sober appraisal of this battle, which since time immemorial has probably raged between forest and field, should make it clear that there are highly concrete limitations to our biological existence. The forest is no longer limitless. Current speculations

[1] M. Hindus, *House Without a Roof* (New York: Doubleday & Company, Inc., 1961), p. 465.

about how to feed the future billions from forest waste, or even through direct forest culture, neglect the obvious fact that presently accessible forests are desperately required for a whole range of other needs. The debate about the forests, and their future as a potential feeding reserve for mankind, is still more dubious, since the forests by and large have been mobilized and actually serve what might be called the world's Luxury Club, *i.e.*, some 450 million well-fed people. Most prognoses of the future of the forests

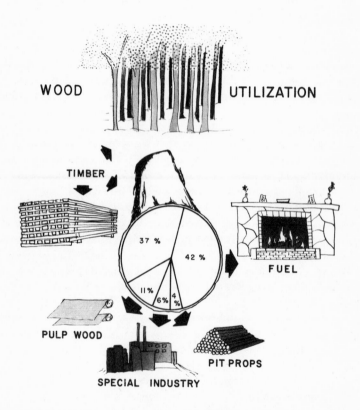

WOOD UTILIZATION

TIMBER

37 %

42 %

FUEL

11 %

6 %

4 %

PULP WOOD

SPECIAL INDUSTRY

PIT PROPS

Fig. 4. Close to half (42 percent) of the world's wood resources are still used for fuel purposes. The graph (average 1958–64) indicates the percentage moving into construction, pulp, paper, pitprops, and special industries. This graph does not take in the 30 to 50 percent of the standing stock that is removed in the harvesting and extraction of the timber and lumber.

take it for granted that this unequal distribution of the world's riches will in some peculiar way remain the pattern of the future. It is, however, a serious fallacy to believe that a peaceful development of the world is possible if its resources are not shared in a more equitable way. Can anyone reasonably defend that one-seventh of the world's population continues to consume close to six-sevenths of what its forests are yielding?

Fuel from the Forest

At least two-thirds of mankind still uses wood as fuel for cooking purposes. The trees, therefore, have both directly and indirectly played a decisive role in world feeding. In many parts of the Far East the inadequate forest resources not only create a serious scarcity of wood for fuel and lumber for timber but affect agricultural production in a detrimental way. The rural population is forced to use as fuel agricultural waste and cattle dung, both of which should be returned to the soils. According to estimates made in Greece and India, the per-acre yields of these countries would probably increase by more than one-tenth if an improved agriculture with composting were introduced. This would be feasible only if the fuel needs could be met in some other way. If we are going to create a world free from starvation, we have to replant forests, protect those we have, and introduce a more rational management as well as a wiser utilization of this important natural resource.

Through good management we will undoubtedly get improved forests as well as larger yields per acre, even though this in many regions will necessitate artificial fertilizing. In the end the forest is faced with the same limitations as the crop production of the tilled land. In a literal sense the old saying that "the trees do not grow to the sky" is applicable in this context.

CHAPTER II

Will Chemistry
Offer Mankind
the Third Freedom?

In a major speech to the United States Congress in January, 1941, President Franklin D. Roosevelt summarized the main objectives of man's strivings as a struggle for Four Freedoms: (1) Freedom of Expression, (2) Freedom of Religion, (3) Freedom from Want, and (4) Freedom from Fear. These ideas constituted major guidelines for the Atlantic Charter, proclaimed later that year as a formulation of the goals of the Allies in World War II and regarded as a kind of Magna Charta for mankind.

Against this background science writers in many countries have elaborated on the theme that chemistry possesses the key to a new freedom for mankind—Freedom from the Green Plant. Man's bondage to the plant kingdom would vanish. Food and feed need no longer come from the produce of the fields but should be available from chemical factories. Basically, though, this visionary Fifth Freedom is identical to the third one: Freedom from Want. This latter formulation also seems to characterize better the potential contributions chemistry would make. Even without unleashing mankind from dependence on the green plant cover, the achievements of chemistry via these same plants are already immense and contribute heavily to alleviating world misery.

This future role of chemistry is mirrored in numerous popular books and articles, with such titles as *Road to Abundance through Chemistry, Factories Give Us Bread, Synthetic Foods, Artificial Bread for the Millions, Our Synthetic Environment, End to the Green Thraldom,* and *The Fifth Freedom, Chemistry's Gift to Mankind.*

The saga of chemistry's new leadership has been described in glowing terms; the farmers and their toiling in the soil will be replaced by the chemists in their white lab coats. How things will change when chemistry in this way has entirely taken over the task of providing mankind with food has been presented in the following manner:

> Meat proteins, which are now the most expensive of all staple foods, and available in sufficient quantities only to a small part of the world's population, will then be available to everybody at a nominal cost. The systematic protein undernourishment of the majority of mankind will cease. Millions of cattle raisers and packing-industry employees will be replaced by a few chemical operators. The disgrace of slaughterhouses will disappear from our cities, and one will have to go to a zoological garden to see a cow. Our grandchildren will hardly believe that we were so primitive and barbaric that we had to eat cadavers of dead animals in order to keep alive.[1]

Science fiction writers did for quite some time elaborate on how the discoveries of science will affect man's feeding. They made their men of the future, in institutional kitchens, cut beefsteaks out of infinitely growing tissue cultures; served synthetic, uniform protein, artificially flavored with chemical additives, this in order to simulate, according to preference, fish, meat, vegetables, etc. In these fancy tales chemistry was hailed as the great savior of mankind, which would stave off the menace of starvation and provide man with limitless quantities of food. By now, science fiction has abandoned the earth altogether and hardly any longer delves into such mundane matters as food, but rather basks in the glories of space.

Chemistry will without any doubt whatsoever continue along its victorious path, persistently adding new conquests to its previous achievements. Knowing that basically our foods are composed of

[1] J. Rosin and M. Eastman, *Road to Abundance* (New York: McGraw-Hill, Inc., 1953), p. 55.

nothing but chemical compounds—admittedly in well-defined proportions—we should not exclude the possibility that future chemists may be able to synthesize proteins, carbohydrates, and fats, and in addition the numerous vitamins a human being requires.

But does it necessarily follow that chemistry will solve our present and future feeding problems? Will, in fact, the food of the future take on the form of pills, easily swallowed and digested? Will farming and fishing be reduced to pleasant leisure pastimes? Will the world's billions be fed synthetic foods, and will the products of agriculture and fisheries become exclusively luxury items, available only to the privileged few? This is more or less the vision of the future encountered in science fiction writings. How does this picture fit in with reality? Are these predictions well founded? Does chemistry in effect possess the key to the future?

Synthetic Food

Let us first scrutinize the absurd notions of pills as food. The difficulties encountered in solving the food problems for space travelers have exploded many of these myths and removed them from mass media and science writing. The amount of organic matter needed during a year by the human body is about 550 pounds. Consequently a daily intake of 250 to 500 pills of one to two grams (1/28 to 2/28 of an ounce) would be required. Besides this, man needs a minimum amount of water. It is unlikely that such a pill diet would leave the gastrointestinal system and its functioning unaffected.

There is very little likelihood that science will be able to find shortcuts that would free man from the intake of any essential part of these substances so that he could survive on air, for example. Such hopes belong to the world of free speculation and lack a realistic foundation. If in the future we are in a position to discover and establish all the compounds required by man, there is all likelihood that chemistry will evolve methods of synthesizing and manufacturing most of these substances. If we thus assume that it would be possible to manufacture industrially most such substances as amino acids, vitamins, etc., that the human body needs, one problem still remains unresolved; these compounds would yet have to be provided in molecules of highly specialized structure.

Furthermore they contain such indispensable basic elements as nitrogen, sulfur, and phosphorus, just to mention a few of the most essential ones. Man will never move outside this general framework of prerequisites for his survival.

Nature actually works with organic molecules built according to very strict specifications. Even the same compound appears in different substructures. There are, for instance, so-called right- and left-turning molecules, constituting mirror pictures of each other. These two variants do not have identical properties, nor do they function in an identical way in nutritional terms. In a few instances the counterpart molecule may even be deleterious. In synthetic production the result is usually a mixture which can only in part be utilized by the human organism. It requires complex, costly devices to separate.

Moreover, factories for synthetic food must be provided with all the required raw materials, even if they are in elemental form. If man wants to get outside of the boundaries of what soils and seas yield with regard to, for instance, carbon, he is by and large dependent on carbon sources such as peat moss, pit coal, mineral oils, and other residues from earlier vegetation periods in the history of the globe. Most of these sources at present constitute the basis for man's energy supply as well. By transferring the burden of food production from living nature to these residues from earlier periods, we actually transfer from renewable to nonrenewable resources. We draw from capital in lieu of renewed production, and thereby accelerate the rate with which these capital assets are depleted. Again we arrive at the basic thesis of this book. Sooner or later we will be forced to live from what we produce, in other words from what we can extract by utilizing the carbon dioxide of the soils, the oceans, and the air.

By resorting to synthetic foods, we gain but a brief respite, a decade or two, which in the long history of mankind would be quite irrelevant. Still worse is that once these synthetic foods have passed through man and livestock, they sooner or later join the air as exhaled carbon dioxide or ammonia. Alternative channels are a decomposition in the spoilage of such foods or feeds and the degradation of waste, ensuing from such synthetic products either via processing plants or sewage installations. In all these circumstances man would be forced to fall back again to dependence on the green plant, with its ingenious mechanism for the retrieval of the airborne carbon dioxide as a coal source, and on ammonia or nitrogen as a source of this element. These would all be widely dispersed in the atmosphere as against the concentrated sources from which the food synthesis once started. Nitrogen could in theory be recollected from the air, but only as long as energy is cheaply available; otherwise there evolves a new, second dependency, namely of the nitrogen-fixing microbial world.

As already mentioned, the dependence on the chlorophyll miracle in the plant kingdom, the photosynthesis, has been called man's green thraldom. This relationship is twofold. Despite all emphasis on organic production the most important aspect of the photosynthesis is not the making of food, in the first place carbohydrates, but rather the release of oxygen. All molecular oxygen available on earth presumably is derived from photosynthesis in earlier millenia. Without free oxygen, men, animals, and most plants would simply not be able to breathe and support respiration.

Photosynthesis

Whether death by suffocation would be the price we would have to pay for such a radical divorce from the plant kingdom and a more or less general reliance on chemical manufacturing of foodstuffs will not be further discussed here. To a certain degree this has been recognized by some experts by visualizing the freedom from the green plant primarily in terms of a chemical synthesis of the miraculous green pigment, the chlorophyll, still leaving the major burden to photosynthesis, but under controlled conditions in huge industrial plants rather than in fields and forests. With the influence of recent advances in modern chlorophyll research, and not the least as a consequence of the conferring of the Nobel Prize in 1961 on the Californian biochemist M. Calvin, science writers have reveled in visionary descriptions of future factories where foodstuffs would be made in continuous process with the aid of such synthetic chlorophyll. Merely by synthesizing the ignition compound—so goes the reasoning—the motor will be made to run. In this way it was thought that man would be capable of mass-fabricating food from the carbon dioxide of the air.

By resorting to such a controlled photosynthesis, man would

continue to reap full benefits from the generously flowing and cost-free sun energy. In effect, the energy account is not the least costly for industrial chemical synthesis, including that of food. On the other hand the argument has been raised that food accounts for only a fraction of the energy use in an industrialized society—less than one-fiftieth in the United States. The corresponding figure for Western Europe seems to be in the magnitude of about one-twentieth.

Such estimates overlook the large additional amounts of energy that would be needed in the actual industrial synthesis of food. A modern grain farm in the United States is actually using more energy than the grain produced has managed to accumulate. Most oilseed-producing farms raise per acre less oil than what is consumed per acre of mineral oil in the running operation of the farm. For example, the binding of one metric ton of the nitrogen in the air requires the equivalent of five metric tons of carbon in the form of energy. The ratio is still more unfavorable in other indispensable processes. The energy account would thus mount considerably, and far in excess of the relatively minor quantity that ends up in the final foods. This additional load is of such tremendous dimensions that it can be greatly questioned if such a big order to chemistry can be filled, even if it were to advance victoriously on all synthetic frontiers.

Additives

Pointing to these limitations is not intended to deprecate the terrific load which chemistry carries in the food field. In effect, it can be convincingly argued that chemistry is our chief defense weapon in our fierce battle on the food front. Besides fertilizers and spray chemicals, chemistry provides additives, *i.e.,* compounds essential to food preservation and processing. Despite excessive manufacturing costs they retain their significance by being crucial in some specialized respect—*e.g.,* in the manufacture of vitamins or supplementary amino acids. It is, however, quite typical of the present world economy that these industries are serving almost exclusively the well-fed nations with their strong markets. Synthetic amino acids, which constitute the building stones of protein, are mainly used as admixtures in animal feed. Poultry and hogs in the

Western countries are, as a rule, even better provided for in this respect than the human beings of these very same nations. This discrepancy becomes more or less absurd in terms of malnourished and half-starved people such as those in Mexico, the Caribbean Islands, South America, the Middle East, tropical Africa, and Asia.

Supplementary Role—Large or Small?

Returning to the central question of the possibility of manufacturing food entirely through chemical means, it is worth noting that hardly any of the popular writings in this field make an effort to estimate the magnitude of this task. Producing food through agriculture and fisheries is in effect a gigantic undertaking. Merely to provide for one single year's added numbers through chemistry —more than seventy million in 1967—would require facilities greatly exceeding the total synthetic-organic industry of present-day United States. An *annual* investment of at least fifteen billion dollars would be needed. Nature works with much more elegance and carries out its complicated synthesis at low temperatures and without costly equipment. In comparison, man is very clumsy. In addition, the water consumption of an equivalent industrial process is manifold. Starches and fats, produced chemically, require about five hundred times more water than when made in nature. This is one of the more obvious reasons why the present industrial development raises demands that are hard to meet even with a repeated recirculation of water.

Synthetic additives, of which several are already being made industrially, may obviously be employed for supplementing the deficient protein of rice, wheat, or corn. Quite impressive figures have been presented in this particular respect showing the great benefits that would accrue from such supplementations. But these estimates represent armchair guesses and remain purely theoretical. They might be arithmetically correct, they might even be sound in terms of individual foods, but in true life most foods are not eaten alone. Most civilizations have been quite ingenious in supplementing the deficiencies of their grain proteins by resorting to daily diets including various other natural food products. The American Indians mixed their corn flour with flour made of beans, and the peoples of the Andean regions still do so today. Fish products are added to rice in Southeast Asia and Japan. The soybean and the Chinese cabbage each have a protein that fits as hand in glove to the rice protein and makes this combination rather complete for human needs; a circumstance the Chinese have exploited for centuries in feeding their millions. Consequently, no sensational results can be expected from supplementation programs, because they would, at best, be replacements to a diet which already has solved the amino acid riddle qualitatively if not quantitatively.

The Vanishing Role of Chemistry

It is symptomatic that almost every popular science review of synthetic food, sooner or later, leaves this subject in its strict sense and slides into a discussion of the manufacture of fats, protein, and vitamins through algae, yeast, fungi, and bacteria. Through the back door, plants are smuggled into the play as a creative natural force. In the chapter "Food and Microorganisms" this fascinating subject of the feeding role of biotechnology will be an-

PERCENTAGE OF PROTEIN OF DRY MATTER IN MAJOR FOODS

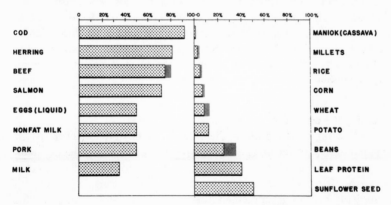

Fig. 5. Protein percentage of dry matter in major foods; animal products to the left and plant products to the right. Shaded areas indicate the amplitude in values. Only animal products or pulses and oilseeds can be effectively used to raise the protein content of a cereal-tuber diet.

alyzed. These applications will probably become crucial for man's survival but will have little relationship to the making of foods through truly chemical synthesis.

Chemistry Economizes with Acreages

Just because synthetic foods are for the most part an illusion with little relevance in reality, even in the future, this does not mean that chemistry is insignificant—on the contrary. Few seem to have realized how tremendous a burden chemistry already is carrying in providing for the present generation of man. This role of chemistry is furthermore expanding at a considerable rate.

It has frequently been pointed out that the synthetic manufacturing of rubber, indigo, coloring matter, nylon, etc., has freed large soil acreages which can now be utilized for food production. The truth is that these industrial crops never occupied any significant part of the world's tilled land. The acreage needed to produce rubber in quantities equivalent to those now delivered from the synthetic rubber factories would not provide enough food for more than approximately twelve million people, *i.e.,* about one-sixth of the present annual increase in world population.

Chemistry taking over the energy provision within agriculture is a far more important factor. The oil refineries of the world have attained what amounts to a key position in the feeding of the Western world. Approximately 250 million people in North America, western Europe, and the Soviet Union get their food thanks to the fact that their farms no longer have to feed horses and other draft animals.

Artificial Fertilizers

More far-reaching as to the role of chemistry, however, is the manufacture of fertilizers. The corresponding feed-producing acreages have been released to raise food. Close to 600 million people depend for their survival upon artificial fertilizers. Without this annually repeated supplementation of the soil with man-extracted minerals, approximately that number of humans would lack food. This relationship may also be formulated in this way: Chemistry saves acreages equivalent to what would suffice for more than half a billion people. It is a common misapprehension that this fact in itself reflects our technological skill when it comes to raising the

GLOBAL USE OF FERTILIZERS

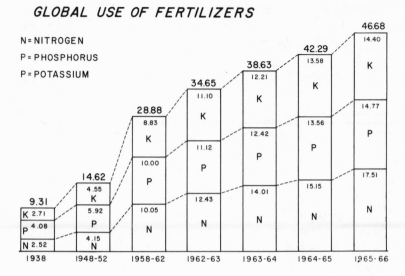

Fig. 6. Global use of fertilizers in terms of nutrients, 1938–66 (million metric tons)

total food production. In several instances it is not a question of an additional yield on top of that which nature provides. The use of fertilizer constitutes an indispensable repayment to the mineral banks of the soils jeopardized due to man's reckless outtakes.

It is extremely difficult to make an exact estimate of how many additional individuals get their daily bread thanks to the fact that chemistry has augmented the food production above what nature originally provided. Basically, this is an economic question. The fact remains that this close dependence exists and will expand considerably during the decades immediately ahead. More and more hundreds of millions will have to rely for their survival basically not on agriculture, but on the continuous, giant supporting contributions to agriculture by the chemical industry, particularly in the form of fertilizers, spray chemicals, and veterinary therapeutics. Man in the developed world has expanded his living to an artificial, elevated level, which to a growing degree is removed from the basic soil fertility endowed by nature.

In itself this is an impressive achievement, but we must not lose sight of the fact that in so doing we have increased the vulnerability of our civilization and actually created an artificial subsidiary platform—a kind of auxiliary man-made support. We are frequently inclined to overlook this dependence on industry, and we fail to enter corresponding investments in energy and in water on the balance sheet. The replacement of the annual removals by the crops from the soil deposits is a process which is not only limited to safeguarding future yields. Due to industrialization and the concomitant urbanization, the local or even regional return to the soil of these extracted mineral riches is no longer feasible. Instead, these minerals are via food brought by millions of tons into urban and suburban areas. In the most favorable cases, they may end up in sewage plants producing manure or fertilizers. The lion's share, however, reaches rivers, lakes, and today even the oceans. Only minor quantities return via artificial humus on sale at sewage plants. Not only are the Great Lakes and Swiss mountain lakes being converted into sewage recipients, but even the sizable Baltic Sea is heading the same way. Man as a "dirtifier"

ARTIFICIAL NITROGEN

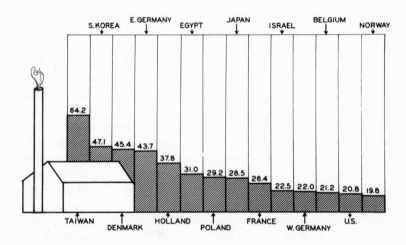

Fig. 7. Man-made nitrogen percentage of daily protein intake. Calculated by author on the basis of an assumed 5/6 loss in conversion from fertilizer bag to harvested crop.

is in this respect adding some hazardous pages to the annals of his history which bring little credit to his ingenuity and farsightedness.

There is in addition a growing concern for the spillover of both nitrates and phosphates from agricultural lands into natural waters. In many regions with intense agriculture an excessive use of fertilizers, coupled with the leaching of these nutrients, which are not held too well by the topsoil, aggravates the water-pollution situation. Nitrates may also become a toxicant of waters, jeopardizing human health. Such instances have been reported in central Europe and North America.

Waste Utilization

On the waste front, chemistry will, on a mounting scale, be called upon to perform great feats to the benefit of mankind, especially when it comes to the direct utilization of compounds like cellulose and lignin, converting them into food digestible in the human body. It is true that cellulose can be hydrolyzed into sugars. But lignin, constituting 40 percent of forest waste, has so far defied efforts toward this goal. These intricate tasks are consequently far from solved in any attractive or feasible way. It is, furthermore, not self-evident that chemistry, even if successful, will really be able to compete in this respect with the ruminants or the lignin decomposers in the soil or those fungi serving the wood-eating insects.

To help in the reconversion of the waste and sewage of the cities into food is another big task in store for chemistry, which has started on only a very modest scale. It has been estimated that if the paper waste of the United States were collected and transformed via chemical methods into sugar, this would take care of one-third of the caloric needs of the United States population. However, calories are not the crucial issue of the world, but rather protein. If the tilled acreage of the United States were used solely for the cultivation of sugar beets and cane, the yield would exceed the calorie needs of the entire world. No expensive chemical syntheses are actually needed for this particular purpose.

Gigantic Future Needs

Looking toward the future, we discern another, much more critical issue. The three billion or so increase in human beings, which is anticipated before the end of this century, can simply not be fed via the natural mineral resources of the soils. At least half of this additional number of humans will depend on the chemical fertilizer industry coming to their rescue. Commercial fertilizers already constitute a heavy burden on the transportation capacity of industrial nations. Before the end of this century this load will be in the neighborhood of 500 million metric tons, considerably more than the total weight of mankind at that time. Probably still more will be needed.

So far man has limited himself to filling the needs for the four key mineral nutrients—nitrogen, phosphorus, potassium, and lime —and this in an inadequate way. But the deficit in terms of some twelve to twenty other elements, which are now being tapped from the soils in a similar way in the cropping procedure, is making itself increasingly felt. The situation is particularly critical with regard to sulphur and magnesium. Besides these two, there is a whole series of other minerals which are indispensable, although needed only in minor quantities, trace elements. The above mentioned quantities will therefore swell and exceed at least 700 million tons in the year 2000. And yet these amounts would not mean a particularly efficient fertilization per acre, merely about one-fifth of what countries like Japan and Holland already consume.

If chemistry is not going to be earmarked exclusively for food production purposes, we must probably reorganize our whole way of life. Cities with their present concentration of humans and waste will probably become an impossibility. The task of returning the mineral nutrients will become an insurmountable obstacle. Yet it is the enormous underconsumption of commercial fertilizers which explains to a great extent the present undernourishment in the world. The entire African continent is using an amount of fertilizers equal to that of Italian agriculture. Most of these fertilizers are employed largely for such cash crops as the cotton fields in Egypt and Sudan or consumed by the white colonizers primarily to feed themselves. Only a fraction benefits the black natives, many times more in number. Huge India, now exceeding 500 million people, uses about the same amount of fertilizers as Sweden, with 7.5 million people, and only twice what Taiwan, with twelve million people, is employing (1965). More than a hundred million acres at present lie fallow in India due to mineral depletion over the centuries. The entire South American continent, which is now seething with a population that doubles in thirty-four years, utilizes

FERTILIZERS

Annual average percentage of world consumption
1963/64–1964/65

Total 38.20 million metric tons

	CONSUMPTION		WORLD POPULATION	
	PERCENT	Σ	PERCENT	Σ
Europe	42.6	42.6	13.7	13.7
U.S.A.	25.0	67.6	5.8	19.5
U.S.S.R.	10.1	77.7	6.9	26.4
Japan	4.8	82.5	3.0	29.4
Others	17.5	100.0	70.6	100.0

One-fourth of the world's population uses more than three-fourths of the world's fertilizers.

Some Telling Comparisons
(in million metric tons)

Annual average 1963/64–1964/65

| France | 2.98 | Scandinavia | 1.23 | Italy | 1.15 | Holland | 0.84 |
| West Germany | 2.04 | India | 0.67 | Africa | 0.89 | S. America | 0.79 |

about the same amount of fertilizers as tiny Holland, and this, too, predominantly for such plantation crops as coffee, bananas, cocoa, etc., *i.e.,* products that are for the most part exported to the well-fed Western countries. More than one-fourth of the fertilizer consumption in the United States is used for lawns and private gardens. Gigantic efforts would therefore be needed merely to meet the present desperate situation in the world.

China and India

The fertilizer industry of the world is at the present time expanding rapidly. The situation on the nitrogen front is discussed in the chapter "Food and Microorganisms." Figure 6, p. 27, illustrates the steeply mounting curves. Yet certain characteristic trends are discernible which point to a disquieting gap between image and reality. This reveals the minor degree to which the gigantic thrust by chemistry in our generation really benefits the hungry. According to official figures (FAO), world consumption in 1962 amounted to thirty million metric tons (calculated as N_2, P_2O_5, and K_2O) nitrogen, phosphorus, and potassium used as fertilizers. Only one-tenth of this quantity went to underdeveloped countries. This lopsidedness continues despite the notable increase taking place in consumption, but mostly within the rich nations.

This is easy to explain. The needs are, in the overpopulated parts of the world, so enormous that it is highly unlikely the fertilizer industry will ever catch up with them. In other words: Is it really possible to raise the productivity of the soils to more elevated artificial levels, in view of the fact that the population figures are rushing upward without any consideration for the resources of the earth? India alone would have to invest something in the order of twenty billion dollars in fertilizer factories to achieve parity and balance. On top of that, two additional gigantic factories would be needed each year only to provide for the annual population growth of more than twelve millions—yet this discussion has not taken into account the time factor. No major fertilizer plant can initiate regular production in shorter time than three to five years.

China has, almost in desperation, changed her development plans and is now diverting capital and effort from the making of steel, construction material, and machinery into creating fertilizer factories. These were in 1962 suddenly given priority ahead of all other industries required for the far-reaching transformation of that country. Both these key nations have long ago crossed the boundaries for what is reasonable and are therefore faced with overwhelming needs.

As pointed out in the chapter "Water and Our Daily Bread," fertilizers and water are inseparable companions. It is hardly likely that India's and China's water budgets will ever allow a consumption of fertilizers of the level being applied in precipitation-rich Japan and western Europe. But even a much more modest plan may break the back of economies of a more robust nature than China and India possess. The U.S.S.R. is faced with the same difficulty in its new large-scale fertilizer drive. This has to be coupled with an equally generous water plan. As explained in my book *The Hungry Planet,* water resources constitute the Achilles heel of the Soviet Union.

The Transportation Load

As mentioned above, it can be seriously questioned if enough water can be mobilized to take care of the enormous input of fertilizers which the world population growth requires, not to mention the doubling that is needed to supply the people that are already starving. Furthermore, it is not at all sure that the transportation facilities of the world—railroads, merchant navies, and road trucks—can be expanded enough to take care of these quantities without neglecting other essential needs. Before the end of this century a transportation volume occupying a substantial part of the nontanker merchant navy of the world would be required for this purpose alone. This would not be a mere one-time operation, but an annually recurrent burden.

A growing part of the world's chemical industry is in fact already being earmarked for food production. Thus it is being estimated that 60 percent, for instance, of Japan's chemical industry is working exclusively for the food sector. No less than two hundred plants are devoted to the production of agricultural chemicals. There is a great deal of boasting about how the individual farmer in the Western world today produces food for so many more people than before. The large-scale mobilization of the chemical industry, in the shape of oil refineries and fertilizer factories, which has taken place in order to accomplish this, is rarely mentioned although it is indispensable. Without this aid the modern farmer of the Western world would cut a rather miserable figure as a producer.

Our Protective Chemical Barrier

A third category of chemical industries that has come to the aid of the farmer is that producing pesticides and fungicides. It is inadequately recognized to what a considerable extent present crop returns are directly dependent upon an extensive use of chemicals. Without such elaborate chemical barriers, man could not shield the lavish tables he currently is spreading in nature in the shape of high-yielding crops and pastures. He is forced to lean on chemicals and the pursuit of an unrelenting chemical warfare. This arsenal of chemicals is indispensable and part of modern man's survival kit. This is frequently forgotten, except when lamenting over the chemical residues encountered in our foods. We do not want to face the fact that without persistently sustaining these chemical barriers, our food supply would be jeopardized. In this respect the globe is already overpopulated by man, as he in effect is involved in an ominous and persistent battle, with ever-changing front lines, for his very survival. On this battlefront nature is constantly fighting back through harmful insects, obnoxious fungi, and micro-organisms; and man, for his part, is constantly forced to devise new, more potent weapons.

It has been estimated that if the insects of tropical Africa could be kept under control and possibly be eliminated as competitors to man, Africa would be able to feed two billion people, *i.e.*, eight times as many as those now living there. These prognoses may be exaggerated, but nevertheless illustrate how big this insect menace is in the eyes of the experts.

In spite of drastic chemical measures, United States agriculture figures an annual loss in excess of thirteen billion dollars due to damage caused by insects, rats, mice, fungi, and bacterial diseases. This constitutes more than one-third of the farm value of agricultural products. A more convincing illustration of the defensive role held by chemistry is hard to find. The very thought that natural catastrophes or war could dismantle this protective barrier is frightening.

In the chapter "Man's Competitors for Food" the hazards we encounter in the chemical warfare we are pursuing in nature are scrutinized. There are not only victories in this struggle but also many defeats. The situation becomes most precarious when we entirely take over the policing of nature and are forced to make our countermeasures permanent. This has largely taken place as regards the locusts (compare p. 109). Despite first-rate weapons, on the whole very potent as well as effective, every year brings large losses to agriculture, even in countries waging this chemical war in full force. As a consequence, many biologists have suggested that man take a new approach; in lieu of killing off his good helpers and depriving himself of their invaluable support in his fight for survival, he should rather mobilize his friends against his foes. From this kind of thinking methods for biological control of pests and diseases are emerging. Several significant advances have already been made along this line, and more are to be expected.

This is the more desirable as many circumstances give support to the notion that the chemical killing squads gradually lose their efficiency or have become truly indispensable.

This development has rather added to our defense burden than reduced it. Evidently we need to focus more of our research on finding more efficient and less crude countermeasures. To kill a fly with a sledge hammer was never considered particularly smart. We need to apply our rich fund of chemical knowhow in a far more potent way by working *with* nature rather than *against* it as now is the case. We need to get much better acquainted with both our adversaries and our allies. These latter may be far more vital partners than we ever realized. It is both costly and inadvisable to take almost everything in our own hands, regarding most animal creatures as enemies or competitors, completely blind to the self-evident fact that many of them constitute invaluable allies in man's great struggle for survival.

Summation

Our analysis may be summed up in the following way: Chemistry has already been mobilized and earmarked, and this to an almost overwhelming degree, for the gigantic task of providing food for man and livestock. Chemistry constitutes an indispensable basis for the present production of food and feed, and thereby for our entire existence. A war which threw this industry into disarray would have catastrophic consequences and result in starvation for hundreds of millions. The idea of placing still greater burdens on this industry is rather unrealistic. Already the present, more limited functions are on the verge of overpowering chemistry. We need to mobilize this science in a much more efficient and well-planned way in order truly to offer man the third freedom, the Freedom from Want. Without the aid of chemistry the program of the Atlantic Charter could never become a reality. A prerequisite is that we refrain from employing chemistry in a large-scale game of hazard, doomed in advance to failure. Chemistry, too, has its very obvious limitations.

CHAPTER III

Could the Yield
Spiral Be Pushed
Further Upward?

There are few areas where the public debate about food is as ill-defined as the question of the yields of soils and the productivity of livestock in meat, milk, and other commodities. The indisputably greater returns from croplands—particularly in Europe, but also in North America and the Soviet Union—during the last hundred years have made economists and a major part of the general public believe that similar and continued crop yield increases can be projected into the future; that we can look forward to constantly mounting yields, and animals will perform ever more miraculous production feats. No limits are recognized. In some cases there are even glib pronouncements about "accelerated" productivity.

Such reasoning gains acceptance and is furthermore often included in development plans for various countries, without any thought being given to the question of meeting prerequisites for such advances. Common sense or simple probing reflection should make everyone realize that this image is deviously distorted and in any case cannot be universally valid. It ought to be clear to everybody that there are well-established limitations for what soils can do in terms of crops as well as what livestock can achieve as producers. We will therefore try to penetrate the verbal facades and discuss the realities that provide the basis for food production.

We will then discover an entirely different picture from the one perpetuated in the almost parrotlike assertions contained in extravagant promises about a future abundance based on record yields by miracle animals and extraordinary soils.

This exaggerated image of possible productivities is even endorsed by prominent economists, and may be characterized in the following way: World agriculture is seen as consisting of flourishing Iowa farms with high crop returns (and practically every harvest a record one); as giant-uddered, high-producing cows; super-quickly grown, bulging hogs; or egg-layers on a continuous belt regime approaching the magic one-egg-a-day ideal. As if this were not enough, most writers go one step further and assume, in all seriousness, that technology and the ingenuity of the human mind will further improve on these global "Iowa farms," achieving still more high-yielding operations. In order to make the presentation below easier to follow, plant crops and livestock are discussed separately.

CROPS

Plants depend on available water and on nutrients, especially minerals, for their development. In addition the climate must be fairly reliable and allow growth and development sufficient to attain final ripening before frost or drought raise implacable barriers. These constitute the environmental conditions for growth and productivity. To this must be added the structure of the plant and its efficiency in utilizing sun energy and the carbon dioxide of the air, as well as the capability of the root system to absorb mineral substances. It is particularly these latter capabilities that plant breeders wish to improve. But it goes without saying that there is always an intimate interaction between the potential of the plant and available production means in the environment, traditionally termed the interaction between inheritance and environment.

In order to make this general discussion more concrete, a grain plant has been selected as representative of most cultivated plants to answer the question: In which ways can higher yield be achieved? There are in principal four alternative ways: (1) The ability of the root system to absorb mineral nutrients and water may be improved, whereby the foliage receives a greater input of matter for its production. (2) The same effect may be achieved if the plant is provided with a larger root system, which reaches more deeply and embraces a greater action sphere in the soil. (3) It is also possible to give the grain plant a larger leaf surface either through larger leaves or more leaves, thus making it capable of catching more of the incoming sun energy. The plant can then produce more in the tiny cell factories of the leaves, but obviously only if the roots can absorb the additional amounts of water and nutrients which are required for such purposes. (4) Finally there is the possibility of enlarging the green chlorophyll machinery of the plant cell as regards efficiency or amount of pigment and in this way manage to convert more sun energy. These four devices are intertwined in an intricate way, and in no instance can yield increases be ascribed to the operation of one single factor.

It is feasible to breed strains of most crops that economize with water, and in this manner increase the yields in these alternative ways. Nevertheless, in the end the plant is, in most instances, dependent upon additional supply of water and nutrients, *viz.,* the margin that is available to honor these new capabilities. Under very specific conditions it is possible, however, to economize with the evaporative losses as contrasted to the water used in the life processes of the plant. Whether a more economical use of water is possible through breeding, *i.e.,* the genetic buildup of strains which would produce more organic matter per ton water, is unfortunately little studied. In those few cases when such fundamental investigations have been made, the gains are modest in relation to man's needs, even when they are big in terms of the plant (15 to 30 percent). Moreover, economic crops differ a great deal with regard to their capacity for using water economically. This fact has obvious implications, actually to the point that this factor almost regularly has been decisive in the selection of crops in various regions of the globe and further explains the present distribution of certain grain crops. This will be discussed further in the chapter "Water and Our Daily Bread."

The Degree of Coverage

We have until now approached the water question from the point of view of the individual plant, but agriculture must look to the total effect of the thousands of plants that cover each acre. Here entirely different laws apply. It is by no means sure that a large-sized plant renders higher acre-yields. The degree of ground coverage is decisive for the end result. A higher degree of coverage is more often obtained with a great number of small plants rather than through a lesser number of large ones. Even close planting gives higher yield only to a limited extent. The point is soon reached where the competition between the individual plants becomes detrimental to the total effect.

The leaf area per land unit exposed to incoming light consequently determines productivity. In a temperate climate the development of annuals is closely in phase with the seasonal changes in radiation. The tropics lack this variation. The climatic resources there are therefore best utilized with trees, perennials, or transplanted annuals like rice. These all provide an almost complete cover the year round. This explains why, from a strictly economic viewpoint, only sugar cane (a two-year crop) merits consideration for these regions in addition to the above crops. These relationships rather than backwardness explain why the humid tropics, with rain-inducing cloudiness, consistently yield far less than the arid tropics under irrigation, and why their yield potential is also below that of the temperate regions (see also p. 72).

Later on in this chapter the combined effect of water, minerals, climate, etc., under the growing conditions that prevail in different parts of the globe will be discussed separately. But let us first briefly review the most common pitfalls in the debate about yield increases in the world at large.

What Constitutes Effective Yield Increase

First and foremost it needs to be emphatically underlined that yield increase, in the true sense of this expression, does not refer to the achievements of the individual plant, nor to the total agricultural production of a country. In agricultural context yield increase should only refer to greater production per acre or other surface unit, *i.e.,* the additional food outtake from each tilled acre. Unfortunately, this is seldom kept in mind when discussing productivity matters. Larger reported crops in volume are frequently due to the cultivation of additional acres and are consequently achieved by the opening up of new land or through new irrigation projects, extending into new lands. Such advances are often interpreted to mean that the cultivated lands are giving evidence of producing more. The increase in agricultural production that has taken place during this century around the globe is primarily the result of the breaking of new land rather than the outcome of more efficient tillage with ensuing yield increases. This applies to China, the U.S.S.R., Mexico, North and central Africa, as well as the Middle East. Still more surprising is the fact that even the larger volume attained in the postwar period—outside of the United States and western Europe—can largely be attributed to expanded acreage. This question is further analyzed in the chapter "New Heavens and New Earths."

Multicropping

The complexity and the intricacies of greater yields are, however, far from exhausted. There are many more factors that affect the appraisal of such figures. For instance, there are many regions on earth where statistical data indicate astounding increases in yields per acre, despite the fact that the harvested crops have not been larger. When two or more harvests are indicated, each crop may well have become smaller than previously was the case. This paradox is explained by the practice of double or even multiple cropping. This implies that crops are grown on the same piece of land as long as the climate permits such additional vegetation periods. This procedure may also be described as extending the sown or cultivated acreage but retaining the tilled surface. There is a tendency to overlook this key factor in appraising soil productivity. A major part of the increases that have taken place in Taiwan, India, Pakistan, and Japan during the postwar period is the outcome of such expanded multiple cropping (see the chapter "Is Large-scale Irrigation Reaching an End?"). Such intense use of the land will not be without repercussions, nor can the gains be obtained free of charge. They require considerably bigger inputs. The soil has to pay the price in extra outtakes of water and mineral nutrients.

The additional outtake of mineral nutrients necessarily increases with yields; more commercial or natural fertilizer must also be added. Yet, in general, the second harvest shows lower acre-yield figures than those for the first summer crop. If steps are not taken to provide for this additional production, such double-cropping usually brings about progressively lower yields due to more rapid depletion of the water and mineral reserves. Ultimately, this tapping of the resources may jeopardize the entire production. Double-cropping is in effect a gift of nature, but it must be paid for with more water and nutrients. There are no miracles, and man frequently has to intervene to repair the damage he has wrought.

The Jump Upward

Multicropping is the major reason for the "knee" seen on curves plotting changes in average yields during latter decades in countries like Japan, Taiwan, etc. This jump upward is often presented as one of the production "miracles" induced by modern agricultural technology, accomplishing yield gains bordering on the unbelievable. The advances are not, however, as impressive as they might appear. The actual productivity has certainly not jumped to the degree these yield graphs imply and certainly not as precipitously as this "knee" might make one believe. This incongruous advance is in effect nothing but a moving into a "second level" after having reached a rather static plateau in the yield from one single crop.

It goes without saying that such advances are not possible, unless the climate allows the insertion of a second crop within the vegetation period. Equally significant is the fact that in many parts of the globe double- and multiple-cropping started long before this modern age of technology. South China started raising three crops of rice a year far back in its history.

Fallows

Winter fallow is in many regions the only way to collect enough water to make a single annual harvest feasible. When cultivation is extended and the fallow eliminated, water needs to be supplemented also during the winter season. No soil can produce crops from nothing.

This development has in principle, judged globally, been one of the major changes in world agriculture that has taken place largely in the past hundred years. This intensification of production has meant that man has further reduced his margin and moved closer to the ultimate limits of the globe's resources. In Canada reduced fallowing is a major feature of wheat growing in the prairies, but this kind of expansion in sown area is not the result of breaking new lands. It accrues from a more efficient use of the lands earmarked for wheat—but a prerequisite has been extensive and expensive irrigation projects, which provide water from other sources than "collecting it through rest," *i.e.,* nonuse of the soils (*cf.* p. 149).

In tropical Africa and Latin America the population is exerting

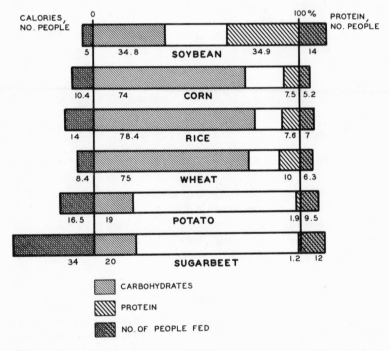

Fig. 8. Comparison between crops with respect to composition (central section of graph) and the number of people that on the average can be fed from one hectare as to calories and protein respectively

such growing pressure on the lands that traditional fallowing no longer can be upheld. The rest period is persistently shortened and in the final stage eliminated, often with disastrous results to human settlements. Desiccation and erosion are the inevitable consequences.

Change of Crops

Another pitfall is that a reported increase in agricultural production may only be the result of a switch in crops or transferring to better soils. Whatever gauge we use for yields—tons, calories,

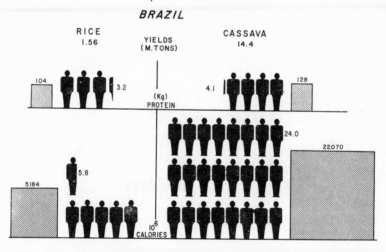

COMPARISON OF NUTRITIVE EFFECT OF RICE AND CASSAVA PER HECTARE, — 1963-65

BRAZIL

Fig. 9. Cassava and rice—Brazil. Cassava, with its higher yield per acreage unit, provides calories for far more people than does rice. But the disproportion between the number fed adequately in terms of protein widens in a disastrous way. The present cassava intake of Brazil needs to be supplemented with more than 2.5 million hectares of soybean to become nutritionally balanced and satisfactory. The coffee acreage of Brazil is 5 million hectares, and the present soybean acreage is less than 0.5 million hectares. This explains the widespread protein malnutrition. Importation does not fill the protein gap.

or monetary value—it is very simple to achieve increased yields through the exchange of one crop for another. Every farmer knows that this is the case. Nevertheless, such gains are usually presented as "agricultural gains" in promotional propaganda and estimates about the future. No production promoting steps need to be taken by the farmer, and yet higher yields may be recorded merely by substituting crops. The table on p. 45 shows this clearly. If potato or sugar beets are cultivated instead of wheat, or for that matter

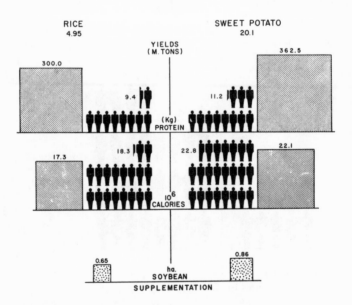

Fig. 10. Sweet potato and rice—Japan. For adequate protein provision sweet potato needs to be supplemented with soybeans from an acreage slightly more (15 percent) than the size of the present soybean acreage of the islands. Soybeans are currently imported in a quantity that would require 7.5 times the present (1964–66) soybean acreage to attain—*i.e.,* almost one-third of all tilled land—in order to fill the void.

COMPARISON BETWEEN CROPS AS PROVIDERS OF CALORIC AND PROTEIN NEEDS

Crop	COMPOSITION					YIELD PER HECTARE			
	Dry matter Percent	Protein Percent	Carbohydrate Percent	Harvested weight Kilograms	Dry matter Kilograms	Calories (millions)	Satisfies (number of people)	Protein Kilograms	Satisfies (number of people)
Soybean	92.5	34.9	34.8	1,450	1,340	4.8	5.0	502	14.0
Corn	88.0	7.5	74.0	2,550	2,240	9.4	10.4	191	5.2
	85.0	12.0	70.0	1,800	3,240	6.7	7.5	216	5.8
Rice	87.7	7.6	78.4	3,430	2,740	12.4	14.0	261	7.0
Wheat	87.0	9.0	77.0	3,500	3,050	11.6	13.0	315	8.5
	86.0	10.0	75.0	2,300	1,980	7.5	8.4	230	6.3
	85.0	12.0	72.0	1,350	1,350	4.5	5.0	162	4.5
	84.0	15.0	69.0	900	760	3.0	3.3	135	3.8
Potato	21.0	1.9	19.0	18,000	3,960	15.0	16.5	342	9.5
Sugar beet	24.0	1.2	20.0	37,000	8,800	30.5	34.0	(440)	(12.0)

By substituting on the same field one crop for another it is consequently readily feasible to register considerably increased yields, calculated by weight, without this in any way mirroring an improvement in the productivity capabilities of the soil. One acre of sugar beets yields fifteen times more in tons and six times more in dry matter than one acre of wheat! Whenever a crop fills the need of more people through calories than through protein, a supplementation of the diet with more protein-rich food is in most instances required (*cf.* Figure 8).

Source: Calculations made by the author, based on certain estimated normal yield figures (by and large North America). The caloric need has been put at 0.9 million annually per individual; the protein need at 100 grams per day, losses not taken into account.

beans, we get considerably more dry matter and thus a larger volume.

This method of agricultural bookkeeping may be the most deceptive way in which the production gains by individual countries or even farms have been misjudged: increased harvest without any basic improvement in the productivity of the soil. Due to these relationships it is also both hazardous and difficult to make a valid comparison in agricultural productivity between various countries and different time periods. Agricultural history is a very tricky discipline, particularly as related to production, since valid comparison in principle can be made only when the cultivation patterns by and large are similar. Otherwise, such comparisons become misleading and often induce incorrect economic conclusions as regards agricultural efficiency in respective countries.

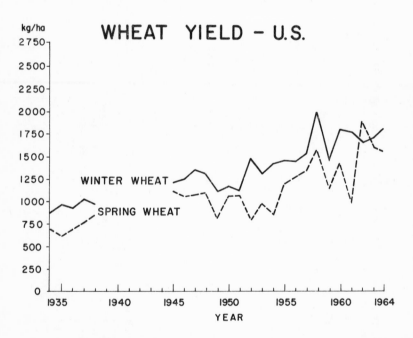

Fig. 11. Comparison between winter wheat and spring wheat as regards yield in kilograms per hectare, 1935–64

Two Kinds of Wheat and Rice

The most striking example of such pitfalls are comparisons between the wheat yields of one country and those of another. Quite often we are dealing with two rather different kinds of plants, though they happen to give fairly similar end products, *viz.,* winter wheat and spring wheat. It is almost self-evident that winter wheat throughout shows higher yields than spring wheat, since it is able to build up the root system in the fall and partly develop and grow in other ways during the fall and the winter. However, the productivity of the wheat fields per week of the vegetation period hardly ever show corresponding discrepancies. On this basis it is almost absurd to compare the total wheat yields of the United States with those of the U.S.S.R. For climatic reasons spring wheat dominates the Soviet scene. Therefore such yield comparisons should nat-

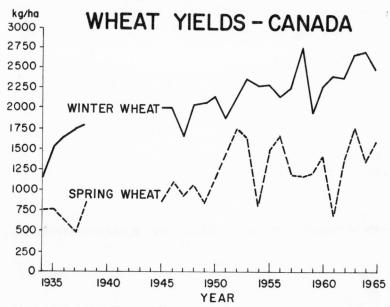

Fig. 12. Comparison between winter wheat and spring wheat in Canada as to yield in kilograms per hectare, 1935–65

RICE YIELD/HECTARE

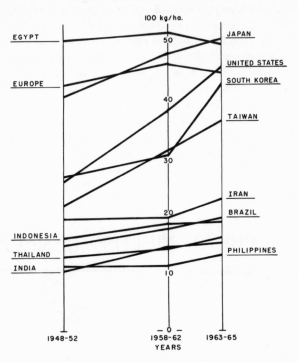

Fig. 13. Changes in rice yields in key countries and regions from 1948–52 to 1963–65. The dramatic yield increases of Japan, South Korea, and Taiwan are primarily due to expanded double-cropping.

urally refer to commensurate crops, in this instance spring wheat. The differences then become far less striking and even minimal in regions with comparable climate and soils. Those regions in the U.S.S.R. that permit the cultivation of winter wheat show much higher yields, also closer to the United States figures for this kind of wheat.

A corresponding major difference prevails between lowland rice (constantly irrigated) and highland rice. The yield is about 3 to 5 times higher, with a similar ratio in water requirements. Most of

India's rice (64 percent) is rain-fed and depends on the irregularities of the monsoon.

This is commonly overlooked in comparing the yields of India with those of Japan. These alleged differences almost vanish when the valid comparison is made between each kind of rice separately and particularly under similar rainfall conditions. Indian regions planted with lowland rice get yields very close to those of Japan—the same is true when results with highland rice are matched. Quality is also in contest here with quantity, since high-yielding rice frequently is down as low as 5 to 7 percent protein content, against 7 to 9 percent in traditional strains. This is too low to satisfy minimal human needs (around 12% of total calories).

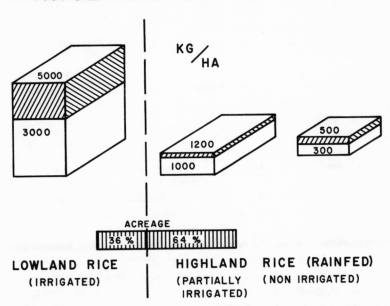

Fig. 14. Most Indian rice is of highland type and grown on rain-fed soils with very little irrigation. When lowland rice is grown with full irrigation, yields came close to those of Japan. The yield figures apply to 1960–1964. The shaded areas indicate the amplitude, *i.e.,* the degree of variation.

Quality vs. Quantity

Finally we arrive at the most decisive factor in evaluating yield increases. It is not enough to produce more in volume. For the food-consuming public quality is more important. It is the capacity of agriculture to satisfy nutritional needs which is decisive. Few countries on earth can afford the luxury of overlooking this and expect to make up for possible nutritional deficiencies in the plant products with additional consumption of expensive animal foodstuffs, in which one has concentrated the needed supplementation in the form of minerals, vitamins, and above all protein.

It is especially in this respect that production records are being misjudged, measuring quantity but overlooking quality. In far too many cases additional production means increased packing of the cells with carbohydrates, *i.e.,* starch and sugar, the primary result of the carbon dioxide assimilation. Protein, the basic life substance of the cells, which constitutes the protoplasm, is being diluted, or pushed aside, as the cells are being filled with carbohydrates. The result looks magnificent—well-filled grain seeds and tubers—but the protein proportion is correspondingly lower, as mirrored in the protein content. Only in very few instances have the plants been able to absorb from the soil enough nitrogen, and with sufficient speed, to keep the protein production in parity with that of fats and carbohydrates.

Misleading Comparisons

Basically, the same factor is behind the relationships we just analyzed, the differences between the yields of various crops. It is no coincidence that the sugar beet and sugar cane produce more calories per acre than any other plants. Breeding for higher sugar production has simply been done by selecting those strains for which analyses indicated the lowest protein content.

This phenomenon has had serious repercussions for the world. Living organisms, whether livestock animals or man, need at least 12 percent of their calorie intake in the form of protein. The ruminants provide an interesting exception to this general rule (see further the chapter "Food and Microorganisms"). This constitutes an absolute limit which man shares with monogastric (nonruminant) livestock animals. So far none within this group has ever been able to bypass the limit, and consequently they are all forced to respect it in order to safeguard body health. Since the protein of plant products is not immediately accessible to digestion and metabolism in the same way as animal protein, man actually is advised to consume somewhat above this minimal amount, approximately 15 percent, in order to be on the safe side. In modern high-yielding rice strains the protein content is down to between 5 and 7 percent, in high-yielding wheat strains to 10 percent, in hybrid corn to 7 percent. We operate consequently nowadays far below this crucial minimum limit, and that is why we need protein supplementation. In the drive for belly-filling calories to meet hunger and the growing number of mouths, man has broken into the crucial defense structure of his body, the protein barrier, and thereby seriously jeopardized his whole defense system.

The United States Secretary of Agriculture, when back from a month-long visit to the Soviet Union and Eastern Europe (in 1963), reported almost with awe about the high protein content of the Russian wheat strains, up to 22 percent! Siberian wheat used to be world famous for its quality. Corn of present-day hybrid varieties must be mixed with protein concentrates to be fit for hog feed. In earlier days hogs could be raised almost exclusively on this grain. Now it has to be supplemented. This relationship may also be formulated in the following way: A piece of cheese or ham has to be added to the sandwich to become equivalent in terms of nutritive value to the same sandwich without any additions around the turn of the century.

This lowering of the protein content can to some degree be counteracted by a late dressing with nitrogen fertilizers, but this involves extra costs, whether it is carried out through air spreading or with a tractor. Plant breeders have developed new strains which are able to withstand such high nitrogen impacts. Early dressings are less efficient in this qualitative respect. They may result in higher yields and even higher yields of protein per acre, but basically through larger plants, etc.—in itself a significant advance, yet less satisfactory from the nutritional point of view. In order to provide for the minimal diet of protein, other tilled land is needed to produce supplementation, whether from leguminous seeds (*e.g.,* soybeans) or animal products. But this is of little avail when the proportion between protein and carbohydrates is pressed downward in a less desirable direction leading to large relative deficiencies in diets and major adjustments in feed formula. It is of little satisfaction to the bread-consuming public to be told that the flour is cheap because it comes from high-yielding fields if the protein content has dropped below the critical minimum and therefore costly extra food is needed, whether this is added as supplementation or purchased separately. In order to avoid deficiencies, protein must be added, and as pointed out earlier, few nations can afford to do this through animal sources. The eventual gain in the costs of flour and bread is illusory to the poor who are forced to make an expensive supplementation by additional purchases of hot dogs, cheese, hamburgers, etc. Nor is the hog in the pen happy if the corn he gets no longer fills his protein needs, even if it happens to come from abundantly yielding fields. The hungry and poor world is paying for such "progress" with mounting figures on protein deficiency disturbances. This risk is particularly insidious, as such consequences are not immediately visible.

The Bread Miracle

Undoubtedly a deep symbolism is embedded in the New Testament narrative of the so-called bread miracle when Christ fed five thousand people on five loaves of bread and two fishes. This points to another feasible combination for filling the protein needs. In this case agriculture is relieved of the task of providing adequate amounts of protein. This key role is abandoned, and agriculture is relegated to the sole and single task of furnishing calories, and this in maximum amounts—almost a complete collapse of the protein barrier. What grains and other crops provide of other ingredients such as protein is gratefully counted in, but an indispensable supplementation has to be sought from the aquatic riches. The agricultural yield increases, which are attained by such an intrinsic undermining of the quality of the products from the soil, are therefore acceptable only on condition that the feeding basis is broad enough to allow such maneuverings.

For most countries this is not the case. From the point of view of public health but also within the framework of the production resource basis of a country, it is in most instances more favorable

eases may cause abrupt changes in harvested crop volumes. Grain production in the U.S.S.R., Australia (see Figure 15), and Canada all reflect such vagaries of the climate, drastically affecting the feeding potential and its reliability to markets and consumption. This explains why grain exports from both the U.S.S.R. and Australia show quite an erratic trait. Both have in some years been forced to import food.

These factors also affect irrigation measures. Both India and Australia, with a high degree of investment in water-storage dams, have found it necessary not only to master floods but to allow storage over more than one growing season.

Pests and Diseases

We have yet another factor to consider. In the chapter "Man's Competitors for Food" those limitations for production are discussed which can be ascribed to plant and animal diseases and

WHEAT PRODUCTION AND YIELDS, 1900-65

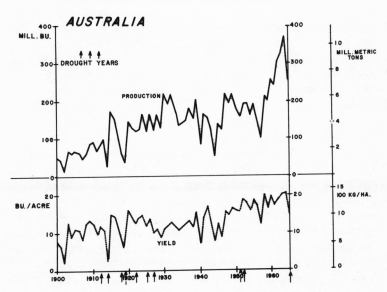

Fig. 15. Australian wheat yields. Note considerable drought-influenced fluctuations.

other competitors that man encounters in nature. Due to this "hostile" world, low yields need not always imply that the soil is poor but rather that agriculture functions under such precarious conditions that much of what is being produced is devoured or attacked by pests and diseases. Exceptionally low wheat yields, which regularly recur in Canada (see p. 47), are to be attributed either to drought or to serious attacks of cereal rusts.

Those of us who live in latitudes where nature, through a harsh winter climate or seasonal changes, gives man an invaluable helping hand in the battle against his enemies, are inclined to draw wrong conclusions in this particular respect. We underestimate the enormous handicap under which most farmers on the globe are forced to till their land and produce. Our spray chemicals and other countermeasures are of little avail when these hostile agents can keep crops and animals under sustained attack. Under these conditions insects and fungi develop and thrive all year round and can launch their campaigns almost at any stage of development and at any time during the year. It is no mere coincidence that the plantation crops of the tropics, even when handled with the aid of all our agricultural technology and knowledge, often fall victim to devastating mass invasions of pests or diseases. It is obviously wrong to gauge soil productivity after elephants, kangaroos, rice finches, or flying foxes have helped themselves from the fields. This is equally true in reference to the more insidious tolls taken by insects and fungi. There is in this respect the need for a whole set of new terms designed to cover all these options.

Natural Catastrophes

One form of destruction with which temperate regions usually are less familiar is damage caused by natural catastrophes. One exception may be hailstorms. During the growing season of 1963, Japan lost close to half its standing crop through typhoons. This was no single instance; each year Japan has to face losses of this or similar kind. Taiwan is hit by an average of twenty typhoons per growing season. For that reason both these countries have to grow sweet potato as an insurance against this type of natural disaster. There may be nothing wrong with the productivity or the yields of the soils, but they cannot be fully exploited due to overpowering natural forces. Yield comparisons between countries become unrealistic when such agricultural drawbacks are not taken into account. In order to correct for such calamities, efforts have been made to relate the crop volume to the acreages actually harvested, rather than taking into account the entire sown acreage.

Naturally, all depends upon the purpose for which such comparisons are made. But in loosely founded estimates of the production potential of the globe such realities are often overlooked. It is as if one counted with a fictional dreamland where no disturbances occur, not to speak of those fantasies where one sees the entire globe cultivated, including the Arctic and the Antarctic, after melting down the ice caps with nuclear power.

Climatic Limitations

We do not want to admit that man has any insurmountable forces against him. That climate sets limitations is, one fancies, merely a transient phenomenon; with modern technology man will subdue the climate. In the chapter "Is Large-scale Irrigation Reaching an End?" those hazards are discussed which we encounter when trying to open up areas that are too dry for plant cultivation. The U.S.S.R. in its vast northern regions, as well as China in Manchuria, have built gigantic greenhouses for tomatoes. But anyone who believes that something is possible other than a supplementary production of certain vitamins, and that we could grow everything that man needs under such artificial conditions, has indeed moved far away from economic and biological realities. The proposals to heat the soils of Siberia and northern Scandinavia with atomic power belong in the same category.

Climate Control

Faced with the rapidly growing billions of human beings, the demand is becoming ever more insistent that mankind should tackle forcefully the climatic obstacles for food production, create precipitation where it is insufficient or lacking, prevent floods when overabundant, eliminate frost ravages, and dampen the unfavorable effects of heat in the warm regions. On the whole, so the reasoning goes, man should take the lead in controlling the climate in the world and not continue, as hitherto, being exposed to its vagaries.

Those who in speech or writing expound such thoughts seem to be little cognizant of the enormous degree to which the survival and progress of the present civilization is already dependent upon the ingenuity and technological skills which throughout the centuries have been applied to this very end of gaining control over the environment and blunting the adverse elements. Though we are far from a climate control, man's efforts to improve the climate have nevertheless been remarkable in scope. This is further discussed in the chapter "Is Large-scale Irrigation Reaching an End?"

Atmospheric Water Truly Global

There is a fairly common belief that the creation of open water areas, from which water would evaporate to augment the atmosphere's stock of vapor, would in turn lead to increased local precipitation. This is a basic misunderstanding caused by misconceptions concerning the hydrological magnitudes involved. In the driest period of a severe drought in any part of the world huge masses of water are still drifting invisibly overhead. The principal cause of drought is almost invariably lack of dynamic forces capable of producing ascending motions. Such movements result in cooling, and hence cloud formation is the first indispensable step in getting any of the atmospheric water down to the earth's surface.

A second misconception concerns the distance scales involved. A molecule of water evaporating from an open water surface ordinarily faces the prospect of drifting ten to hundreds of miles before it ascends, via turbulent diffusion processes, to altitudes high enough to give it a chance of entering clouds and eventually being condensed and precipitated. Almost all precipitation, whether rain or snow, has typically originated in evaporation from some oceanic water area, lying far upwind of the site of precipitation. Not more than about one-tenth of the precipitation falling on the Mississippi watershed involves water evaporated from continental sources; nine-tenths has an oceanic origin. The fact that large water surfaces in arid regions, *e.g.,* the Caspian Sea, sustained via the Volga and the Ural from distant watersheds, do not relieve local aridity, is a further evidence of this global relationship.

Precipitation is, however, mostly induced through the action of some lifting mechanism bringing water into lower temperatures and inducing condensation and rains, rather than through the presence of nearby water bodies. This factor is furthermore the key to cloud seeding operations, mountainous areas showing the most favorable results due to the updrafts over such regions. It is therefore still a very controversial matter whether crystal seeding has ever affected precipitation in nonmountainous areas such as flat open plains within no major land barriers.

Rainmaking

Man's direct efforts to influence the climate go back to ancient China. When, in order to achieve precipitation, we go up above the clouds and release billions of small dry-ice crystals, *i.e.,* crystallized carbon dioxide or silver iodide, which spin down through the air, constituting condensation nuclei and thus create drop formation, we are relying upon the same basic mechanism that lay behind the cannon fire of the Middle Ages and the prairie fires of the American Indian used for the same purpose. Dust particles and crystals initiate a drop formation which in turn leads to rain when the drops become sufficiently heavy.

When rainmaking saw its heyday in this country some years ago there were no less than five hundred companies which dealt in rain. About 350 million acres (150 million hectares), *i.e.,* one-third of our tilled acreage and pastures, were contracted for such artificial rain supplementation through crystal seeding of the clouds. Even when costly large-scale experiments were made, the meteorologists have been rather reticent to draw scientifically binding conclusions about the reliability of such methods.

Rainmaking is nonetheless not the same as cloudmaking. To get rain there must be clouds. Only if there is a surplus of water in the air, so-called oversaturation, can man manipulate rain. Nobody can go up and spread crystals over sun-drenched regions and expect rain. The water must be there. Mountainous areas show the most favorable results because the updrafts created lift the seeding crystals to effective heights. There is as a consequence still no convincing evidence that rain can be created on flat plains. Water cannot be manufactured through some secret magic trick. The magician who pulls the rabbit out of his hat is as everybody knows actually not so smart, because the rabbit has been there all along. It is he who creates the rabbit who is worthy of our admiration. The same applies to rainmaking. Man can at the most manipulate the final mechanism for rain release, but he creates neither water nor rain.

In far too many of the thousands of tests that have been made it was found that in regions distant from the testing areas fog or drizzle appeared. Likewise, certain results indicated that regions that normally receive ample amounts of rain no longer got it, since the cloud masses had been tapped at an earlier stage. Many lawsuits were filed in the United States by people who, paradoxically enough, felt they were deprived of rain through rainmaking. Only if the end result is additional precipitation over a large area can a truly positive effect be established. To change the order of nature to facilitate agriculture in other regions than those which normally receive rain thanks to dominating wind directions and cloud transports is not very smart. From the point of view of a country or a continent it is of no advantage if one part can occasionally get a little more if another area, as a consequence, may suffer serious drought with ensuing crop failure.

Crystal seeding of clouds has been tested around the entire globe where drought periods are a regular feature. In most cases such regions are cloud-free. It has also been tried in several areas where cloud formation takes place—in addition to the United States, in Canada, New Zealand, Australia, England, and even in precipitation-rich Scandinavia. It is, however, still a matter of faith whether these operations have given any concrete results. Be that as it may, meteorological research is not yet that far advanced that man can control the weather. In those cases where our manipulating of the mechanism may possibly have had an effect, it has still not provided a reliable basis for increased food production. One may even go one step further and assert that most likely completely other methods are required to guarantee, in a reassuring manner, precipitation for specified regions. On the basis of our present knowledge, such a possibility seems highly unlikely, and in any circumstance distant in time. We can certainly not issue any checks for the future on this score, since there is little prospect of honoring them in our generation, when the population growth will reach critical dimensions.

Air Pollution

Man's negative role as a climatic factor stands out most con-
spicuously in the staging of his own slow suffocation on a global
scale, through the enormous quantities of carbon dioxide which
he daily allows to be exhausted from cars, factories, motors of
all kinds, as well as from the burning of wood, peat, coal, and
oil. The green plant cover of the globe, which has become drastically reduced through, among other things, deforestation and
the man-made stone deserts of the cities, is no longer capable of
absorbing all this carbon dioxide and its content in the air has
slowly but inexorably been rising since the 1870s. The globe is
furthermore being converted into one tremendous hothouse, since
with reduced plant cover more warm sun energy is absorbed by
the air. It gets warmer, a dubious gain for those regions of the
world which already languish under too much heat. It seems
rather unlikely that this can bring a net gain for world food
production, despite the fact that fertilizing with carbon dioxide
in some regions, where the shortage of carbon dioxide limits full
photosynthesis, may induce yield increases.

Air pollution has already had a large scale impact upon the
growing conditions of crops, particularly around large cities,
partly through smog, *i.e.,* a cloud cover formed by polluting particles which reduce the penetration of the sunrays as well as the
photosynthesis of the leaves. Still worse are directly toxic substances which are deposited on the leaves and damage or kill
them. But even more disquieting is the process by which the
sulfur of the carbon period is returned within a relatively short
period through the coal-driven electrical power plants. From
these installations alone, ten million metric tons of sulfur dioxide
is hurled out into the air over the United States annually, and
this quantity is rapidly mounting, poisoning man, animals, and
plants. If curbing measures are not taken, the estimates are that
this volume will double or triple before the year 2000.

Man as a Negative Climatic Factor

Through the measures mentioned above, man has caused a
deterioration of the climate, and to such a degree that in many

regions he is now jeopardizing his own existence. Man is talked about as the future master of the climate, but silence prevails about man as the great perturbing factor—in effect transforming, mostly in a detrimental way, the climate through the ages, but above all during the last hundred years. It is estimated that during that period desert and wasteland increased with approximately twelve billion acres (five billion hectares) primarily through man's intervention. In deforested regions the water balance was for the most part so upset that drought and winds emerged as formidable and devastating forces of nature. If we add to this the gigantic outtakes from surface waters and groundwater for irrigation and for increased agricultural production, we have the explanation, despite investments amounting to billions of dollars on all continents, for our inability to repair the damage done by our shortsighted and reckless operations. Experts of various kinds more or less agree that the Sahara by and large is a man-made desert and not the result of some large-scale climatological catastrophe. Beneath its sand the remains of the vegetation of bygone times are hidden, even trees, as well as the relics from once-flourishing civilizations. Through intensified irrigation and overgrazing of the pastures along the edges of the desert, it is currently expanding southward by some two to three miles annually. The big lakes of Africa are dwindling, not through any mystical secular process but largely due to deforestation and enlarged irrigation projects in Ethiopia and adjacent countries.

The Caspian Sea is also swiftly vanishing from the map, mainly through man's intervention. Hundreds of fishing villages, which as late as 1939 were in full fling, are now located tens, even hundreds of miles from the coastline. In twenty years the water level has fallen more than six feet (two meters) partly because the U.S.S.R. has created its own Nile Valley in the lower Volga River, partly due to accelerated industrialization and the building of electric power plants. The Volga has been overrated as a water resource. According to the Soviet hydrologists themselves, the proud Caspian Sea will, prior to 1980, have fallen another six feet. The proposed plans to revert the flow of the Petjora River (a tributary of the Irtysch), now flowing into the Arctic Sea, and to convey its water via the Vychegda and Kama, subsidiaries to the Volga, in order to supplement the water flow of the latter river, now seems to be the only answer. This would not, however, restore the Caspian Sea to its former dimensions, but hopefully it might put a halt to further shrinkage.

PLANT PRODUCTIVITY

Returning to the plants and such factors as determine their productivity, briefly mentioned at the beginning of this chapter, we encounter quite a number of limitations the plants impose on man's manipulations. We will discuss for each one of them the possibilities of advancing our positions further.

The Precipitation Pattern

Misconceptions are common with respect to water and precipitation. In elementary textbooks we read about the average annual precipitation for various parts of the globe and generally compare them with those of our own state or region. From this we draw conclusions as regards the potential for plant cultivation in other parts of the globe. Those who, like this author, have seen the enormous dams erected in central Uruguay are inclined to be cautious in appraising the relationships between rainfall and production. The average annual rainfall of Uruguay exceeds 80 inches. This is 2.5 times that of Michigan. Why then these big dams? Even with such ample rainfall the paradox of limiting factors is operating and severely affecting productivity. Averages rarely count in the world of reality. In Uruguay it happens, and not infrequently, that an entire year goes by without any rainfall that counts. In such catastrophic years the crops not only wither but the animals succumb by the hundreds of thousands. These dams have been built to reduce the effect of such calamities. It goes without saying that one cannot store all the water needed for a whole year, but the damage can be blunted and losses reduced and some plant and animal production sustained. Even in precipitation-rich Sweden, twenty-five years out of a hundred are critical drought years which affect the yields adversely.

The distribution of the precipitation over the year is another factor. In many important areas of the world rainfall is very erratic. The rain must come in the right season to serve the crops.

This is not the case in many regions. When the presowing rains fail and (or) rains jeopardize the crops in the harvesting period it does not help much if the average annual precipitation is adequate. Torrential downpours provide much water, but frequently its efficiency in plant production is minimal. Much is lost through excessive runoff.

Imbalances of these kinds partly caused the failure of the huge peanut project that the British government started as a future basis for its fat supply in Tanganyika when the Second World War ended. This project was located in a region where agricultural experts had established that one could only count on seven good years out of nineteen and only one further year with reasonable yields. Eleven years out of nineteen are catastrophic. Either rain is not forthcoming, or locusts ravage the area. It is not surprising that the large multimillion-dollar program became a resounding failure, in spite of the first-rate experts employed and ample funds available. In this case one could not blame the miscarriage on the natives, their apathy and technological backwardness, as we otherwise are so inclined to do. Certainly the outcome of the Tanganyika project and similar failures should make us more humble when advising underdeveloped countries.

Too Much Water

With regard to the individual plant, water availability is decisive for its producing capabilities. Water must constantly be pumped through the plant in order to sustain production. But there is a limit to what the plant can take. Most of us have seen the distressing result when too much water is given to potted plants in the desert climate of our modern homes with central heating. The pores of the soil soon get filled up with water. The air is pushed out of the soil. The roots and rootlets can no longer breathe. The limits for the functioning of the plant are in effect determined by the availability of air. But long before that critical point is reached, the law of diminishing returns has gone into effect. The same volume of water does not yield identical additional results when approaching the limits of the water uptake capabilities of the plant. Paradoxically enough, a similar phenomenon of reduced efficiency of water is encountered under arid conditions, when more water is required for an equivalent production. Wheat grown in Australia takes approximately 2.5 times more water than is needed for the same production in the United States Midwest. California-grown crops use far more water than comparable crops in Michigan. The same is true of North African and Mediterranean crops as compared to those of Scandinavia. Besides the transpiration of the plant being affected by the higher temperatures, the evaporative losses are much greater. In terms of water economy it therefore pays much better to irrigate in humid areas for additional crops than to make the "desert bloom." The role of water in plant production is further discussed in the chapter "Water and Our Daily Bread."

Aeration and Drainage

Irrigation is, in more than one way, an art of balancing in order to strike the right amount of water for delivery to the crops. In most arid lands there is great risk of overdosage, resulting in seepage which gradually may give waterlogging. This phenomenon is accelerated by the formation of an underlying hardpan through microerosion. Seeping water carries with it tiny particles, which finally settle in the fine pores of the soil at a certain level as the downward rate of water movement slows. These relationships lead to the paradoxical situation that too effective irrigation has its limitations and may well result in declining yields; as when plants cannot "swallow" water, and even prior to this point. But in global context drainage has played almost as big a role as irrigation. Considerable areas of marshlands have been drained.

Among the characteristic features that are used to classify soils is the relationship between pores and dry matter; in significance to man's feeding, this competes with the elaborate drainage increasingly required to remove saline water from cropped lands under irrigation (see p. 195). The porosity determines aeration. Soils

	MARSHLAND	MORAIN
Measured depth	20 cm. (8 inches)	100 cm. (40 inches)
Airpores—volume	6.7 %	64 %

show major discrepancies in this respect and in the resulting water-storing capacity, which, for example, is 943 mm. (profile depth of 100 cm.) in muck soils, in contrast to 360 mm. in morain soils.

Soil—Prime Water Source

In terms of crop productivity it is rather the amount of water available for the root system to utilize, which determines general crop ecology and yields. At the optimum in temperate regions, sandy soils hold 30–50 mm. (1.2–2 inches) of water as compared to mulch soil—500–550 mm. (20–22 inches). This difference in water-binding capacity determines to a large degree crop yields, and rather more so than precipitation and evaporation as such. The figures above give clear evidence of this, as they considerably exceed annual precipitation in magnitude. Those simple relationships are complicated by the differing withholding capabilities of the soil, which retains certain amounts of water with forces insurmountable to the suction force of the root hairs of the plants. At any rate, rain prior to the vegetation period may be equally important to the crop returns as rain during this period. This is why rapid losses of organic matter in warm, tropical soils reduce their capability of holding water, and thus make them less productive. Our spaceship has its peculiar, often unheeded, limits in the depth of the soils.

The Mineral Substances

Approximately the same laws as for water are in operation as regards the plant's absorption of mineral nutrients. Thus no plant can produce without being able to absorb continuously through the root system nitrogenous compounds and salts of potassium, phosphorus, calcium, as well as an additional twenty-some substances in minor amounts. The higher the yields, the lesser as a rule is the effect from additional fertilizing. In extreme cases the mineral content in the soil may become so high that growth is retarded. Available water is not adequate for a desirable degree of dilution. It is generally recognized that Germany during the thirties suffered from a nitrogen depression, *i.e.,* the yields fell despite the use of higher amounts of fertilizers. Even in this case an obvious limit is encountered in the capability of the plant to use added amounts of minerals effectively in production. No plant can survive in concentrated salt solutions. Eventually breeders may develop plants and strains which are capable of absorbing more, but such increases in productivity are as a rule small as compared to the gigantic needs of the global household for one and a half to two times the present harvests.

Although both Holland and Japan may already feel the law of diminishing returns as affecting their agricultural productivity, too little rather than too much better describes the world situation with respect to minerals. Most countries are far from optimum and certainly have not passed this range. It is today an exception when Dutch agricultural experiments achieve statistically valid increases of more than 1 to 3 percent. In quite a few countries also in the developed world the mineral balance is, on the whole, negative, *i.e.,* crops remove much more from the soil than the amount of minerals returned as dung or fertilizers. This type of operation can be labeled as a kind of soil mining. As a rule the shortage first becomes apparent through deficiency symptoms tied to specific trace elements, *i.e.,* essential nutrients that the plants absorb and require only in minimal amounts. These signs of shortage are not always heeded, and due to the small amounts involved, they were and still are overlooked in planning and pro-gramming, although they may be limiting to production. De-ficiency symptoms gradually also show up in macronutrients, *i.e.,* minerals needed in larger amounts. This whole field is highly complicated. In several instances reduced yields rather than de-ficiency symptoms may be the sign of inadequate sources of minerals.

If we go back to a period, documented in history, when new lands were broken on the North American prairie, the mineral content of its topsoil was about three times higher than today. The Australian wheat soils, which on a large scale were brought under cultivation in the 1870s, showed decreasing yield figures up to 1890. It took until the 1910s before fertilizing returned amounts adequate enough to bring back the original acre-yields. Only by the use of persistently higher amounts of fertilizers was it possible to reach up gradually to the present yield figures, which are about 25 percent higher than those obtained when the wheat lands first were opened up with the plow. There is furthermore every indication that the soils of both India and China have been continuously tapped of their minerals. In India the result is that currently more than 125 million acres (fifty million hectares) constitute unproductive wasteland, which in all likelihood will remain so due to the prohibitive costs of restoring their mineral riches. China has tried desperately to hold the mineral losses of the soils down by returning night soil as well as other sewage. Yet only partial compensation has been accomplished.

Ever since the beginning of recorded history man somehow intuitively seems to have understood that something had to be returned to the soils in order to replace what was removed in the cropping. Classic writers, particularly Pliny, list all measures taken to this effect. In a few regions of the world man has been able, painstakingly, to restore the productivity of the soils to the natural initial level, and maintain this over the decades through large-scale fertilization. For ages the easiest way was via cattle dung or grazing animals returning through feces and urine considerable quantities of minerals originating in their feed. Defending this battlefront in the topsoil requires relentless vigilance. As pointed out in the previous chapter, close to 600 millions of the world's people are in our time dependent upon the industrial manufacture of fertilizers for their food supply. We ought to keep in mind that in such a world, wars and natural calamities have more far-reaching effects than direct devastation. Indirectly many hundred millions may be affected besides those directly involved.

Yield increases to be ascribed to fertilizing are consequently highly difficult to assess. In other words the greater yields attained in this way cannot be appraised in a correct way without some knowledge of the history of the soil. It goes without saying that soils impoverished with respect to one or several nutrients should yield more when the limiting minerals are supplied. But basically this is rather a repairing of the soil productivity, bringing it back to a more "normal" or "natural" level but frequently interpreted as a net gain to the credit of fertilizing, thus elevating soil productivity.

There are special cases of quite an opposite nature. The globe carries many soils that from the beginning seem to have been lacking one or more trace elements, *e.g.,* the ninety-mile desert of Australia, and where even very small-scale supplementation may give returns in sizable harvest increases or even make otherwise barren soils usable for plant cultivation. In terms of nature the phenomena are identical, but in terms of the role of man's intervention there is a big difference between making up for a "damage" and upgrading a resource.

Soil Erosion

Nevertheless, "mining" of the soils constitutes a highly questionable venture in such areas of the world—and they are certainly not few—where soil erosion through wind and water aggravates the losses by carrying away additional amounts of nutrients. Cropping here faces another difficulty limiting productivity, namely the maintenance of the topsoils. In many instances man has aggravated these destructive forces by depriving the earth of millions of acres of protective plant cover, in this way exposing the soils to these kinds of erosion. Primarily this has been done by removing forests or grass.

Soil erosion is a worldwide phenomenon and one unmistakable sign that man has overextended himself. The topsoil does not stand up to the strains of cropping and grazing. The truth is that in many parts of the globe the available land should be shrunk (reduced) in order to save the topsoil. More than half of India's tilled land is afflicted by soil erosion, one-third so seriously as to jeopardize the future of the topsoil. It is not easy to accomodate for soil conservation measures and the idling of tilled land when the pressure of the millions is exerting itself. A recent study of Turkey recommended that the present livestock be reduced by one-third to avert disastrous soil erosion through overgrazing and that one-fifth of the tilled land be reconverted to pastures to protect the topsoil.

The Interaction Between Water and Mineral Nutrients

Decisive to agricultural yields is another basic relationship, *viz.,* between water and mineral nutrients. It is of little avail to supply commercial fertilizers to agricultural regions that have a limited supply of water. The opposite is also self-evident. Irrigation helps little when the mineral nutrients are lacking for the growth and development of the plants. Thus there is a visibly close interrelationship between these two major factors. It is easy to deplete the water reserves of the soil by too extravagant fertilizing, which is especially harmful when done in the initial stages of plant growth. The water resources may be used up before the plant reaches maturity and full development. Such plants simply wither and die. Several examples of this kind could be reviewed from various parts of the globe. One of the most notable failures of this type took place in Nebraska, when the alfalfa yield was increased dramatically through fertilizing, but at the same time the demand on the water stored in the soils rose so sharply that when these fields were broken up and resown, nothing would grow. The topsoil was desiccated, and the area became for all practical purposes a desert. In a very brief lapse of time approximately thirty (!) years of precipitation had been consumed.

The Chlorophyll Miracle

Many popular articles have been written about the green pigment in the leaves, the key substance for manufacture of starch in the carbon dioxide assimilation. A great deal has been said about the poor return of energy in starch and sugars when rated against the liberal influx of sun energy. No photochemical reaction is, however, more economical than that of the chlorophyll miracle. In relation to what is being produced, it is the most efficient of all known photochemical reactions. The conversion efficiency in terms of absorbed photons related to the chemical energy of the manufactured starch is notably high. Popular writings on these matters base their comparison of inflowing sun energy mostly on the energy content of the final product of the tilled land. Measured in this obtuse way, the return is merely fractions of 1 percent.

Since two-thirds of the inflowing sun energy never reaches the plants but is thrown back into the universe, it is obvious that we should count only that part of the energy flow which actually hits the plant. But even in this case the ratio between the energy which hits the plant and the amount which is finally stored up in starch and selected compounds is rather unfavorable. It is commonly said that roughly 1 percent is returned this way. This is a very misleading notion. The major part of the energy absorbed by the plant is actually used to evaporate water. Without this key operation, which cools the plants, the crops would soon become overheated and possibly scorched. The yields are furthermore net

DAILY TOTALS OF THE UNDEPLETED SOLAR RADIATION RECEIVED ON A HORIZONTAL SURFACE

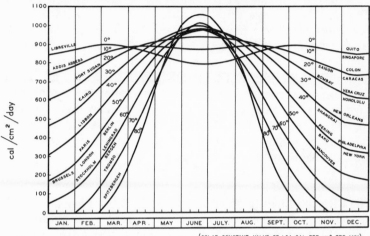

(SOLAR CONSTANT VALUE OF 1.94 CAL PER cm² PER MIN)

Fig. 16. The influx of sun energy measured on a horizontal surface at various latitudes. (The flowing sun energy is a fixed amount: 1.94 cal per cm² and min.) A Michigan farm receives in summertime more sun energy per acre than farms in the equatorial zone of the tropics.

figures. The plant is binding and actually manufacturing two to five times more than what it finally produces as a net gain and yield. The amount that is not incorporated into food is required to sustain the life of the plant, its respiration, and other metabolic processes. Therefore, the relationship between night and day temperatures gains special importance. Yield of a crop is the resulting balance subsequent to various organic compounds being used up in the daily respiration and metabolism. This finally determines the net gain, what we generally call yield.

Furthermore, it is often overlooked that man utilizes as food only a portion of what the plant actually produces: the seeds from grain crops, the tubers from the potato plant, the leaves from spinach, to name but a few examples. There are large amounts of nutrients in the roots, stem, leaves, etc., which return into circulation and must reasonably be taken into account in any appraisal of plant productivity. Comparisons between the productivity of the soils and that of the waters become totally misleading if these factors are not considered. The cool Nordic regions as well as the high plateaus of the tropics offer much more favorable conditions for higher yields than do the warm nights of the tropical lowlands. Therefore comparable crops show the highest acre-yields in temperate regions. These have in addition the advantage that during the vegetation period the daylength is much longer, which means undisturbed production, compared to the five to six hours shorter daylength of the tropics. During this period the energy flow from the sun is also considerably higher in the temperate regions (see Figure 16). Another factor of fundamental importance in this context is the length of the vegetation period. Valid comparisons can only be made of the productivity in producing stages—preferably in terms of calories or poundage per week.

The Ultimate Limit for the Productivity of Green Plants?

Some apprehension is noticeable in recent years as regards the possibility that there is an ultimate limit to the productivity of green plants. On theoretical grounds it can hardly be doubted that such a limit exists but so far we do not know the true nature of this ultimate capability. Indirect evidence points to the likelihood that it might be in the photosynthetic mechanism. If one takes the highest yields achieved with agricultural plants and furthermore selects high-yielding strains, in other words focuses attention on maximal organic production, one finds that the relationship between the energy supplied to the plant and the amount of energy built into the final plant constitutes 2 percent. The same figure actually emerges regardless of agricultural region.

There are also many indications that there are strict limitations for the total volume of nitrogen and phosphate the plants of a given crop can absorb from the soil. It even appears that this total quantity might be independent of crop and the maximal values identical for sugar beet, potato, and wheat. Possibly the nitrogen binding crops like peas and beans deviate from this general pattern. This whole area gives the impression of being a highly neglected field of research. But there are obvious limits to the creative capabilities of the plant, about the true nature of which we can so far only speculate. All life has limits, and it has been a serious fallacy to operate and program as if this were not true. At any rate the limit cannot be very far removed from the top yields discussed above.

Weather—the Yield Barrier

The superseding influence of climate, water availability, day-length, and influx of sun energy are factors far too little recognized in development programs and projected estimates as to future crop yields. The farmer certainly knows what difference the weather makes. This overriding factor has rightly been called the weather barrier, constituting the chief obstacle to the realization of the full yielding potential of any crop. Selecting the right varieties, providing adequate fertilization inclusive of liming, applying inoculation (in the case of leguminous plants), employing optimal plant spacing, preparing the soil in the most appropriate ways, maintaining an ideal control of weeds, insects, and diseases—all these measures are certainly conducive and essential to yields. Nevertheless, they are almost wholly nullified by shortcomings in the weather. This is frequently overlooked by agricultural experts.

The amount of rain is not the only crucial factor. Each crop has one or more critical phases in its growth and development when lack of rain is more detrimental—when availability of water is more indispensable—to final yields than at other times.

An abortive frame of mind is represented by those economic analysts who neglect, belittle, or brush off references to these critical and decisive limitations to productivity as "deterministic" and replace them with a firm belief in the economic forces of demand and purchasing power. They take refuge in an abstract verbal world far removed from the stark realities of our globe and its staggering food needs. Even the best agricultural practices come to nought when the weather fails.

LIVESTOCK AND POULTRY

A great deal of what has been said above about plants also applies to livestock and poultry. For their production they depend on feed, mainly from crops and pastures. Their yield per acre in meat, milk, eggs, etc., together with their efficiency in feed utilization is in the end the only gauge that truthfully reflects the economy of animal husbandry.

It can be seriously argued that the science of animal feeding shows most progress of all research disciplines in the agricultural field. In addition it is safe to say—although it is in itself an absurd state of affairs—that in modern intense animal production, poultry, hogs, and cows are better cared for nutritionally than even our own children. We know much more about the specific needs of livestock and poultry as to amino acids, vitamins, and minerals than we know about human requirements in this respect. This has led to unexpected progress in feed conversion and in the general health conditions of well-fed animals. It is almost un-believable that the broiler industry now works so efficiently that five to six pounds (2½ kg.) of feed produces two pounds (one kg.) of living weight. To a certain extent this remarkable result is a consequence of the fact that, simultaneously with the progress in animal feeding, a feed industry has emerged which produces ever more perfect feedstuffs and feed mixes with less and less bulk. The "natural" feed, which was used earlier, contained too much material not needed. It should be pointed out that at the same time steps have been taken to reduce the animals' utilization of feed for other purposes than those in which man has an immediate interest such as his food. Thus, egg-laying hens are confined to cages in order to make them produce as many eggs as possible. They are not allowed to roam around freely, wasting energy. High-yielding cows are supplied with extra feed and are not, if it can be avoided, permitted energy-consuming grazing. Other examples are millelactaries and "urban" feedlots for steer.

Yet, despite all this, it should still be obvious even to the lay-man that no animal can produce from nothing, that the produc-tion depends upon the feed supply, and that there furthermore exists a limit beyond which we cannot go. To most people this is more evident in regard to animals than to plants. There are many signs that livestock and poultry as suppliers of animal products have been pressed beyond a reasonable limit. Many indirect symptoms of overexertion and wear and tear have been recorded. The eggshells become thinner and more brittle; there is either not enough lime in the feed or—even when sufficient quantity is supplied—the body of the hen is not geared to the handling of such huge quantities. There are physiological limitations. Mastitis among cows, *i.e.,* infections of the udders caused by microbes, are rapidly rising in frequency under the stress of intense milk production. The bacteria find it easier to penetrate overstrained udders, which are forced persistently to perform at peak. In other words, their microbial resistance becomes undermined. Milk fever induced by shortage of magnesium is another critical issue.

We can of course breed larger animals, cows with proportionately larger and more efficient udders. Undoubtedly, we are also able to improve further their feed conversion efficiency, especially if more is revealed about the master tricks of the rumen (*cf.* Chapter IV, "Food and Microorganisms"). But the law of diminishing returns applies also to animals. When we approach the limit of what is possible, the production gains become more costly. The yield figures in milk for a cow or in number of eggs per hen are thus not true measures of productivity. More telling is how much milk, meat, or eggs the respective animals are able to produce from a given amount of feed. Too frequently this important ratio has not been adequately considered in the evaluation preceding prize awards. What really counts is not the amount of milk or fat a cow is capable of producing, but rather the return on feed. As regards broilers, similar misleading gauges have long been abandoned. The birds are appraised basically as to their capacity for producing meat from a given amount of feed, or simplified, their gain in live weight.

There is further a decisive difference between the bulky feeds of early days and the refined, complete feeds of today, requiring costly mixing, evaluation, and supplementation. This has created a whole new branch of agricultural activity—the efficient feed manufacturing industry. Frequently the greater returns have paid off this large-scale investment, but much of this is not paid by the farmers or the food consumers.

Quality

As in crop cultivation, animal husbandry must also strive not only to produce more but to improve quality. There are many indications that yield increases have been accompanied by a lowering of the quality. It is also common that high-producing cows give milk that contains more water and less minerals and vitamins. The carotene content of eggs, *i.e.,* the yellow coloring substance, decreases, and as mentioned above, the shell deteriorates. In both cases the keeping quality and nutritional value are affected in a negative way. To avoid misunderstanding it should, however, be pointed out that such negative effects do not appear if the production increase is kept within reasonable limits. The additional amounts of nutrients required to protect quality have to be provided through the feed, and corresponding adjustments must be made. Neither animals nor plants can perform production miracles from nothing. Some writings on these matters make you believe that this is considered feasible. Provided the animals are not subjected to undue strain, they are nevertheless capable of converting considerable amounts of additional nutrients.

It should be added that high productivity can only be maintained by a relentless chemical battle against man's competitors. Unfortunately, this has created more hazards, this time from residues of spray chemicals or by a deterioration of quality, in some cases so serious that the product may not be marketable. In these as in all other circumstances, gains have to be weighed against losses and a reasonable balance sought. The limitations of the producing machineries of our animals are, however, clearly felt in modern high-pressure production and far from always mastered.

Feed in the Tropics

Evidently the feed composition is another vital factor in regard to quality. As already indicated, livestock animals, with the exception of ruminants, require in relative terms as much protein as do humans. Like man, they cannot live and produce on energy-calories alone; they need protein as well as adequate amounts of other nutrients. In Western nations this was learned through hard-won experience, and modern animal production no longer can afford to neglect a strict observance of the demands raised by the feed formulas for proteins, amino acids, minerals, and vitamins. Particularly in this respect false notions prevail in our advice to countries with a different climate, when tacitly assuming that the lush and juicy grasslands of the humid tropics offer feed values equivalent to those of the grasses of our own pastures. In effect the differences are enormous.

The tropical grass strains are usually rich in water but poor in minerals and above all in protein. Large amounts of fertilizers are needed in order to make them approach to a reasonable degree the corresponding figures for temperate regions. The response to fertilizers is as a rule considerably less effective in the tropics, compared to the responses in our climate and latitudes. This factor contributes to the higher returns from Africa's wild hoofed animals as compared to livestock. The former eat the seeds and pods of several wild legumes and acquire in this way valuable protein supplementation. Most soils in the humid tropics do not stand up to permanent grazing. This has the surprising consequence that besides a low return from natural pastures comes a need for large extra acreages. These require a hazardous harvesting, and costly preservation is called for, and yet the use of commercial feed concentrates may be necessary—all procedures that many Westerners would believe to be superfluous in warm latitudes.

Consequently these limitations, raised by inferior feed, have nothing to do with backwardness. Even when modern agricultural methods were fully applied, *e.g.,* by the cattle raisers of Hawaii, it was discovered that the locally produced feed was wholly inadequate. Concentrates and other feed must be supplemented to compensate for the low protein output of the pastures, even when lavishly fertilized and supervised.

In the dry tropics, as well as on the steppes and many natural grasslands of the earth, shortage of water drastically limits the possibilities for livestock production. Furthermore the disease risks of the tropics are higher, a menace which is dealt with in the chapter "Man's Competitors for Food."

Climate

Like plants, animals depend on the climate. The exceptional measures taken in our animal production to provide high-producing livestock and poultry with a controlled artificial environment through airconditioning installations testify to this fact. But the dependence upon climate is often overlooked in yield comparisons between nations. Breeding stock of animals are readily available today on the international market. But in far too many instances such transferred animals meet with entirely different climatic conditions and completely new hazards. The menacing diseases are new to them, and frequently these are much more aggressive against high-producing, overly susceptible animals introduced from other climatic spheres. In such instances diseases have a much more devastating effect. High-breed animals normally have high susceptibility to primitive and adverse ecological, microbial, and parasitic factors. The production machinery becomes disturbed or collapses under the strains, *e.g.*, the exposure to different daylengths and abrupt temperature changes. Despite many efforts the tropics still lack efficient milk-producing cattle, outside of the buffalo.

Large regions in Africa and certain parts of Brazil are so affected with sleeping sickness, rinderpest, and other ravaging diseases that man has had to concede defeat despite large-scale efforts over a number of years to build up protection for the livestock and eradicate pests and diseases. These biological limitations are further review on pp. 125–126.

Game Cropping

Finally it deserves to be noted that great advances in the field of animal husbandry and impressive productivity gains notwithstanding, there still are regions on earth where man's livestock cannot compete with wild animals in yield per acre. This is true of tropical Africa with its many hoofed animals, which through the centuries have probably become immune to prevalent diseases and other enemies. Properly managed, they yield in some areas greater amounts of meat per acre than the average farms in the same general region, and this despite the fact that the ranchers, thanks to highly efficient crop cultivation and improved pastures, produce more feed than nature provides.

We touch here upon a far-reaching and important subject, *viz.*, the biomass, or the entire living mass within an area. In practical terms agricultural cropping actually means that man selects a sector of the biomass and develops this at the expense of almost everything else with all the impending risks and possible gains such a procedure involves. But it is by no means self-evident that we surpass nature in terms of productivity by such maneuvers. Man cannot repeal the law of the survival of the fittest. Under the relentless rules of this law within the hierarchy of living beings of a richly faceted fauna and flora, there is a tough competition going on among the plants, the animals, and between these two. Each species utilizes different niches in this intricate living system and as it seems at a high level of efficiency. At the same time this entire ecosystem is constantly being readjusted through complex biological feedback and kept in balance so that no single component gets the upper hand. The end result is frequently a total production that is larger than that of the more imbalanced system created and controlled by man within his agricultural framework.

In warm and dry areas man has especially overestimated the agricultural potential. We are in this instance confronted with a phenomenon similar to the destructive effect of overgrazing. Far too many cattle have been let loose on the pastures with the result that the grass cover is trampled. The soil is laid bare. Wind and water continue the damage. The consequences are especially disastrous in the arid regions. Today there is considerable agreement that such overgrazing has been the cause of the serious erosion prevailing in large parts of Australia. Instead of restricting or even reducing the grip of the deserts by extending the border regions employed for plant cropping, man has added extensive wasteland regions to the world household. This has happened with the Sahara and Kalahari deserts (see the chapter "New Heavens and New Earths"). The goat has been the primary marauder in those regions, since it grazes much closer than other livestock. Admittedly, however, the goat in many areas, *e.g.,* Pakistan, India, and Egypt, has become the poor man's cow because it is satisfied to feed on plant-stuffs which otherwise would remain untouched.

Confronted with these limitations for animal husbandry in arid regions, man almost since time immemorial has brought in water. Making these dry areas "bloom" and produce obviously required considerable effort and frequently large-scale spending. But again: What price is man willing to pay, and how far are we willing to go, in order to push such frontiers farther out and beyond economically reasonable limits? Anyhow, far greater efforts than our present ones will be needed to meet the orders placed by the burgeoning populations. Mankind will, in any case, be forced to recognize that the globe, after all, is limited, and water may well become our first critical resource. Biological restraint and a revamped economy represent the only path that will lead to health and peace for mankind. The difficult art of restraint always has been looked upon as a sign of nobility, but we have now reached the point where its practice on a universal scale constitutes the only road to salvation.

The Protein Swindle

In the Rich World, livestock raising has unfortunately lost almost all contact with the soil and its productivity. Grazing pastures with silaging and feed storage on the farm was more conducive to a better touch with reality. Modern commercial feeds for cattle and broiler establishments, and cage methods for egglayers in the hundreds of thousands, are the melody of the day. The feedstuffs are purchased, and little thought is given to the amount of land required to produce their huge quantities, whether these acreages lie in distant exporting lands or come from within the country. Animal husbandry has more and more taken on the character of industry, small as well as giant, with feed as input and food as output. Very few farmers of North America and western Europe look upon their livestock in relation to the yields of their own land acreages. Very few, indeed, can tell how many acres are needed for each cow or for ten hogs. On the whole, it has been stated, when the yield spiral moves upward, and the harvests are getting larger, automatically more animals can be fed. This may not necessarily be so. In the raising of most animals it is even more crucial than for humans to fill the minimal protein needs. Trade statistics testify to what extent the transoceanic flow of feedstuffs moves between the rich and well-fed nations or flows in from the Hungry World, still further boosting the privileged standing of the rich. Of the United States soybean export, 57 percent goes to western Europe to make fat for the margarine industry and feed for dairy cattle, other livestock, and poultry. The residues of the oilseed pressing, by and large, move in the form of oilseed cakes (presscakes) to the same destination. Crowning this swindle, the Western countries receive nine-tenths of the world's fish-meal production.

Some selected figures (see p. 236 and tables, pp. 239–40) show indirectly to what a surprising degree the protein provision for dairy cattle and poultry, particularly in Europe (both east and west), has become dependent upon transoceanic shipments of feed and upon fish meal from the oceans. This latter source is equally vital to the poultry industry of the United States.

Proteins from United States soybeans are in a similar way indispensable to North American dairy production, so that only a trifle amount of this first-rate human food is allowed to flow into the needy, hungry world. The stark realities of traditional economics ru'e this state of affairs, but weighed in terms of the global human household, it is neither rational nor economic.

The hungry world cannot expect increases of significance in their animal production. The protein shortage sets a harsh and unyielding limit to such expansions. Within foreseeable time, the poor countries simply cannot afford to raise the protein supplies up to the artificial level to which we have pushed them in our parts of the world. Our glittering achievements are basically products of the almost monopolistic preference the western world enjoys on the world's international feed market. In addition this is centered upon the number one shortage commodity of the Hungry World, protein. We are in a position to outbid any competitor on this market easily, and we readily do so, no matter the magnitude of his needs and demands. On the basis of any kind of rational allocation principle the well-fed nations are the least likely to be selected as recipients of these invaluable nutritional riches. Sometimes one wonders how many Americans and western Europeans have grasped the fact that quite a few of their beef steaks, quarts of milk, dozens of eggs, and hundreds of broilers are the result, not of their agriculture, but rather of the approximately two million metric tons of protein, mostly of high quality, which astute Western businessmen channel away from the needy and hungry. In latter years Japan has followed suit and is copying the Western world to provide for its aspiring livestock industry; some feed is purchased, but primarily these advances are based on the floating fishmeal factories, which in summertime operate in the Bering Straits and in wintertime along the African west coast off Angola. There are already unmistakable signs of Japan's retracting from this kind of extravagance. A growing number of these factory ships are now manufacturing raw fish flesh, ground and frozen on board, for subsequent use in the manufacturing of fish sausages. By spanning the globe in these operations, it is easy to lose contact with reality, and it becomes hard under such conditions to realize that there are critical limitations for human existence also in the affluent world. The livestock of our Western farms are not as miraculous producers as is commonly believed; in the end they draw upon the entire world as a basis for their production and also upon the plankton pastures of the oceans—this latter also in the United States.

HOW MANY?

The futile question is often raised: How many can the world feed? This depends primarily upon which standard one has in mind; whether we want to live like Chinese, East Indians, or Americans. All three can be adequately fed, but the composition of daily food, the ratio of animal to plant products, is highly different. If this question is posed in relation to the causal factors discussed in this chapter, the answer takes on a somewhat different character. It is in this particular respect that the wildest conclusions are drawn and the most generous promises are made.

Most experts look at their own little research sector and draw from such findings lofty and even whimsical conclusions. The energy researcher sees everything as an energy problem leaving unconsidered the elementary nutritional needs of man as well as his dependence upon a long list of specifically built molecules, isomers, essential fatty acids, and amino acids, vitamins, etc. He calculates that the sunflow to the earth would be enough to provide food for 900 billion people. Long before that stage has been reached, most accessible coal of the globe would have passed over into human bodies, and thus the whole machinery would have been brought to a standstill at a much earlier stage when the resources and reserves of other commodities, essential to man, were exhausted.

The nutritionist calculates that man eats about 1 percent of what the earth produces and that it should thus be possible to cater to more than ninety-five times as many as the numbers of the present world population. He overlooks that other living organisms not only have a right to food but also are indispensable to man's existence, *e.g.,* spiders, insect-eating birds, cats, etc., not to mention our big friendly armies among the microorganisms. This type of estimate also overlooks the fact that a much larger portion of what is in the global trough already is required to produce the food we now consume, in effect six to seven times more than the 1 percent figure might make one believe.

The soil experts take inventories of the soils and are usually more moderate in their promises, but they seem inclined to reserve too little for forestry and for human settlements (housing developments, and such other human activities as industries, airfields, etc.). Finally man will even be short of standing room, already reflected in the creation of skyscrapers. Frequently, in order to be in the run for the highest bids, the soil scientists visualize most agricultural land as tilled, although evidently large expanses always will require plant cover protection.

The plant breeder and his colleague, the animal breeder, measure the achievements in improved yields and multiply them glibly on a global scale, without previously surveying available water, mineral reserves, and other productional means. The successful farmer in North America and western Europe looks at his own returns from crop production and livestock and believes that they can be copied the world around. The fertilizer expert eyes the world in his particular light, calculating the enormous markets merely waiting for exploitation, without taking into account the limiting factors discussed earlier. The economists analyze trends, price quotations, and foreign trade, not considering their fundamental basis in resources: forests, water, and soil. The law of diminishing returns seems to be completely forgotten, and limiting factors "technology" cannot overcome seem not to be admitted. The yield figures are expected to continue skyrocketing in some miraculous way, seemingly without limit, if only the holy profitability can be safeguarded.

By and large everyone sees his particular sector function on the productivity scene as the driving force of world agriculture. Nobody disputes that there are prime motors driving us ahead, but we are far too little trained to think in a coordinative manner and fit the details into feasible programs. Sight is lost of the categories of reality. What happens in the real world is not determined by all these individual factors, but to a much greater extent by those factors that limit the functioning of the whole, the bottlenecks of production. Our entire academic training has fallen victim to this kind of analytical outlook, thinking that in some peculiar manner a fine mosaic pattern is going to emerge by putting the pieces together. In effect very little attention is paid to the kind of pattern achieved. The synthesis fails or is neglected in our feverish analyses. Means are placed ahead of goals. Tactics and tactical maneuverings are given precedence over strategy. It has been our great fallacy to believe that by willing the means we would reach the goal, in this case feeding the hungry.

Every Increase in Yield Has Its Price

The most salutary viewpoint when probing into the crucial question, How much further can the yield spiral be pushed upward? is perhaps the realization that as a rule each effort toward

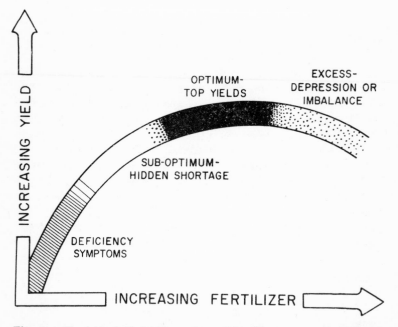

Fig. 17. The law of diminishing returns. The effect upon productivity of various amounts of input such as water, fertilizers, etc., gradually levels off and may even reverse itself. The higher the yield, the smaller the net return of each additional identical amount of input.

this goal places big extra demands on capital in the form of investments and above all in terms of basic resources such as waters, soils, and their mineral nutrients. The question is: Are we willing to pay this additional price, and then, are we capable of doing so? In theory it is evident that the United States could feed as many as China harbors today and yet maintain its high standard of living. We could without any doubt produce the huge quantities of meat, eggs, butter, milk, etc., which this would require, but are we willing to pay the price when already at the present level of production water is getting in short supply in both the South and the West? Thus parts of the North American continent share with several other sections of the world the feature of taking out in many key areas more water than the hydrological cycle is returning. The United States is moving toward a crisis. In the crucial areas—Texas and southern California—water resources are being emptied, and this basically through what might be called a mining of water, Pleistocene in origin and accumulated over thousands of years. It can be safely concluded that an operation like feeding a United States population in number equivalent to that of present-day China (780 million) simply cannot be implemented without drastic changes in our present nutritional standard. The United States is currently rapidly moving toward such figures; with present rate of growth a population figure exceeding 1,000 million could be reached a hundred years from now.

So gigantic an accomplishment as feeding 780 million within the United States has many other consequences. A prerequisite for this would presumably be a total mobilization, with drastic political consequences, where the decried Chinese communes can be glimpsed at the end of the road. But in more concrete terms such a giant operation is most likely to require a considerable tapping of our major freshwater reserve, the Great Lakes, the largest such reservoir on earth. Are we prepared to lose St. Lawrence Seaway and the Mississippi water artery merely for the dubious pleasure of cramming together three-quarter billion people within our present borders? Are we prepared to build the hundreds of fertilizer plants this would take and construct the additional highway system the delivery of fertilizers would necessitate? Such are the types of questions we should be pondering in this context.

What Do We Do Next?

The most important question of all is perhaps: What do we do next? There is no indication that the United States could stop abruptly at the three-quarter billion figure. What does the next generation do? They will be bound by exactly the same natural laws that pertain to us. No technology on earth, no scientific breakthroughs can change the basic premises for man's existence. For this very reason the common talk that science and technology will solve our dilemma is both glib and irresponsible. We certainly need all the ingenuity, creativity, and innovation that humankind can master to cope with the frightful dilemma we are facing, that of feeding those 3.5 billion now living on earth, of which only 1.1 billion are reasonably adequately fed, and only 300 to 350 million eat as well as the average American. It is therefore imperative that we abandon our present hazardous ventures in favor of realistic and workable programs that take into account the obvious limitations that prevail for man's existence, on which this book elaborates. Already the present feeding burden is overwhelming, not to mention that of the future billions.

CHAPTER IV

Food and
Microorganisms

When relating food to microorganisms, most people have in mind primarily the armies of destructive agents in the form of yeast, mold, and bacteria, which take their toll in damaged and destroyed foods on the fields, in storage, and during distribution. It is evident that these kinds of losses despite numerous counter-measures are a heavy burden on the common household of the world. Even in a highly developed country like the United States, the annual losses through microorganisms alone are estimated to exceed two billion dollars. This despite the fact that we take comfort in the notion that chemicals keep pests and diseases from our fields. With such chemical means we have created strong barriers around our crops. Yet these obstacles are not impenetrable.

Food scientists are inclined to point out how modern preservation and storage methods have largely disposed of the risks for microbial attacks, not only temporarily but rather permanently. In England fifty-seven-year-old cans were recently opened, and the contents were found to be first rate. Canned foods of even higher age have on earlier occasions been tasted and analyzed without registering noticeable damage.

We forget that these technological methods, from which we

benefit daily in *our* part of the world, are either far too costly or too complicated for application in countries where the technical and economic development is not yet on our level. Furthermore, we close our eyes to the fact that we ourselves often fall short of the goals and suffer considerable losses both in the storage and the preservation of foods. Man is in effect involved in a constantly raging battle for his food. There are in this area no finite victories. The microorganisms fight back, and often in unexpected ways. The canning factories are involved in an ever-sharpening struggle against a number of heat-thriving microorganisms which develop at high temperatures, thermophiles (heat-loving) which cause a great deal of harm. The cold storage facilities select another type of microorganism, the psychrophiles (cold-loving). These reduce the efficiency of chilling procedures. Other fungi and bacteria adjust themselves to such of our preservatives as benzoic acid, and some of them even learn to thrive on them. In the living world of microorganisms there are no final successes or victories. Man is involved in a never-ceasing struggle for his existence. The microorganisms constantly open up new battle fronts, and man has to mobilize his full vigilance and keep a permanent guard.

With the growing importance of institutional feeding, new types of food poisoning appear from time to time. Furthermore, each case involves so many more people, due to this type of feeding. It is not at all rare that one single contaminated food supply may affect hundreds, even thousands of people.

The Intestinal Flora

Ever since the discovery of the microorganisms a vivid discussion has been going on about whether these agents are friends or enemies of man. In reality they are both, and we may safely assert that without the aid of the microorganisms man would not be able to survive. In everyday life we are apt to forget these immense armies of faithful servants which occupy our intestinal system and assist the body in the transformation and utilization of food. It is still an open question to what degree this flora takes a part in supplying certain nutrients. We do not yet know to what degree some bacteria are capable of converting food ingredients into such indispensable substances and making them accessible as food supplement. Research in this particular field has been neglected. Not even studies of the feeding of microbe-free animals have given reliable information in this respect. The discomfort and risks accompanying the intake of antibiotics against perilous diseases may be an indication of the indispensability of our intestinal flora, if for no other reason than to stave off the invasion of still more dangerous attackers than the original ones. At any rate, some antibiotics may cause havoc among the regular intestinal flora, another reminder of the asset microorganisms represent to man. When that protective flora is lost, life may even be jeopardized.

Two facts are well acknowledged: (1) Man has associated himself with certain kinds of bacteria which even during infant nursing take the lead and become dominant to stave off invasion of hazardous microorganisms. (2) If this microbial defense system of patrol guards is disturbed, man may fall victim to diarrhea and may even die. Despite, as mentioned above, our information being scanty about the intestinal flora, it appears that under certain circumstances it may provide supplementation to man's diet in the shape of certain vitamins. It is therefore important that our diet is composed in such a way that this friendly flora is kept flourishing. When the balance is upset, there may be danger ahead.

The Microbial Feats in the Rumen

This singular intestinal flora has been discussed in some detail, as it gives us the clue to the understanding of another similar chemical conversion center where microorganisms of various kinds play a key role and perhaps in a manner more decisive to man and his standing on earth, not the least as a basis for his food supply. This applies to the rumen, the first one of the four stomachs of the cow. In the rumen the feed consumed by the cow undergoes its first degradation before the rechewing (cudding). Bacteria, protozoans, and many other microorganisms are active here in harmonious cooperation. From the point of view of man, two circumstances are of particular interest in this context. One is the fact that plants make certain compounds in large quantities, such as cellulose, which the human intestinal system cannot digest, but they are readily transformed in the rumen and used in the feeding of the cow—finally rendering milk. Furthermore, by starting with simple inorganic nitrogen salts, the flora of the rumen is capable of synthesizing amino acids which are in turn building-stones of protein. It is no coincidence that the ruminants constitute such a dominating group among the wild animals in the world, perhaps not in number of species, but in number of animals. To this group belong bisons, buffaloes, llamas, gazelles, deers, antelopes, giraffes, and many others.

The ruminants—cows, sheep, goats, and camels—also form the largest group among the domesticated animals, with the cow in the lead. Measured in living organic biomass, the cattle of the world consume two and a half times more than does the total number of humans. This might also be formulated in this way: To the immense benefit of man, the cow has been able to create a massive bridgehead in the plant kingdom by utilizing the cellulose resources which man's gastric system is not capable of using. The cow has thus been able to provide man with a major share of his meat and milk. This is one reason the disappearance of the cow would not render the net gain claimed by vegetarians, in particular since the rumen can operate entirely on inorganic sources.

In recent decades a great deal of interest has been bestowed upon another group of animals, which might have a similar role, namely the insects. Nitrogen-fixing bacteria have been found in the intestinal systems of many insect species. The termites are known for their ability to devour wood. Perhaps man would be well advised to look for future livestock animals among the insects! Locust swarms and larval rains have ever since biblical times been looked upon as godsends for the hungry.

Nitrogen Fixation

In discussing the rumen, we touch upon an entirely different section of the human food front where the microorganisms are of key importance to man's survival. I have in mind the nitrogen fixation in nature. This takes place partly through microorganisms that live freely in the soil and are capable of converting the nitrogen of the air via a series of processes into protein. The leguminous family of plants has, however, attracted most attention in this respect. In this case the nitrogen-fixing microorganisms live in the roots and rootlets and deliver amino acids directly to the plant, which in turn becomes part of the protein synthesis in peas and beans, both in the seeds and other parts of these plants.

There has been a great deal of discussion, not the least between the scientists in the West and those in the East, over whether the freely living nitrogen-fixers of the soils are of vital significance. It is easy to figure out that approximately 500 to 1,250 pounds of organic matter is needed per acre to feed the free-living bacteria, thereby keeping these miniature nitrogen factories in full operation. In most soils this feed demand would not only create practical problems but also be too expensive.

It is noteworthy that, despite all agricultural research, in many parts of the world we still do not have a clear picture of the nitrogen balance in the soils. There are many indications that the mobilization en masse of chemically produced nitrogen, amounting to 15.5 million tons annually (1967), may have put many of these our unpaid helpers out of business. One could say that the nitrogen-fixing bacteria soon discovered they no longer had to go to the trouble of collecting nitrogen from the air, as ready-made nitrogenous salts were lavished upon them by man in his fertilizing. At any rate most experiments indicate that these nitrogen-fixing microorganisms react in this manner. It is therefore quite possible that man has taken upon himself a considerably larger burden than is actually necessary. More than half a billion people depend today for their protein supply upon artificially supplied nitrogen in the form of nitrogenous commercial fertilizers. The majority of these people live in the rich world. We the well-fed could afford this kind of operation, but when we turn to the poor world with advice and instructions, such wastefulness is not equally commendable. The contrary might in several instances be more appropriate. If India, Indonesia, China, Africa, and tropical Latin America are going to improve the productivity of their soils fast enough, there will not be time for the construction of fertilizer factories in sufficient numbers. This is explained in detail in the earlier chapter "Will Chemistry Offer Mankind the Third Freedom?" Besides, the true fact is that those countries cannot in effect afford this procedure. They will have to mobilize some of nature's own resources, and this cannot be done to greater advantage than on this neglected front of nitrogen fixation.

The Secret of Rice Cultivation

As many have pointed out, and as was analyzed in detail in my previous book, *The Hungry Planet* (1965 and 1967), protein is the most critical shortage facing mankind. To maintain an adequate supply of protein, a constant supply of several raw materials is required, but above all nitrogen and sulfur. A fascinating aspect of this question is the fact that rice cultivation around the globe has well withstood the test of the generations thanks to the thin layer of blue-green algae growing on the soil surface and developing in pace with the rice plants. Man as a cultivator has presumably been little aware of this key factor in rice growing and its benefits. But on the other hand the empirical procedures evolved through centuries took this into account. In this case it is not primarily bacteria that operate, but it seems to be these blue-green algae that perform the trick of binding the nitrogen of the air, thereby manufacturing nitrogenous substances from which protein subsequently is synthesized in the rice plant. Possibly these algae cooperate with certain bacteria. They also have a second important function, namely that of providing the roots with oxygen, quite vital since the rice plant stands in water and according to all rules should be hampered in its growth by a limited access to free oxygen. Besides, certain snails are indispensable to ventilate the producing soil layer and transfer the calcium of their shells to the surface. Some minerals come via irrigation water.

What kind of additional role do the algae, not only those belonging to the blue-green category, play in the agriculture also of the developed world? Again we encounter a neglected field of research where only fragmentary observations have been made, despite the fact that most soils are invaded on the surface by a great number of such organisms growing filaments, fronds, or single cells. The Japanese have understood the importance of tackling these complications in a realistic and efficient way. They have constructed small machines, operating on water from hot springs, or on natural gas, for the cultivation of a certain blue-green algae with special capability for fixing nitrogen. The particular strain being used was originally discovered in Borneo (Indonesia) and brought to Japan. By cultivating this little plant in these miniature factories, a kind of village industry has been created. Each unit produces an amount of algae adequate for spreading over 750 acres (300 hectares). Such bacterial fertilization is repeated biannually. This is the kind of invention that underdeveloped nations need and can afford to procure and operate.

In the chapter on the role of chemistry it is pointed out how much steel and energy are required for each ton of nitrogen when converted into fertilizer in a factory. Such costs make the application of these methods in poor countries difficult. They are rather well advised to avoid such wasteful adventures. In addition the water consumption is considerable, and frequently comes into direct conflict with the water needs for the crops. To see to it that the microorganisms in nature function efficiently and get adequate assistance in their supporting service to man is consequently a far cheaper and more effective alternative in securing food for the hungry who also are poor.

The Food Front in the Soil

Topsoil contains a teeming multitude of living organisms, dominated by microorganisms. In addition there are worms, insect larvae, centipedes, and many others. As already pointed out, the primary producers in the soil, capable of rendering organic matter starting from the carbon dioxide and the nitrogen of the air, are in effect the algae. They may be called the feeding partners of the soil. In addition the soil receives a great deal of organic matter through leaf wastes and the root systems of the crops when they die off after the harvest. Thus many nutrients become available to such consuming microorganisms as fungi, bacteria, protozoans, etc. Without this continuous degradation of organic matter, man would soon suffocate under the burden of immense quantities of waste. Perhaps the oil resources of the earth once originated in this way. But in this intense, many-sided microbial activity there are certain aspects which are especially important in regard to agricultural production and thereby man's food.

In their growth and development the microorganisms con-

SOIL ORGANISMS kg/ha

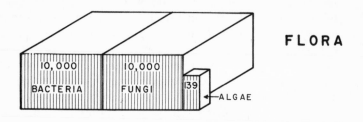

FLORA

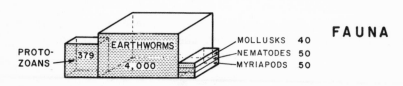

FAUNA

Fig. 18. Soil organisms in kilograms per hectare in well-cultivated soil

tribute to the freeing of calcium, phosphate, potassium, etc., in the soil. All these minerals and many more which the microorganisms assimilate in order to grow again become available upon their death. They have a life-span of a couple of days, sometimes merely hours, and assist in this way in what is termed the mineralization of the soils. Many soils bind minerals and make them inaccessible for the uptake of the roots of various crops. In this light, these path-clearing activities of the microorganisms take on particular significance. Since they make these nutritive resources more readily available, they are in many cases a prerequisite for a reasonable growth of crops.

The grand armies of microbial billions thriving within the topsoil layer of a first-rate pasture consume in terms of organic matter an amount equivalent to what a cow generally takes when grazing above soil. A field of grain crop or a pasture should be looked upon in those terms, remindful of the fact that the consumers invisible to the human eye are equivalent to a grazing cow. These living organisms in the topsoil must be fed if it is to bear and to yield persistently. In this living world of microorganisms below the soil surface a struggle for survival is also raging—a fight involving life and death, and quite as intense as the struggle above ground. The bacteria are grazed by protozoans, microscopic unicellular organisms with certain animal-like qualities as predators. Within a few hours they can devour immense quantities of bacteria on which they feed, at the same time keeping them in check. Our knowledge is far too scanty about this kaleidoscopically changing, living world of the soil and its laws. The fact that most plants have an individual satellite system of a special microbial flora surrounding the roots constitutes an interesting indication of how complex this microbial world is, and it is becoming increasingly evident how fundamental it is to agricultural productivity. Maybe each one of these species makes a particular and singular contribution to the well-being of the plant or protects it against intruding spoiling agents.

Fermented Products

The preserving of foods by means of various microbial fermentation processes was a method man derived early in his history. Such fermented products are clearly distinguishable from spoiled foods, this being the result of a detrimental decomposition. Empirically man developed methods of fermentation which rendered preserving compounds such as alcohol, lactic acid, and several other substances antibiotically active. In this way the foundation was laid, even in primitive stages, for the manufacturing of cheese, acidified and fermented milks, wine, beer, and sauerkraut, all with reasonably good keeping qualities. Food preservation through fermentation is the basis of modern feed silaging. Together with products preserved through the application of salt, fermented foods have been fundamental features in human diet for thousands of years. Sometimes a combination of both methods has been employed.

China and Japan have a whole array of fermented soybean products; such as *natto, miso, tofu,* etc., which in a way correspond to our rich collection of cheeses, but based on the protein of soybean instead of that of milk. In the Indonesian islands coconut is preserved in a relatively similar way and transformed into a cheesy pulp. In Southeast Asia, fermented sauces are made from fish, a counterpart to fermented Baltic herring but decomposed to a much higher degree, and served with almost every meal. In extreme cases a liquid as transparent as water, *nuoc-mam,* is produced. This is nothing but liquefied potable fish protein obtained through lengthy hydrolytic breakdown. Undesirable microbial spoilers are kept out simply by adding salt.

Unfortunately, modern research has failed to take guidance from these lessons of history in producing cheap, storable, and nourishing foodstuffs. An intriguing aspect is the relative absence of food poisonings induced by these products, which superficially judged might seem potentially hazardous. There is every reason to expect that such fermented products will take on greater importance when poor developing countries are looking for economical and reliable methods to safeguard food and feed.

Waste into Food

The decomposing activity of microorganisms becomes especially important in the utilization of waste which would not otherwise be useful to man, such as sulfate solution from pulp factories, mash from breweries and alcohol factories, whey from dairies, and perhaps the most important, human waste from our cities, which moves into sewage plants. In all these cases man depends on microorganisms, either for the decomposition of organic matter taking place on a major scale in sewage plants, or for the production of microorganisms, particularly yeasts or fungi, which can be used as feed or food.

Man already is consuming a considerable amount of food, resulting from microbial activity. Yeasts are ingredients in several types of food such as bread, soups, beer, etc. Many kinds of cheeses have a rich microbial flora on the surface. Despite recommendations to eat also the rind on cheeses such as Camembert, a great deal of good nourishment is discarded in the removal of this protective cover. The Chinese and later the Japanese cultivated fungi long before mushrooms were raised in Europe. Some fungal gardens were created on tree trunks, which had either fallen down

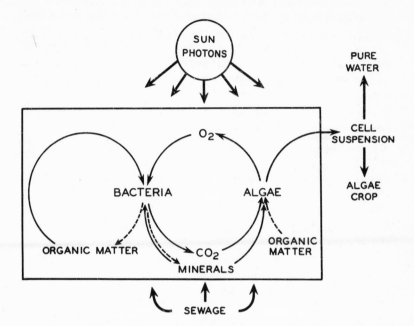

Fig. 19. Sewage "purification" through the growing of algae coordinated with bacterial decomposition. Oxygen is released and organic matter builds up in algal cells.

themselves or were felled for this specific purpose. This kind of "gardening" still takes place. In many parts of the world wild mushrooms are collected as well as preserved but merely a pittance of the thousands of wild species have been taken into cultivation. Today morels can be produced in factories and there are many signs that a great many other fungi could be cultivated in the same way and be utilized to give variation to the human diet. How the sewage plants of the future will convert sewage into food with the aid of microorganisms in the form of algae, fungi, and bacteria is described in the chapter "Tomorrow's Dinner." Most likely this conversion will not be limited to such a production of mushrooms and yeast but will proceed further by utilizing these products as feed for the raising of fish, shrimp, or ducks.

It is particularly favorable to marshal microorganisms for food production, as in this way it is feasible to produce protein at a high conversion rate. In any case the time involved in making protein is much shorter than with cattle, hogs, and other livestock. Within a few hours the yeast fungi perform a production miracle which it takes beef cattle months to accomplish. In other instances, as in Germany during World War II, fat was produced from various types of yeast, but under normal circumstances this alternative is far less urgent than the manufacturing of protein.

The Find of the Aztecs

Only recently was it possible to identify an item in the food larders of the Aztecs. Tenochtitlàn, the Aztec capital (now known as Mexico City), was surrounded by lakes that have since vanished in the Mexican quest for water. On the surface of the lakes a blue-green algae grew, forming a scum that was collected, dried, and molded into small loaves. These were cut in slices and eaten, for they constituted good protein food. Saharan tribes living around Lake Chad still make a similar product.

This blue-green algae and the Aztec way of processing it was discovered by French scientists, and it has since been grown successfully in pilot projects in southern France. The nutritive value of the protein was given a good rating. Poor people in present-day China get protein through an inexpensive product called *lan,* prepared in a similar way from blue-green algae growing on pond and lake surfaces. Further research will undoubtedly prove the future value of this microorganism, not as livestock but as a regular crop, based on the nitrogen-fixing capability of blue-green algae. Possibly its cell wall is less elaborate than that of other plant cells and thus more readily available to man's gastric juices. Several blue-greens, however, make compounds toxic to man.

Microorganisms as Livestock

Time is not the limiting factor in the making of microbial food. It is rather the restricted access to feed for the microorganisms, this livestock of a new era, as they have been designated. Microorganisms too must be fed. In principle they function in the same way as man's livestock. They cannot themselves produce everything they must consume in order to grow and develop and need to be provided with a series of special compounds as feed. As long as waste is used for this purpose the economic feasibility is considerably enhanced. But resorting to products raised on tilled land for the feeding of the microorganisms makes these ventures highly questionable.

A similar weakness applies to the present discussion about the cultivation of microorganisms on the waste from oil refineries for the purpose of producing protein. It should be evident that such oil residues provide, at the most, the carbon source. Sulfur, phosphorus, and other substances required for microbial growth must be added from other sources or be available in the oil residues in adequate amounts. Such a procedure is naturally quite feasible, but these external raw materials should be added to the balance sheet in any appraisal of this method. In order to produce food it is therefore far from sufficient to have oil residues. They constitute only one source of raw material, basically the carbon. They provide only part of the feed required for these rather demanding microbial creatures. The main difficulty with this manufacture of protein is, however, that the oil resources of the world are already in a squeeze as an energy source and will be so still more in the not too distant future. Man would get involved in a direct conflict between food and energy if he were to resort to this way of processing food.

Sooner or later synthetic foods, whether they are made on a purely chemical basis or with the aid of microorganisms, will pass the human body. They then break down through the metabolism into carbon dioxide, ammonia, and other compounds. In view of the nonrenewable nature of these carbon resources (oil or coal), man will once again be thrown back upon the dependence of the unsurpassed capability of the green plant to collect and convert carbon dioxide. Mineral oils can therefore at best alleviate man's critical situation only temporarily, even if this project were on the whole economically feasible. In the long run truly synthetic food offers no real solution to the food shortage of man. At the most such foods will offer him a brief period of grace. Synthetic foods are by no means any permanent and true extension of man's domain (biosphere) but merely a short-term conquest. Man will soon again be pushed back within the limitations for his existence, as set by nature.

Microbial Vitamins

We shall discuss two instances where microorganisms in a decisive way contribute to the feeding of man. One vitamin, B_{12}, which was discovered as late as 1928, has the surprising feature, as far as is known, of being produced only by microorganisms. This may be expressed differently: Man is in this instance dependent both for his health and survival on the producing machinery of the microbial realm. In sewage, with its intense microbial activity, this vitamin is so concentrated that it is even found in the bottom silt of recipient lakes. The surface of certain marine algae is covered with a rich microbial flora, which among other things is engaged in the production of B_{12}. Both fish and shellfish take in B_{12} via the microbial flora of water. Along intricate channels B_{12} does transfer, or migrate, from microorganisms into meat and milk, as well as becoming enriched in brain, liver, and kidney tissue. The soil with its rich microbial flora also contains B_{12}. In many regions of the globe people obtain this vitamin by direct eating of soil (geophagy) and manure. To what degree the human intestinal flora normally, or merely under certain circumstances, supplies this vitamin to the human body is still an open question. Vegetarians frequently get low in the B_{12} level of their blood, which might indicate that the intestinal flora is not too effective a provider or at any rate not dependable. Many grazing animals seem to be furnished with B_{12} this way, particularly the ruminants via the flora of the rumen.

Today B_{12} can be produced in large quantities both from sewage and lake silt and at a low cost. Since this vitamin plays a decisive role in the full utilization of plant products this source may be increasingly important as the world is forced closer to a vegetarian diet. In this case such supplementation is indispensable. It is also possible to manufacture B_{12} directly in factories with the aid of high-yielding microbial strains.

The Sulfur Front

Still more conclusive perhaps is the role of the microorganisms in the sulfur cycle of the world. Search for the origin of the large sulfur quantities in the air has long been proceeding. Even when calculating with the increase in carbon combustion caused by industrialization—with its ensuing sulfur buildup in the air via smoke, principally from coal-driven electricity plants—there are still several million metric tons of sulfur annually thrown out into the air oceans, for which we cannot account. Some time ago it was discovered that large coastal areas, when exposed through the withdrawal of tidal waters, release hydrogen sulfide to the air through the metabolic activities of an abundant flora of sulfur bacteria. In several locations, the Black Sea and certain sections of the world oceans, for instance along the southwest African coast and off Peru, considerable amounts of hydrogen sulfide are produced at great depths. Off and on such gas forces itself to the surface and reaches the air due to turbulence and aberrations in current flows. The overloading of waters with waste has given man an additional source of sulfur resulting from the decomposition of waste at the bottom of lakes, rivers, and ocean stretches. It has been suggested that the gondolas of Venice were painted black in order to conceal the discolorations most likely induced by hydrogen sulfide. These changes were too easily noticeable when the vessels were painted in lighter colors. All this hydrogen sulfide is the result of microbial activity—but essentially valuable to man since gradually it has become quite evident that sulfur is one of mankind's critical elements. Sulfur shortage is becoming increasingly felt in agriculture as phosphate fertilizers no longer are being produced with sulfuric acid. As the direct combustion of coal became history, sulfur via air pollution also was reduced; This is now switching back due to the upsurge of coal-driven electricity plants.

So far it has been far too little recognized that both sulfur and phosphorus constitute key substances in the buildup of protein, whether referring to plants, animals, or microorganisms. Without these elements life as well as protein production is inconceivable. It is therefore more than an academic question to what extent the receding protein front of mankind may be attributed to the shortage of these two cardinal substances.

Long before there are any signs of sulfur shortage showing up in crops, the proteins of grown products have as a rule lost some of their sulfurous amino acids. Only oysters, some fish species, and eggs contain these important nutrients in quantities adequate for the human diet. Grain, peas, beans of various kinds, and also nuts, milk, and meat are all in relative terms short in this respect when measured in terms of human need. This applies both to feed and to food. Several primitive civilizations sought out, entirely on an empirical basis, foodstuffs, particularly plant crops, which contributed these essential sulfurous amino acids such as sesame seed of the Middle East, funio of the Nigerians, and the amaranth of the American Indians.

Sulfur-containing amino acids are essential in many ways, not the least to the fat metabolism in the body. It is quite possible that they constitute one key element to the understanding of the disturbances in the fat metabolism, which have become so widespread in our time. The bacteria of the rumen possess the priceless capability to transform simple inorganic sulfate into these complicated organic sulfur-containing molecules—not only amino acids. Several of these are key elements in the metabolism of both nitrogen and phosphorus, in turn decisive to protein synthesis.

It is quite surprising to find that a number of mushrooms which are traditionally collected during the fall in the U.S.S.R., Scandinavia, Poland, and Germany are rich sources of methionine, one of these sulfurous amino acids. Today, eggs and certain freshwater fishes are almost the only foods in the everyday diet of Western countries which provide adequate quantities of methionine. Whether modern intensive meat and milk production has induced changes in the composition of the foods in this particular respect is an intriguing but yet open question. The diet of several primitive peoples appears, however, to be better in this particular. It is further food for thought that in modern feed mixtures, especially for poultry, a supplement of methionine is almost mandatory. Methionine is also deficient in the diet of many nations.

Supplementation with Amino Acids

Maybe one of the most important future contributions of microbiology will be to assist in the production of those amino acids that are obviously short in the diet, among which methionine deficit is the most serious handicap. Supplementation with specific amino acids in short supply seems less likely, since most civilizations have succeeded in various ways to combine in their diet foods such as fish and rice, soybeans and rice, beans and corn, and this in such a pattern that most amino acids are present in adequate amounts. Compare the earlier chapter "Will Chemistry

Offer Mankind the Third Freedom?" If any amino acid has been persistently low, it has been methionine. This compound can already be manufactured on a factory scale through microbial synthesis. An alternative would be to investigate what can be done through plant breeding in order to provide our regular food as well as feed with an adequate amount of this amino acid.

The Responsibility of Microbiology

It is easy to explain why microbiologists have been placed on the bench of the accused in the current debate about world misery. Largely through their doings has the population explosion taken on such frightening dimensions. Not without justification it has been pointed out that man's spectacular successes in the fight against diseases and our world-wide sanitary measures are main culprits to which the declining death rates can be attributed. In combination with man's refusal to pay the price for these gains, in the form of an efficient birth control, this has caused the steep climb in the population curve.

It was therefore not so surprising that microbiologists in the summer of 1963 were called by UNESCO to a conference in Stockholm, Sweden, less for ventilating scientific details than discussing what could and should be done to deal effectively with the mounting misery in the world. The motto of the meeting was "Global Aspects of Microbiology." This formulation mirrored a feeling of keen and growing responsibility on behalf of this discipline for the destiny of mankind, and it demonstrated a desire for concrete action.

Scientists can no longer persist in behaving as if these matters were of no concern to them. A general stock-taking of man's knowledge as to the relationship between food and microorganisms unveiled astounding gaps but also mapped several realistic ways of coping with this dilemma. One point became quite clear to all participants in the Stockholm meeting: The task facing mankind in the immediate future is enormous in dimensions, even if global birth control is generally accepted and practiced. Progress will not come easily, and few victories are likely. We have already taken on such tremendous feeding burdens that wise planning and purposeful production programs are required in order to bring health and satisfactory diet within reach for everybody.

CHAPTER V

Man's Competitors
for Food

Man likes to think of himself as master of the globe. Neverthe-less, even a superficial scrutiny of his powerful position reveals that a multitude of organisms compete with him for rank. Further-more, many of his competitors are rather difficult to cope with, and they help themselves to considerable portions of his crops and livestock, and of course his stores of food and feed. There is even reason to speak about a massive mobilization of nature and its forces, inimical to man, keeping him under constant fire. What else can we expect when we spread our sumptuous tables in the form of high-yielding fields, right in the lap of nature. Thanks to the elevated yield levels, they are even more overflowing than nature's own wildlife plots. All living organisms help themselves from the bounties according to the basic law of nature about the struggle for survival.

For a farmer in the upper Michigan peninsula, who has trouble with deer visits and mole invasions or foxes occasionally ravaging his poultry yard, it may be hard to understand that these are minor afflictions compared to the massive attacks that are routine in many nations on earth with more favorable climates. China's flocks of sparrows, numbered in the millions; India's fifty million monkeys and hordes of antelopes and elephants, which run wild;

Africa's soil-burrowing termites; and Australia's irksome and costly kangaroos, dingos, and flying foxes are just a random selection of some major menaces. The devastation and massive invasions by all kinds of wild animals constitute phenomena of a totally different magnitude than those we normally encounter in temperate regions. Still more harrying in scope are the rampages of the African giant snail in India, on Formosa (Taiwan), in Japan, and among the Pacific islands. Several species of crabs ravaging the rice fields of southeast Asia are other telling examples. The raids of finches in India and the weaverbird (*Quelea*), a scourge of Africa, cause serious concern in many quarters and decimate the crops.

When the North American continent was opened up and the frontier moved relentlessly westward, until finally the Pacific was reached, large marshlands were discovered along the coast, especially in the northern parts. These were almost completely drained during the fifties, and at a rapid pace in order to compensate for the land losses to urbanization. The ducks, geese, and other aquatic birds that used to frequent these marshlands on their annual migration have seen their feeding grounds dwindle. This ruthlessly taxed the bird stocks, to the degree that this important food source was eliminated. But man did not stop there. The water levels were lowered, which exposed shallow shore expanses loaded with botulinus bacteria. Mass poisoning took place. Another development was that many water fowl on their migrations northward in the spring and southward in the fall gradually found a substitute and made it a habit to visit the cultivated fields, since their customary feeding places had vanished. The losses inflicted upon the farmers made it profitable to establish special feeding areas. These are, however, not large enough; the migratory birds still settle on some of the cultivated fields for their meals. Large flocks of birds also hold the rice plantations in southern California under constant attack and tentatively the flying intruders are attacked by chemical weapons. When northern Australia tried to convert a large wild-rice region into a rice bowl for Asia, a series of unexpected obstacles was encountered (see *The Hungry Planet*, p. 194), among them the fact that migrating birds helped themselves to almost half the rice harvest.

The adaptation of wild nature to man's domain, primarily

created to guarantee him food and feed, has involved many complications. Even though nature in several respects has accommodated to the gigantic man-made reserves, now devoted to agriculture and in a terminal way withdrawn from wildlife, we tend to forget that the border skirmishes may still become fierce. Break-ins happen constantly. Most of the phenomena discussed above are basically nothing but indirect consequences of the disturbances man has caused in nature's biological balance. To a point this has been inevitable in man's strivings to secure an empire exclusively his on earth, but it can be seriously contended that we have pushed our frontiers too far and become a threat to almost all living creatures on earth.

Rats and Other Rodents

The rodents are entitled to a section of their own, since their devastations are so enormous and their struggle with man incessant. War on rats in the form of eradication campaigns are continuously waged in this century of urbanization. The mice are equally evident, and in the fields the field mice take their tribute. According to estimates, the rodents of the globe eat or destroy indirectly an amount of grain, tubers, etc., corresponding to the average consumption of 200 million people. As is well known, in addition they contribute to the spreading of diseases to still more millions of humans. As a rule they support themselves by robbing from man what he has stored for his own good. The rat is therefore without any doubt man's most important competitor. Indisputably, it is the only higher animal which nowadays can contend with man in numbers, according to random tests taken in some United States and European cities. The rat has reached this numerical strength in the shadow of man.

United States federal authorities estimate that a rat eats about forty pounds (eighteen kilograms) of food or feedstuffs annually, but destroys or contaminates at least twice as much. Rat hair is one of the most common findings in quality control of processed foods. In stored, nonprocessed food it is still more frequent. The number of rats in the United States is officially estimated at 120 million, and they cost the American economy more than one billion dollars annually. Their role as a dangerous disease spreader is not included. To their account various diseases can be credited, plus quite a few instances of food poisonings through salmonella bacteria and tapeworm. A rat bite often causes fever. Rats roam around in livestock barns and may further harm poultry, young hogs, and calves.

Proceeding from our own progressive country to others with more primitive arrangements for food storage, sanitation, sewage disposal, and garbage collecting, the ravages of the rat are still more damaging. It may therefore not be an exaggerated statement at all that in some countries the rat destroys or damages up to one-third of the grain, beans, and other stored foods. In the Egypt of old the cat was a sacred animal, an honor it shared with the ibis bird and the serpent. Together they were basic to the flourishing of the Egyptian civilization. Each one of them guarded an important section of man's frontier, which was under constant attack from his competitors. Of these we will first take a look at the defense perimeter of the ibis, that of the insects.

Are the Insects Taking Over?

The world's leading biologists have seriously debated if man actually holds supremacy in nature. They have pointed to the victorious inroads made by the insects into man's biosphere. We deal in this case with one of his most successful contenders. According to estimates, insects eat or destroy at least one-tenth, in several countries up to one-fifth of what the soil yields. As is well known, they also tackle our stored foods, especially the basic and crucial ones like grain, beans, etc. In India insects annually consume more food than the entire nine million population of Michigan eats. Such losses can doubtless be reduced, but there is good reason to tone down our generous promises about what can be achieved along these lines when similar conditions can be recorded also in countries where man has created powerful chemical barriers around his lush fields and even resorted to war gases in his fight for victory and survival. Nevertheless, the U.S. Department of Agriculture estimates that merely the insects cause losses to our nation in the range of four to five billion dollars annually. Our total agricultural production is valued at only six times that amount. The U.S.D.A. has furthermore figured out that we would need in excess of ninety million additional acres (thirty-seven million hectares) of cropland to compensate for the present annual losses in the fields due to insects, and sixty-five million acres (twenty-six million hectares) to counterbalance the losses in stored foods. This means that the annual loss due to insect attacks corresponds to the yield from a tilled acreage almost three times that of Iowa, or close to the total of our southern states or one-fifth of our national total. We trust that our modern technology in all its ingenuity and efficiency will protect us. Such is by no means the case. Our promises to the destitute world, holding out total victory in the battle against pests, are therefore not realistic; at best we may be somewhat more successful than hitherto. In this struggle there are, however, no finite victories.

No informed estimates have been made of the costs for such indirect ravages of insects as spreading various diseases—bacteria, fungi, even intestinal worms—to man, animals, and plants. This is an increasingly important sector of our battlefront against the insects, where man has to beef up his defenses and where at any time dangerous breakthroughs may occur.

In recent years there has been a noticeably increased awareness of the high costs involved when man takes over the policing of nature. Despite all the spraying on the ground or the showering from the air, the insects seem to outsmart us. They learn not only to cope with our toxic substances, but in some instances they thrive on them. Examples in the hundreds could be given that man's interference may have aggravated the situation by giving free rein to still more aggressive insects than those we may have exterminated or reduced in numbers to less threatening proportions.

Locusts, Leaf-cutting Ants, and Termites

A British expert, who spent a lifetime studying the insect problems of Africa, stated in a lecture to the Royal Society (1960), the counterpart to the U.S. Academy of Science, that the locusts, whose ravages were drastically described already in the Bible, used to constitute a menace to African crops about each tenth year. In the postwar years this threat became permanent. Airplane squadrons are on constant spraying missions over all the continents in the warm belt where grasshoppers thrive. Despite intense precision attacks against key foci in Sudan for the African locust, this insect succeeds year after year in breaking out in giant swarms toward both east and west. In 1959 Indian agriculture was exposed to no less than 109 devastating large-scale attacks by desert locusts. Perhaps only those who, like this author, have seen with their own eyes how everything is ruthlessly stripped by marauding locust swarms, may be able to grasp the gravity of this menace.

In the summer of 1946 locusts ravaged hundreds of acres of tangerine plantations in the Argentinian province of Corrientes. What they did not eat directly, *e.g.,* the older leaves, fell off a few days later, since all nourishing young leaves and sprouts had been devoured. It is a queer sight in the middle of the summer to look out upon hundreds of acres of bare and seemingly dead trees.

Locusts have caused considerable havoc on the North American continent, particularly in the dry prairies. The locust swarms of the 1870s, several miles in length and breadth, awed the pioneers of Nebraska and the Dakotas and nearly created a national catastrophe. Locusts still constitute a persistent menace to wide areas of the United States West. One type, the mormon cricket, is particularly perilous to the Western rangelands. Salt Lake City has a monument dedicated to this formidable foe. Twenty such locusts per square yard consume on an acre as much as one cow. The largest outbreak on record occurred in the late 1930s. Today constant surveillance is kept over their build-up, and better control is available through modern sprays; nevertheless, locusts frequently cause losses in the millions of dollars.

Almost as devastating is the Brazilian leaf-cutting ant, the sauva, when its armies march up and each ant cuts out a piece from a leaf, exactly the size it manages to carry to the mound. In a few hours they make a clean sweep. There is a stark reality behind the Brazilian saying: "We must eradicate the sauva or the sauva will destroy our country." It is a deadly serious battle, not merely some advance skirmishes or rearguard actions. The activities of this diligent insect are fascinating to observe, but the effects are frightening.

Termites not only attack wooden furniture and houses, books, and all kinds of human belongings; they also invade the fields with their own high or deep mound constructions. In the Argentinian province of Misiones they have infested many cultivated areas bordering on forest lands. The soil is completely undermined. The Congo is one of many regions involved in an uneven battle against this particular intruder. Several strains build mounds several yards high.

A couple of years ago the newspapers reported from China on the mobilization of millions of people in a battle against birds, which were consuming the coveted and invaluable rice crops. Triumphantly the party leaders proclaimed success in this campaign against the marauders. But the rejoicing did not last long. The elimination of the birds was followed by an even more devastating insect invasion. This is merely one of many examples how a unilateral campaign against our competitors may be followed by even worse calamities. Experiences from the African locust swarms, as well as thousands of observations by various scientific experts and by practicing farmers, testify to the fact that in our shortsightedness we often deprive ourselves of supporting forces in nature. Recklessly we exterminate everything, even our aiding friends among the animals. This costs us dearly. It is by working *with* nature not *against* it that we have a chance to defend our biosphere. Despite our overwhelming numerical strength, it is naïve to believe either that we can afford to take over the role of policing nature or that we even possess the capability of doing so.

The Worm Invasion

The worms are another large group of animals which have penetrated deep into the domain of man. They have staged what almost amounts to an invasion of both livestock and crops. Among them are liver worms, flatworms, hookworms, roundworms, tapeworms, and many others. Even man himself falls a victim. It is a shocking fact that more than 500 million humans carry hookworms. As told in the chapter "Is Large-scale Irrigation Reaching an End?" the bilharzia (nowadays mostly called schistosomiasis), a serious disease induced by a snail-spread worm, has in many parts of the world increased in pace with the expansion of irrigated lands, especially in those regions where irrigation has been pushed from a seasonal to a permanent nature. The experts are presently deeply concerned over the further spread of this disease the new Aswan Dam will generate among the already severely infected Egyptians. In many villages with irrigated land, more than 80 percent of the people are already afflicted, and experts fear that this figure will reach 100 percent.

What then has this to do with the limitations for man's existence? Thoroughly sick people, whose strength and health are undermined, are not efficient producers. Around the third Aswan Dam, the degree of infection by this scourge rose from 2 to 75 percent in three years after switching to year-round or permanent irrigation. Similar catastrophic developments are registered in other areas around the globe introducing permanent irrigation, *e.g.,* Iraq, Algiers, China, and Japan. The Umshandige Dam in southern Rhodesia cost nine million dollars to build, but within ten years the irrigated region simply had to be abandoned and the inhabitants evacuated—a capitulation of man to the worms. A leading parasitologist, who in 1961 analyzed the victorious path of bilharzia and man's defense measures, stated: "Looking into the future, one prediction is safe—the bilharzia will continue to spread. There will not merely be more cases in already infected regions, but it will continuously expand to new areas the more energetically we push the irrigation drive."

Recent studies show that filarial worms, responsible for a sickness called river blindness, frequently win out over man in tropical Africa in areas favored by river water and consequently more humid conditions than the surrounding savannahs. These worms are spread to man by a tiny but fiery fly (only one-fourth of the housefly in size). The worms are carried with the blood and frequently get caught in the eye, causing blindness. There are many villages in tropical west Africa where most, even all elderly people are blind chiefly from this cause. Good farmland has furthermore been abandoned where efforts to eradicate the fly and the disease have failed. Palm-oil-producing areas of west Africa show low frequency for the disease as this oil, due to its high content of vitamin A, delays or possibly eliminates the accumulations of worms in the eye.

Trichinosis and tapeworms have in no way disappeared from the arena. The Ethiopians, for centuries holding the world record as consumers of raw beef, almost boast about the number of tapeworms they harbor in their bowels, and yet these voracious worms are competing for the food taken in by the host, particularly critical when inadequate in amount. In east Africa, half the population is infected with tapeworm from beef. The more the population density rises, and above all, the higher the number of cattle, sheep, and other grazing animals crowding the pastures, the greater the threat has become. The percentage of infected livestock has actually risen despite modern worm-killing (antihelminthic) remedies. With increased water pollution this menace has regained serious dimensions in the technologically developed parts of the world, particularly where sewage water is being utilized for irrigation, in itself a commendable measure.

The nematodes are in many ways man's most serious competitors. They may rightfully be classified as the most common category of living organism on earth. These worms invade the roots of a series of crops such as sugar beet, potato, wheat, and rice. Almost all important Indian crops are highly infected with nematodes. The California fruit growers must each year submit the soil to a thorough soaking with chemicals in order to hold these saboteurs at bay, and yet success is only partial. Potato eel (a nematode) still constitutes, along with potato scab, the most serious threat to potato cultivation; in some areas the crop has even been forbidden due to eel invasion and in an effort to contain the enemy. Experts estimate the annual toll taken on a global basis by this single group of worms to exceed 750 million dollars in value.

Parasitologists who have studied historical indications of nematode ravages are by and large in agreement that they played a fateful role in the Roman Empire, among the Mayans, and several other civilizations. The nematode menace was once so serious that it was on the verge of making further sugar beet cultivation impossible. We like to believe that, with modern agricultural chemicals, new resistant strains of plants, counteracting crop rotation, and special cultivation techniques, man may block the way for these enemies of his. But our defense must constantly be on the alert, our combat patrols forever active, and our reconnaissance in persistent pursuit. Defeats are not uncommon. Indonesia's pepper plantations on the Bantu Islands, which as late as 1953 had twenty-two million bushes in prime condition, were invaded by nematodes and only about one million survived, despite a number of radical countermeasures.

Weeds

One battlefront, where man all over the globe is in constant action to stave off the reconquest of cultivated lands by the remnants of the wild vegetation, is represented by the weeds. They were discussed in the Bible and have been a constant nuisance to man's cropping endeavors ever since, despite modern herbicides. All kinds of estimates have been made of the losses caused by this category among man's competitors. Canada's grain-growing states—Manitoba, Saskatchewan, etc.—expect average annual losses ascribed to weeds of 10 to 15 percent; England from 7 to 10 percent of its grain production; India 20 to 30 percent. If the weeds could be eliminated, the Indian subcontinent would under prevailing growing conditions obtain a 25 percent larger harvest. Still more surprising perhaps is that the United States, despite full use of modern chemical weapons, suffers an annual loss valued at four to five billion dollars. The weeds compete with the crops in various ways; they compete for light, space, nutrients, and water. In grain cultivation it is by no means rare that the weeds rob the soil of so much nitrogen that the protein content of the grain goes down. This could be labeled a hidden damage.

Just as modern chemicals interfere in the balance of various kinds of fungi and insects and frequently give completely new pests and diseases their chance, so have new strains of weeds intruded upon man's domain in the wake of weed-killing chemicals, effective against one or some weeds but not others. This explains why wild oats, a weed botanically closely related to cultivated oats, has become a worldwide hazard. According to Canadian appraisals (1962) no less than sixty million acres (about twenty-five million hectares) of Canada's tilled acreage have become infested with this weed, seemingly irrevocably until the time when research eventually finds a remedy; up to one thousand plants of wild oats per square yard have been found. Various cultivation techniques supplemented with chemical weapons have so far not managed to overcome the wild oats and this weed has outsmarted man.

In Idaho another embarrassing weed staged an invasion in the fifties, the Medusahead grass. From some few thousand acres it quickly spread to no less than three-quarter million acres. This weed is detrimental in many respects: it suppresses other vegetation, cannot be eaten by cattle—the barbed seed coatings penetrate the eyes, nose, and mouth of the grazing animals—and finally, the dead plants do not break down, so the residues pile up on the surface of the soil. Prairie fires have even been recorded as caused by this waste. The annual losses to Idaho from this weed alone amounted in the beginning of the sixties to 3.5 million dollars annually. There is considerable apprehension that it might invade all the grazing lands of Idaho and thereby render livestock raising impossible. Another equally annoying weed has invaded the United States from India and is rapidly spreading in the southern states. It lives as a parasite on the roots of corn, rice, millet, sugar cane, and other species. Its popular name is witch-grass.

In the fifties an African bush entered Cuba and spread with frantic speed over the country, covering both tilled land and uncultivated land with dense thickets to a height of 8 to 12 feet. Chemical spraying met with little success. Efforts to eliminate the bushes with bulldozers proved expensive and also inefficient. What has happened lately in this respect is not known due to the severed ties with Cuba. Oxalic acid poisonings, which have plagued sheep and cattle, especially in Nevada, are caused by another such invading weed, halogeton, which reached the United States in the thirties. This species now covers almost 2.5 million acres in Nevada and is spreading to neighboring parts of Idaho and Utah.

When the chemicals do not work, special culturing techniques creating conditions less conducive to the growth of weeds constitute the only resort. But the large grazing ranges are rarely ever touched by the plow and as a consequence lie open to weed invasion. This chiefly explains why this category among man's competitors poses particularly serious menaces and why weeds frequently are quite successful in their intrusions upon the domain of man. Certainly the weeds represent one of the most ominous threats of all to man's crops. A feature indicative of the situation is the fact that the total acreage sprayed each year in the United States against weeds is larger than the area where the battle against insects and crop diseases is waged.

Man's successes in weed killing are neither finite nor lasting; we constantly encounter severe reverses and have to face new intruders. Thus it was believed that St. John's wort, which had overrun the California pastures, causing big losses, was finally conquered when a Japanese beetle was found with a hearty appetite for this weed. But in the wake of the eradicated weed, another one is now invading the liberated areas.

A note should be added about the large weed invasion in the fifties, staged by the water hyacinth in most tropical waterways of any economic importance. The breaking of new land, with ensuing erosion, the increased use of commercial fertilizers, and growing pollution represent some of the factors that paved the way for this water pest. When the plants are killed by chemical spraying, they sink to the bottom of the riverbed, where they undergo troublesome fermentations which jeopardize fishlife by using up the oxygen. Presently its use as feed or fertilizer is under consideration (see pp. 260–261).

Prevention Preferable to Cure

As always, preventive measures are preferable to remedial cures. This applies to the detrimental agents discussed in this chapter: insects, worms, rodents, and weeds. Seed control may serve as a good example since seed improvement partly consists of the careful elimination of weeds. It is highly likely that seed control has been the most efficient measure ever taken to raise the productivity of crop cultivation. Stalin stressed this in a conversation with Churchill during World War II. In principle the same basic ground rules apply in the battle against trichinae, cattle tuberculosis, flies, etc. This fact is behind the present debate about the potential threat of agricultural chemicals. Preventive measures have been neglected, and too much trust has been placed in the efficiency of our chemical weapons. We must guard against resorting to sledgehammers to crack nuts!

The big issue about the further spread of spray residues in the life cycle, their accumulation and long-range effect in soils and upon people and animals, are all important issues, into which we cannot enter here. But they should not be overlooked, because they provide an indication that the new border fortifications man tries to erect for his existence are not easily defended and rarely permanent. It also shows that there are risk limits we would be wise not to press too far in the use of our new weapons. These facts should be borne in mind when, in an almost thoughtless manner, we make generous promises to take care of twice as many people or more on our globe, already now overpopulated. Merely to provide for those now living raises tremendous demands, and it is not the least on the biological battlefront that the borders for man's existence are hard to defend and the battles are fierce.

DISEASES

This large category of indirect competitors both on land and at sea is usually not regarded as such, but we prefer to call them "diseases." Microorganisms and parasites expose crops and livestock to a veritable bombardment. By and large they make their conquests at our cost. These agents are detrimental in two ways, by weakening or even killing the hosts or victims, but also by stealing nutrients wholesale or retail. These damaging effects apply both to man and to his livestock.

On the Horizon of the General Public

Urbanized Americans rarely ever give a thought to the pests and diseases hampering the farmer's crops and animals. Occasionally there may be a news item, to which little attention is given, about foot-and-mouth disease in South America, grain weevils, or rust attacks on wheat. There is still less awareness about the combined losses inflicted by insects and fungi in storage as well as in the fields. Whenever such matters are brought up, the general notion is conveyed that modern spray chemicals have almost completely removed such threats from the American scene.

World Menace

Among us, living under the conditions described in the previous paragraph, it is naturally quite difficult to mobilize enough imagination to realize in all seriousness that plant and animal diseases still represent a real and acute threat to man's existence. Every month catastrophes of this type are reported from some part of the globe and even where modern spraying techniques or potent therapeuticals have been applied. According to estimates the highly developed agriculture of the United States registers annual losses on the average of at least ten billion dollars due to such causes. Approximately two billions of this sum are attributed to the microorganisms, insects account for five billion, plant diseases for three billion, and livestock diseases for half a billion. We will return later to the important question, how, despite all countermeasures, the annual toll does reach such alarming figures. But we ought to keep in mind that this is an extremely telling evidence of the magnitude of the vagaries under which agricultural production operates, be it raising crops or livestock.

In all our deliberations on world food production, in most development programs, and not the least in economic estimates of feasible production increases and production trends, we rarely ever take these risks into account. Mostly the tacit assumption is made that maximum producton will be reached. There is little realism in the debate and attention is rarely paid to the limitations that nature raises for food production despite the fact that we almost daily receive reminders of devastating attacks. They are still basically looked upon as incidents, bad fortune, irregularities, or something out of the normal, in spite of the fact that such calamities belong to the regular pattern and are very much part of normal life.

Man Coresponsible

It is actually not so surprising that the multitudinous world of insects and fungi as well as many parasitical worms suddenly emerge as formidable enemies of man. When man, through his crops and livestock, eliminates wild vegetation and animals competing with us, then those fungi, insects, and worms become extremely favored, specialized upon the kind of plants and animals we utilize in our battle for food. The table is not only set *for* them and *by* us, but frequently to overflowing. Under wildlife conditions their feeding basis is far more limited and large-scale attacks unique happenings. They also then feel the brunt of competition. They are, in effect, never allowed to grow numerous enough to become a real threat, capable of extensive devastation. There are many indications that man himself is an important disease-spreading agent and directly transfers detrimental organisms from one region to another. Recently the head of the African section of the World Health Organization warned against livestock diseases and pointed out that in a few years several dangerous pests have spread through man's own doing from endemic reserves in central Africa over wide expanses, and especially northward to Ethiopia and Egypt. Through man's intervention they had been given the opportunity to break out of their isolation and invade large territories.

But man has also indirectly been party to their spreading. The small farm units of old have grown into big plantations, kolchozes, or specialized farms with corn, wheat, soybeans, etc., stretching for hundreds of miles. History testifies to the fact that the spreading pattern by and large has been the one outlined above, with man as chief acting agent. Frequently the involved area has in size been out of all proportion to the original disease center. Who remembers today that it was the rust fungi of coffee which made the British a tea-drinking nation? A disease spread all over the coffee paradise of Ceylon, created by the British, and hit the endless expanses planted with coffee with devastating force. Coffee cultivation became impossible on Ceylon, and the same rust disease traveled with man's help to the Philippines and India. The tea bush came to the rescue, and so far man has been fortunate, since this plant has been capable of staving off several fungal attacks; serious disease threats have been recorded, however, so there is no guarantee for the future.

Large-scale Catastrophes

We have all read in the history books how the potato blight caused famine in Ireland and initiated the emigration of millions in the middle of the past century. But it is far from the only incident where these fungi have written world history by striking crops. In 1943, in the middle of World War II, the state of Bengal in India was hit with a mass invasion of the rice fields by a particular fungus. Rusts, attacking grain crops, have inflicted upon mankind a great deal of harm throughout history, which cannot be reviewed here. We will confine ourselves to one particular aspect of this question.

The United States' entrance into World War I was probably delayed due to the devastating rust attack which hit our wheatlands and other grain crop fields and brought about a national food crisis in 1916–1917, when at least one-third of the harvest was lost. Although exact figures are not available, there are several indications that the loss was even greater. England managed, thanks to foresighted plant breeders who had developed rust-resistant strains of wheat.

It was at this late time that the United States followed Europe in a relentless battle against the barberry bush, on whose leaves the winter spores of the rust survived until the next season. This also gave momentum to resistance breeding, whereby through suitable crossings a protective system is built up within the plant itself. The procedure seems simple and is invaluable, though time-consuming. Nevertheless, during the Second World War, the United States got a new shock when it was reminded of the enormous variability of fungi. The plant pathologists had repeatedly issued warnings against this high degree of diversity. Each species, and consequently each fungal disease, exists in tens of thousands of strains and varieties; through cross-fertilization their number constantly mounts. This means that man here has a frontier that must be persistently defended, and with new weapons, in order to meet the incessant regroupings. The wheat rust hit the prairies in 1948, when North America was at the peak of its aid to a war-ravaged world. This time, however, man was prepared, thanks to science and a major program of breeding resistant strains. As early as in 1952 almost the entire wheat acreage was switched to these new strains, resistant to the new invaders. But another time the preparedness may not be as good!

Potato Diseases

The potato has many such vicious enemies as scab and late blight. This latter causes brown rot in the tubers. Breeding of resistance against these two has been most complicated. Hardly had a variety resistant to scab or blight been put into cultivation before a new race of the disease-creating fungi outsmarted it.

Closely related to the potato blight is a fungus which frequently ravages banana plantations and can take a toll of up to 10 to 30 percent of the crop.

When cultivated in warm regions, potatoes undergo a rapid degeneration, induced by the spread of virus diseases. Virus is the smallest among disease agents and frequently attacks and kills bacteria too. Unfortunately, virus creates much havoc among both crops and livestock. In bygone days new potato varieties were developed from seeds, which explains why Europe had close to three thousand potato species at the start of the century. Each new variety was involved in an uneven struggle against virus diseases and only managed to sustain itself on the outer fringes of cultivated acreages, in areas where the aphids did not thrive due to low temperatures. This group of insects spread most of the virus diseases among crops. Other viruses attack the cocoa plant, causing disastrous "swollen shoot" disease.

The Tropics Most Critical

It is not only the plantation system, *i.e.,* large-scale plant cropping, which explains that the warm regions of the globe, the tropics and adjoining areas, have provided the stage for the most devastating mass attacks of disease agents which actually have stifled entire production branches. Special significance must also be attached to the fact that the agents are little decimated through climatic effects. For those who live in the temperate regions of the globe it may be difficult to conceive what a powerful ally they have in the winter, when both insects and fungi are killed on a massive scale or forced to seek protection. Even when storage facilities are available, the potential loss risks in grain, beans, peanuts, etc., are considerable in warm regions. The activities of the destructive agents under these conditions are never halted by unfavorable temperature; they proceed unimpeded all year round. In general it is both more hazardous and more costly to arrange for effective food storage in underdeveloped countries, the majority of which are located in warm latitudes, than in our cooler latitudes.

The same applies to the cultivated fields. Unfortunately, the notion is widespread that the warm areas of the world run less risks than we do. The lush vegetation of the humid tropics seems to point to greater exuberance and greater vitality of growth. Such simplified reasonings, have their roots in false assumptions. Man has actually suffered and still suffers his most crushing defeats in warm latitudes. As mentioned above, several pests and diseases have made headlines around the world through their ravages among the coffee plantations, not only in Ceylon, where these were wiped out, but also among the coffee crops of Brazil (*broca*), the bananas of South America (*sigatoka*), tropical Africa's cocoa trees (*swollen shoot*), and in recent years the coconut palms of the Philippines (*cadang-cadang*), etc. The major diseases hitting those crops are indicated in parentheses.

Many examples could be given from various parts of the globe showing that pests and diseases have made crop-raising hazardous and in some instances even entirely impossible; they have won the battle and put stringent limits to man's cropping. He has so far not been in a position to overpower and far less push back their advanced positions. The *moka* disease, caused by a bacteria, raises havoc with banana plantations and has made banana production impossible in large regions along the Pacific coast of Central America as well as in certain parts of Brazil and Venezuela. *Sigatoka,* another enemy of banana cultivation, and the virus disease "swollen shoot" of the cocoa tree have caused multimillion-dollar losses. The latter is spread by insects, and all our chemical counterattacks have so far proved ineffective. Both in Ghana and Nigeria, man was finally forced to resort to a felling and burning of all infested cocoa trees to stamp out the disease.

In the Philippines the coconut palm is threatened by a devastating virus disease, *cadang-cadang*; the leaves turn yellow and the trees die in the millions. One fears in all seriousness that the important income from the copra export, the number one source of foreign exchange, will be lost altogether. Of late, a ray of hope has entered the picture, since there seems to be some justification for the suspicion that the "disease" has its origin in such trace element deficiencies of the soil as lack of copper, aluminum, and others. This in turn causes physiological disturbances which either have a direct killing effect or undermine the resistance of the plant to the degree that the virus in question gets free rein. In the Caribbean Islands a similar yellow virus disease has in many areas made impossible the cultivation of coconut palm, a highly important crop for this region. Jamaica has thus no coconut plantations left in the western part of the island, one third of the entire area.

Late blight with accompanying brown rot in the tubers still constitutes a critical menace to potato cultivation in the temperate regions, as soon as temperature and humidity conditions offer this fungus an opportunity. Despite spraying against late blight, the fungus spreads around causing bad potato years with heavy tuber infection. This is immediately reflected in yields in the developed countries, but still more in subsequent storage losses. In warmer regions the charcoal rot seriously hampers potato cultivation. Every year losses in the millions of dollars are registered in the southern United States as well as in India and South America due to this particular disease.

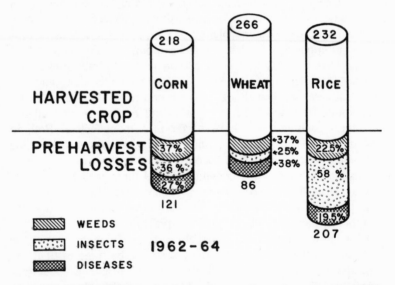

Fig. 20. Global preharvest losses in three major grain crops. Harvested quantities and total losses are indicated in million metric tons. Note that rice is most seriously threatened by insects (data compiled by H. H. Cramer, 1967—see Chapter References).

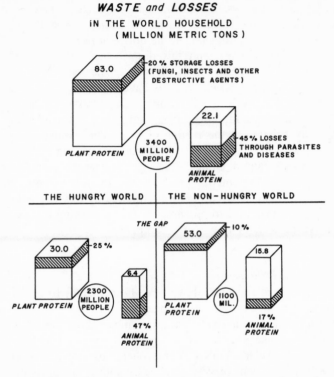

Fig. 21. Estimated losses in plant products subsequent to harvesting and in animal products during raising of livestock (data compiled by author)

The Rust Diseases

No light has been shed on the origin of the rust diseases. Already during the campaign against the barberry bush at the time of the First World War, the primitive airplanes of those days could, through sampling, show how the spores were spread in wide circles from one single bush and reached as high as thousands of feet. The rust fungus has two stages: summer spores, which develop on grain crop plants, and winter spores on the barberry bush; under certain circumstances the fungus may skip the winter stage. In the United States it was, however, gradually found that large spore clouds traveled from early wheat plantings in

Mexico and brought about mass infection in Canada and the United States when weather, wind, and air currents favored this. Similar harmful phenomena appear in India, where the spores spread from cultivated regions in the northern parts of the country to the southern regions, and this despite the fact that the host plant, the barberry bush, reportedly was eradicated.

Throughout the ages, cereal rusts have been regarded as man's arch enemy. The Bible uses the combination "moth and rust" as a symbol of insects and fungi as our adversaries, not alluding, as many may believe, to the rusting of iron. The Romans held religious festivals to appease the rust god. Some years the black rust of wheat caused United States grain growers losses in the range of six million metric tons! During the First World War, more wheat was destroyed in North America by this single disease than England managed to procure, chiefly by plowing the pastures in their large-scale "Grow More" campaign.

Our Victories Ephemeral

The examples discussed above have been included to illustrate the basic fact that cropping is subject to obvious biological hazards. The battle for survival as a law of nature does indeed apply, not merely to the jungle, but on the whole to all wildlife. It is equally operative in man's own biosphere, despite his efforts to achieve supreme control. We may well smother our enemies, but in so doing often pave the way for their many competitors. In the fields of bacteria, fungi, and insects new or minor diseases have emerged as serious in the wake of our own successful dimunition of major contenders. It is only natural that living nature exerts considerable resistance against man's monopolizing endeavors and avails itself of every opportunity to regain territory and intrude on man's domain. In nature there can be no sanctuaries or reserved seats. The more man extenuates his battlefront, the more vulnerable he becomes. The living world is ruled by its own intrinsic laws of maximum utilization of all available chances for life. Despite man's modern toxic chemical weapons he has certainly not won the war, only some battles and skirmishes. There is every good reason for the assumption that there are no finite victories in this kind of warfare. All evidence points in the opposite direction. The more man specializes his crop production, the greater are the risks involved, and the harder the blows he must take.

How large a tribute the diseases take, even when modern cultivation and spraying techniques are fully applied under best expert management, may be exemplified by the complications that faced the crops of processing peas in Wisconsin. One single fungous disease, root rot, destroyed in one single year, when it first appeared, one-tenth of the harvest. Other diseases took together another one-tenth. The entire pea crop covered 100,000 acres. The total damage thus corresponded to a loss of 20,000 acres. Any number of similar examples could be given in order to demonstrate how far from reality those popular concepts are that countries with a highly developed plant production are safeguarded, and that only backward, underdeveloped countries are subject to such hazards. The truth is rather that we all, poor and rich nations, are exposed to the same menace, even though we, the rich, at great costs have reduced the risks but certainly not eliminated them by a long shot. In several instances we are forced to pay high running costs for vaccinations, which frequently have to be renewed at intervals.

Defeat in the Battle Against Livestock Diseases

When, toward the end of the Second World War, England understood that in order to guarantee the nation's food supply, it had to create a feeding bastion elsewhere than in Australia, New Zealand, and Canada, it started large peanut projects in Tanganyika (*cf.* p. 64) and Nigeria. An almost equally grandiose project was initiated in Gambia in tropical Africa for the raising of poultry. In this latter case the failure was even more resounding than in Tanganyika. Despite the application of first-rate knowledge available to modern poultry science, all kinds of vaccinations, and adherence to scientifically formulated feeds and feeding regimens, the outcome was most disappointing. The birds fell victim to a whole series of diseases, and the project had to be abandoned. Further, feed was critically short.

Paradoxically enough, tropical Africa is the scene for the most dramatic conquests over man—staged by livestock diseases. The

most serious, almost ferocious, case was undoubtedly the rinderpest which will be further discussed later. The most persistent
conquest is that of the tse-tse fly, ruling almost unperturbed over
most of tropical Africa and still spreading sickness and death
(sleeping disease) both to man and beast, and this despite energetic counterblows by man, so far almost wholly unsuccessful.
The fact is that economically feasible livestock and poultry raising
remains in doubt for a large belt across the African continent,
stretching in a narrow strip along the coast of Guinea and in a
broad zone across the center, from southwest Africa into a slightly
narrower belt on the east side, covering parts of Uganda, Tanzania, etc. This is the domain of the tse-tse fly spreading through
its bites *nagana, i.e.,* sleeping sickness, to the livestock. In sections
of Tanzania we still encounter foci for rinderpest, the cattle plague
which probably in the Middle Ages traveled to Europe and
simultaneously with the scourge of the black pest among men
took its heavy toll of livestock. It reached tropical Africa with
devastating force at the end of the nineteenth century, wiping
out hundred of millions of wild hoofed animals as well as cattle,
causing starvation and death among man. The tse-tse fly has retained its power position in central Africa despite innumerable
efforts to eliminate it. Both plant diseases and disease agents
plaguing livestock have maintained a firm grip over this continent,
severely limiting the possibilities for food production. These restrictions may naturally in the future be removed or rolled back
by new chemical devices, but the agents will always be there and
require constant vigilance, since we must anticipate surprise attacks at any time. There seems to be little chance for man to
control or expect to improve permanently to his benefit the over-
all ecology of this region. When beneficial to man, it is most
likely to be advantageous also to some ever-present disease agents
or to entirely new ones adjusting to these changed conditions.

New Attacks

The new large United States research institute for foot-and-
mouth disease, located on isolated Plum Island off Long Island,
which cost more than twenty million dollars in construction,
testifies to the serious threat this particular disease constitutes.

Epizooties are constantly being recorded from some corner of the earth, and are rarely confined to the place of origin but spread to other countries and continents. As is the case with plant diseases, new strains constantly emerge. Vaccination has thus not become the efficient protection it was once thought to be. It is a countermeasure which rarely can be applied to plants. Animals can readily be provided with antibodies aiding them in staving off disease attacks. But, as indicated, this weapon, effective as it may be, also has its obvious limitations, due not only to the multitude of strains but to the fact that it is rarely possible to achieve permanent immunity. The effect is usually limited in time. Each new animal has further to be provided with an arsenal of vaccines.

Several animal diseases adapt easily to new hosts, and we must therefore anticipate that new diseases regularly transfer from wild animals to livestock. In many parts of Europe and North America it was generally believed until quite recently that man had achieved complete success in the eradication of bovine tuberculosis, when suddenly afflicted cattle appeared. Closer investigations revealed that avian tuberculosis had spread via poultry to cows and even to man and had managed to accomodate to its new hosts. A whole series of new types of tuberculosis have also been found. So far it has only partially been possible to establish their origin or true nature.

In October, 1967, Britain was hit by a ferocious outbreak of foot-and-mouth disease. More than 420,000 diseased cattle were slaughtered and burned, inflicting losses in direct compensation and indirect costs in excess of 250 million dollars. The infection was traced to imported lamb meat.

Artificial Rearing

It is certainly food for serious thought that a highly developed agriculture like that of the United States estimates that one-third of its production is lost due to plant and livestock diseases. At the same time it constitutes a resigned acceptance of defeat, almost amounting to capitulation, when modern animal production is moving toward, or at any rate is seriously investigating the possibility of no longer exposing livestock and poultry to the strains of nature. So far such methods have been employed for hogs. The piglets are delivered at birth by means of sterile operations, and the subsequent feeding takes place in artificially conditioned and air-filtered rearing establishments. In this way the mortality among suckling piglets has been reduced by up to one-third, with the losses of animals reduced to a trifle. Experiences from the world of humans indicates, however, that individuals and peoples who grow up under good controlled sanitary conditions and are exposed to few infection risks often become excessively susceptible. In this vein it has been seriously discussed if polio is not rather the result of a too hygienic childhood environment, depriving the individual of the chance to build up a gradual body resistance through a kind of self-vaccination from ubiquitous polio reservoirs in the intestinal system.

Anyone who ponders over these intricate biological relationships, and furthermore takes into consideration the actual conditions in various parts of the world, soon realizes that such extremely protected animals never will become, in a global context, the food producers of the future. On the contrary, we would be better advised to take the opposite track, move in the direction of resorting to breeds and types of animals which are capable of withstanding adverse and primitive conditions as typical for most of world agriculture. We should be selecting animals less susceptible to diseases and capable of surviving and producing under adverse conditions, with respect to both climate and exposure to diseases. This undoubtedly is the only feasible way if man is going to defend his position at a reasonable cost, and in the world at large and not withdrawn to luxury cuvettes.

New Deal

The biologists have by and large been pushed aside while the technologists practiced their seemingly fabulous magic tricks. But nature has struck back, and even in those instances where technology had free rein and where money and resources were no issue. At the moment we are about to enter upon the exploitation of the remaining reserves of the humid tropics, primarily the Congo and the Amazon basins. There are many unmistakable signs that our present agricultural techniques, with pastures and livestock-raising supplemented with outside feed, in many parts of the tropics, actually yield less food, measured in protein, than what would be obtained through a systematic and calculated taxing of wild animals. Nevertheless, man by and large persists with his agricultural pursuits in the traditional pattern. It is an interesting sign of the times that several of the new African governments are supporting, at least in the preliminary stage, what might be labeled game cropping. In principle this means that man takes over the previous role of the predators, and himself harvests a regular annual toll of the hoofed animals, thereby also keeping their numbers down in order not to overtax the plant cover as the main feed resource of these herds (see pp. 78–80).

These observations should not be interpreted to mean that man's technological methods and scientific achievements are valueless in this context. On the contrary, the total fund of engineering knowledge and agricultural science of the world are desperately needed, but they must be applied in a radically new way. The notorious failure of the peanut project in Tanganyika hopefully signified the end of an easy-going era when man recklessly destroyed wildlife. The indiscriminate use of the bulldozer may stand as a symbol for this era. Thus man opened up much new land, as in mankind's infancy—but now on a more gigantic scale, and this time very much to the final detriment of man— operating heedless of the laws of living nature and unaware of the creative forces of nature with which he needed to cooperate. For man's survival new devices and new symbols are required, recognizing the need for operating *with* nature, not *against* it.

We revel in name-calling, designating our competitors in nature as marauders and saboteurs of man. A thorough, objective analysis of these issues shows, however, that in many essential respects, man himself has staged a gigantic sabotage of nature, jeopardizing both himself and the creative forces of living nature. In order to have even a slight chance of mastering the critical problems confronting man today in this teeming world of humans and not run the risk of being victimized, he must learn to marshall full support from his many friends in nature. They must be mobilized as our allies in a joint battle against formidable foes and this in a massive way and on a very broad front. There are a great many fungi, insects, and worms which could be of great value to us. On a limited scale this has started in the so-called biological control of insects. For this purpose man has to learn respect for the laws of nature. Even the predators may have a role to play as our fellow combatants. Already in the sixteenth century the British philosopher Francis Bacon understood these basic relationships, which he poignantly formulated in the sentence "In order to rule nature, we must learn to obey her." This may constitute an entirely new vantage point for our operations, which might be formulated in this way: It is up to man in his own self-interest to arouse a minimum of hostility as well as a maximum of cooperation. This will require restraint in goals and recognition of limits.

Above all, however, man needs to put an end to his shortsighted way of handling this as well as many other matters related to the world food issue. Anti-rat campaigns are basically poor substitutes for better householding, which deprives the rodents of access to man's food stores or of a thriving sustenance on his wastes. The removal of symptoms is in the long run both a futile and costly way of operating. We need to supplant tactical devices with strategic plans of operation. Presumably this will automatically involve not only less people but also a far more efficient and prudent marshaling of support from the potentialities of living nature.

CHAPTER VI

Water and
Our Daily Bread

In everyday life few people probably realize that man consists mainly of water. Yet close to 70 percent of the body weight can be attributed to this single substance. In addition to what we drink to maintain this level, we get water in most of our food, although in varying quantities, from less than one-tenth of the weight in nuts to one-half in meat and six-sevenths in milk. The appearance of our foods is deceptive in this respect. We speak about liquid and solid food. But there is actually a higher water content in lettuce, spinach, and melon than in milk, in spite of the latter being a liquid.

In the Human and Animal Body

Water is not only our most basic food. It is fundamental to life itself. Water carries all mineral salts and water-soluble vitamins, carbohydrates, etc., conveying these vital nutrients to all parts of the body with the flow of gastric juices, blood, and lymph. Finally, it is by means of water that the waste is transported out of the body via urine and transpiration. By far the greatest number of life processes in the body take place with water as a key substance. Water is also involved in the metabolism of fat. Each pound of fat, when metabolized in the body, ends

131

up yielding 1.07 pounds of water. The hump of the camel or that of the zebu cow with their stored fat is consequently in principle a kind of indirect water reserve. Experimental animals may lose practically all their body fat. They may be starved, to the degree that almost half their body protein is used up, and still survive. But they cannot live for very long without water. When the water loss reaches the modest amount of one-tenth of the body weight, they die within a few hours. The water produced through fat metabolism in the body is called metabolic water. Each pound of starch and protein, when metabolized in the body, also forms water in the amounts of 0.55 and 0.41 pounds respectively.

At a temperature of 76° F. an adult man consumes on the average around 1,100 pounds of water contained in his "solid" food per year. He drinks an additional 900 pounds of water in its liquid form and in beverages in order to maintain the liquid balance of the body. This adds up to a water requirement of 2,000 pounds annually (around 5.5 pounds, or 2.5 quarts, daily). The metabolic water formed constitutes 200 pounds per year.

Behind our daily need of water, about 2½ quarts (2½ liters), regardless of whether it is taken directly from the faucet or in the food we eat, there is for food a chain where water is required at every stage: on the field, in the cattle barn, in harvesting and hauling, in storage, in slaughterhouses, dairies, and processing plants, in the large food-distribution network, and also at the preparation in the kitchen, whether at home or in institutions. This indirect water account is staggering (see p. 148).

The Lifeline

The entire living world may be said to be dependent on an unbroken lifeline of water. It may therefore seem still more surprising that the entire artificial existence man has created for himself, with modern industrialization as its crowning achievement, is also based on water, and this to the degree that this large, man-created sector is beginning to outgrow man's direct use and needs. Water employed for industrial purposes in an increasing number of countries not only threatens to exceed what nature provides, but it enters into direct competition with our daily bread. In the fifties an important crossroad was passed in this regard. During that decade the actual water take by industry in most of the technologically developed parts of the world, including the United States, grew larger than that of agriculture. Until that time food production had directly or indirectly been the most water-demanding activity under man's control.

In the chapter "Is Large-scale Irrigation Reaching an End?" the reasons for this development are further elucidated. First we need a clear picture of how water functions in the plant, producing organic matter, which in turn yields food in the shape of grain, potato, fruit, vegetables, etc. Let us therefore follow the water on its road from the fields to the dining table.

The water lifeline of mankind starts with the raindrops. The sun, the enormous power station of the universe, incessantly hurls forth its hecatombs of calories. Among other things, this generates the mass evaporation of water on earth, thus keeping

THE HYDROLOGICAL CYCLE

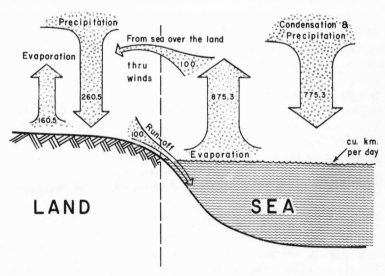

Fig. 22. The hydrological cycle of the earth (in cubic kilometers per day)

nature's huge water circulation machinery moving, given either the designation of the Great Water Cycle or in more scientific terms the hydrological cycle. About 95,000 cubic miles of water are annually lifted from the land masses and ocean expanses. This is carried along with air currents, gathers into clouds, and returns —though unevenly distributed—to earth mainly as rain or snow. About three-fourths of this water (71,000 cubic miles) falls into the oceans, and one-fourth (24,000 cubic miles) on land. The runoff moving back to the oceans is 9,000 cubic miles—equal to what ocean evaporation annually contributes to precipitation on land. This is the annually renewed source of freshwater at man's disposal.

We try to improve on the effective utilization of this water by building enormous dams and distribution canals, and through replenishment of the subterranean layers. Naturally, part of the water seeps through the soil and finally reaches the groundwater. The surface water gradually is returned to the sea but is impeded on its way in lakes, rivers, and marshlands. Four-fifths of the precipitation hitting the land area evaporates or passes through the vegetation, be it forest, cultivated fields, or the plant cover of untilled lands. In other words, some water returns to the atmosphere only after being pumped through the plants with their transpiration as the driving force. Only about 1 percent remains in the plant as part of its buildup.

The Pumping Machinery of the Root

The lifeline thus starts with the raindrop, regardless of whether it goes to the groundwater, the surface water, or up in the air. In order to serve food production, it must obviously be absorbed in the soil or directly by the plants. Water fills all the small pores and channels of the soil, but in the first stage it wraps each one of the billion soil particles as in a thin veil. In this water layer the nutrients of the plants are dissolved. The roots are equipped with millions of absorptive tubes, root hairs, giving the surface a fluffy appearance. These hairs encapsulate the particles and suck the nutrient solution on the surface. A fully developed rye plant which is four months old has hundreds of thousands of roots. Plant physiologists have measured their total length as more than 400 miles; their total surface has been estimated at

2,420 square feet. To this shou'd be added the innumerable tiny root hairs which are the actual absorptive organs; their number per rye plant is estimated at about fourteen million in active work. Their combined length amounts to many more miles than the roots, and their surface has been calculated to exceed 4,300 square feet per average-size plant.

These figures give an idea of the gigantic pumping machinery that each single plant possesses, be it potato, rye, or wheat. The

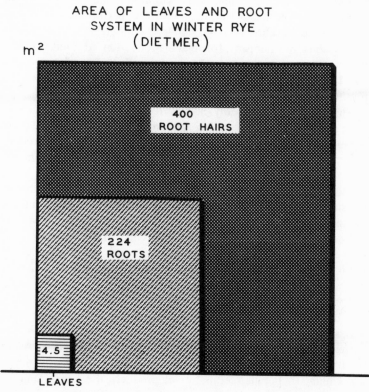

AREA OF LEAVES AND ROOT
SYSTEM IN WINTER RYE
(DIETMER)

m²

400
ROOT HAIRS

224
ROOTS

4.5

LEAVES

Fig. 23. The efficiency of the pumping machinery of the green plant depends on the water-collecting surface represented by the roothairs, the roots, and the rootlets. This area exceeds many times over the evaporative surface of the leaves (in square meters). Figures refer to one single plant.

topsoil layer is literally interwoven with roots and root hairs in search of water. A great number of minerals and other nutrients are conveyed from the soil to the plant via water, this constituting a prerequisite for photosynthesis and thereby for the manufacture of starch and sugar. This in turn yields protein, fat, and other nutrients after transmetabolizing with other compounds.

Plant Crops Water-gobblers

Somebody has said that it is within the laboratories of the small plant cells that the master miracle is performed of converting a piece of clay into delectable, edible fruits. In the cells the various mechanisms for plant production are located, but how much water, the most basic prerequisite for life, do these cell laboratories require in order to sustain photosynthesis, respiration, and other key metabolic processes?

Plants vary considerably in this respect. Some use an abundant amount of water, others economize with it. But under all circumstances large amounts of water are needed to produce one pound of organic matter suitable as human food. The highly water-demanding rice plant consumes, in the hot climate of the tropics, 2,200 pounds of water for each pound of organic matter produced. Wheat needs 350 to 500 pounds for each pound of organic substance. As a matter of fact in terms of water required for our food, a great deal more is needed in both cases, since man only utilizes the kernels as food, and the remainder of the plant employs for its growth an equally large amount of water per pound of organic matter produced.

Evidently the differences in the water economy of the plants has been decisive for the cultivation pattern of the globe. The water economy of crops has, in effect, written world history. An extremely frugal water economy is typical of the millets of Africa as well as of the related species grown in the highlands of northern China. In popular terms, millet produces the largest amount of food with the least amount of water. Its cultivation has consequently made it possible to extract food in regions where water is sparse. In 1942–1943, during the Second World War, when the Soviet Union found itself isolated from the rest of the world, the much-debated scientist Trofim Lysenko—in effect a plant physiologist but controversial largely due to his genetic ideas—advised Stalin not to jeopardize the food supply by sticking to traditional crops, but coolly calculate with the recurrent risks of drought and consequently switch to the cultivation of millet on largest possible acreages. Lysenko thus initiated the growing of Chinese millet, which gradually was extended to twenty-five million acres (ten million hectares).

Share of the Plants in the Precipitation

The amount of water required for food production may be measured through another method, namely by establishing how many inches (millimeters) of rain a crop consumes for an average yield. Luckily, wheat is one of those plants capable of producing even under comparatively dry conditions. For the wheat acreages of the United States, ten to twelve inches (275 to 300 mm.) of precipitation is needed annually, part of which is stored in the soil; so it need not fall during the vegetation period. The Russian wheat strains need approximately the same amount. In the new west Siberian grain regions these figures are not reached when drought hits, which happens quite often. Thus a narrow water margin is a characteristic trait of the climate for the entire interior of the Eurasian continent. Therefore a Soviet prime minister runs twice as great a risk of encountering drought as an American President. Furthermore in the U.S.S.R., when drought does hit, it is on an average twice as serious as on the North American continent. Water plays its capricious but fateful role independent of political system! Even major powers are then reduced to puppets.

Western Europe also experiences dry years now and then, which put a brake to agricultural production. There are many indications that water is a decisive or limiting factor in Swedish agriculture; in any case, on an average twenty-five years out of a hundred are characterized as drought years. This probably explains why Swedish acre-yields have not mounted in pace with the large investments and the modernization of agriculture that have taken place in recent decades.

Some recent soybean data from South Carolina bear out the key role of water as the chief limiting factor to yields:

WATER AS LIMITING FACTOR TO SOYBEAN YIELDS

	AVERAGE YIELD BUSHELS PER ACRE	RAINFALL (INCHES) DURING POD-FILLING AND MATURING *
High-yielding counties	23.7–26.3	2.35–3.46 (2.82)
Low-yielding counties	17.7–21.3	0.45–2.45 (1.19)

* Average rainfall in parentheses.

Over the entire globe yield statistics show significant fluctuations over the years (see Figures 11, 12, 15). Plant diseases and insect attacks play their part in these phenomena, but in the overwhelming majority of cases it is water that is operating behind the scene as the chief limiting factor. The abrupt increases in the acre-yields for winter wheat in the United States in 1958 (48.5 percent) and for spring wheat in 1962 (83.2 percent), as compared with the preceding years, were primarily due to unexpectedly high precipitation favoring good crops in the main wheat-producing states. Similar fluctuations are recorded for the spring wheat of Canada. The United States wheat surplus was to a large extent the result of such record crops. In the opposite case one single year of drought, comparable in intensity to the droughts that hit the prairie lands in the thirties, could easily reduce the yield figures in an equally drastic manner. More than half of mankind already lives in nations where special measures have to be taken in order to secure minimum water needs.

The Water Economy of the Plants

Unfortunately, the closer we get to the limits of available water, the harder the plant seems to work in order to produce, which in turn requires more water. This explains why the Australian wheat strains demand more than twice as much water as the American ones—850 as against 350 pounds per pound of organic matter. Poor soils with low fertility also raise the water consumption. Thus productive soils in good mineral balance economize better with water, an important fact to be considered in comparisons between primitive and modern high-yielding cultivation. The same amount of water cannot always be expected to give identical returns in yield and in food. It may also be formulated in this way. More water is wasted in poor soils in order to produce a certain amount of food than in good soils, and this even when the climate is equivalent. These causal relationships must not, as sometimes happens, be interpreted to mean that higher yields obtained through more fertilizers are procured at no cost in terms of water. Obviously, more water is needed for each additional pound produced, but for each metric ton of water an additional yield of some ounces is obtained if the soil is in good productive shape.

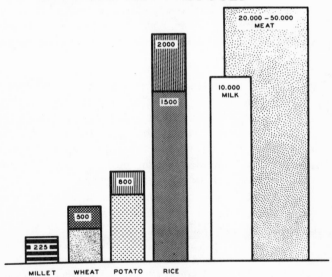

LBS OF WATER PER LB. OF DRY MATTER PRODUCED

Fig. 24. The amount of water passing through the green plant and evaporated into the hydrological cycle in producing foods. Even a water-demanding crop like rice requires far less than animal products, calculated on the basis of the water needed to grow the feedingstuffs required for their production in livestock. The top shaded area for wheat, potato, and rice indicates the degree of variation in crop yields.

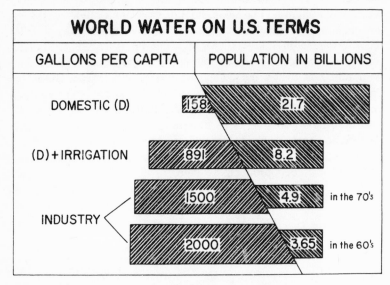

Fig. 25. The number of people who could be provided with water on the United States consumption level. The industry figures are alternatives.

This issue of the relationship between plant nutrients and water will become a key question in the immediate future with the massive offensive in favor of commercial fertilizers which has now been launched both in China, the U.S.S.R., India, and the United States. There is no doubt that the shortages of mineral nutrients in the soil are sizeable, the more so since in so many areas harvest upon harvest has been extracted with little or no return of nutrients to the soil. Nevertheless, in many cases available water is not sufficient to counterbalance the huge amounts of additional fertilizer which are either needed or now being planned with the aim of pushing production upward. Commercial fertilizers inexorably raise the water needs—see further the chapter "Could the Yield Spiral Be Pushed Further Upward?"

Water to Wet Regions

India and China possess together more than half of the world's irrigated land and have for centuries had dams and wells with quite extensive networks for water. Their development in this respect always led the world, and many of their ancient installations are operative to this very day. But both these countries are fast approaching the limit for their water resources, and there are many signs that China in several key regions already has exceeded it. The gambling spirit is implicit in man and exemplified in his invading of arid regions in order to "make the deserts bloom," as the Bible describes. In this context we will merely point to the fact that a great number of even large irrigation systems are located in regions which are fairly well provided with precipitation. But the population growth constantly raises the demand for higher yields at any cost. Examples of this are many irrigation installations in southern France, in Germany, as well as in considerable portions of the rice-growing areas of China and Southeast Asia. In the United States larger investments are currently being made for irrigation in the mild humid northeastern regions than in the arid and semiarid areas of the West and Southwest.

Since the turn of the century Canada, the huge "Land of the Future," has constantly expanded its irrigation facilities, and large costly projects are presently underway in both Manitoba and Saskatchewan. In this case, as in most others, little is being said about the return on these investments, which have reached the range of 800 to 1,000 dollars per acre. Such outlays are not taken into account in the general bankruptcy. They commonly enter into overhead costs and are in no way reflected in food prices. Even California farmers only pay a fraction of the actual cost of their irrigation water. The lion's share is placed directly on the taxpayers' account. No wonder man's concept of the crucial role of water in his feeding is so blurred. Both politicians and the public, and surprisingly, also many categories of food experts have very vague notions of the paramount place water holds in plant production, and as a consequence, in world feeding. Thirst and hunger are in effect phenomena of a Siamese-twin nature.

Mining of Fossil Water

In this very century man has staged a gigantic tapping of invisible groundwater reserves over the entire globe. Since the consequences are not immediately noticeable, the recklessness has been tremendous. Innumerable scientific studies have established the disastrous consequences and have been able to ascertain the excessive toll taken from surface waters in a number of European countries as well as in Canada and the United States. Many miles of rivers and rivulets have gradually dried out, lakes have dwindled and vanished. This has reduced the refill of groundwater reserves or the feeding of aquifers.

For the tapping of groundwater reserves, wells have been drilled by the thousands, and not the least in arid regions like South Africa, Australia, Saudi Arabia, and many other locations. The experience was always the same—the groundwater resources were poorly appraised prior to exploitation. They became overtaxed. The groundwater level kept dropping, and as it receded the wells dried out and soon uneconomic levels (below 200 feet) were reached. At these greater depths saline water is often encountered and sucked into the freshwater aquifers.

The main factor in this ultrarapid depletion was in almost every case a persistent underrating of the gigantic water requirements

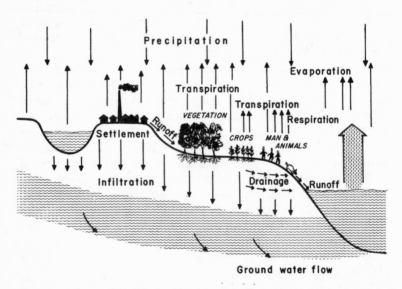

Fig. 26. The multitudinous channels through which water moves in nature

of crops. The need for food was the main culprit in creating thirst. There is a poorly recognized intimate relationship between food and water famines. In harsh hydrological terms this can almost be formulated to mean that groundwater reserves *never* should be used for regular crop production but be held in abeyance for drought relief in critical times.

Plant production in many parts of Australia and South Africa, and other parts of the globe with similar limitations, has come to a standstill. Utilizing such nonvisible underground water reserves for irrigation results in their rapid depletion, but this becomes noticeable only indirectly and gradually. This has had both insidious and disastrous effects on most people's thinking about these matters. But such unheeded depletion has raised sudden and very grim hindrances both to development in general and to food production in many regions around the world.

Several key areas in the United States are faced with the ominous choice between agriculture or industry, food or factories, due to the limited availability of water, no longer to be found within reasonable distance. This dilemma facing the rich world is even more pronounced in countries where food is a shortage commodity. The development plans for poor countries must take water into consideration and can simply not afford our extravagance, since as a rule the water margin is much narrower. This will be discussed in more detail in the next chapter.

The wisdom of our programming and planning may be questioned right in our own part of the world. When regions in the northeast of our country, well-suited for cropping, are rapidly being gulped by huge metropolises, while the raising of food is being relegated to areas with much less favorable conditions as regards rainfall and climate—*e.g.,* around the Great Lakes and in the dry prairies—this appears less than prudent, and at any rate extremely shortsighted.

The Tapping of "Invisible" Groundwater

Daily bread has an essential part in this massive depletion of groundwater by man. Groundwater available within one mile in a top layer of the earth's crust constitutes around one-tenth of all available freshwater resources. Consequently it is easy to empty such reserves even in regions well provided with water, particularly since plant cultivation requires 300 to 2,000 times more water than is being produced in organic matter. As a temporary supplementation measure in times of critical shortage it would not be so ominous, but when the dependence becomes permanent and entirely rests upon man-controlled acquisition, such resources dwindle quickly. Groundwater constitutes a precarious basis for daily food, at any rate in an era when humans are counted in the billions.

By and large our present outtakes exceed considerably what the gigantic hydrological cycle of nature returns. Due to man's own doing, the land masses are losing water and the oceans are expanding. Out of the world's 3½ billion people, some 600 million are chiefly to blame for this. Europe has the record in this regard, since that continent takes out three times more water than the annual return adds to available water resources. North America follows with a rate of outtake twice that of replenishment, this being the pace at which we are presently tapping the groundwater. This is the sinister truth behind the receding groundwater levels and the increasingly larger depths from which pumping has to be carried out in most areas.

Yield Increases Mean Additional Outtake of Water

In whatever context food is appraised, it emerges as a water robber on a large scale. In the developed parts of the world, the greatly elevated yields have raised the water requirements consistently, far above what was employed in earlier periods with more modest yields. Here we encounter another relationship that is often overlooked. To a large extent the extra yields have been obtained through a larger input of water. By and large this water would otherwise have trickled down to the groundwater reserves. The higher crop yields of western Europe have in this century meant an additional outtake of water corresponding to between 1.2 and 1.8 inches (30 to 50 mm.) of the annual precipitation. Only a minor portion of this water has been taken from water which otherwise would have evaporated. Higher yields consequently have a desiccating effect. This also accounts directly or indirectly for a share of the groundwater depletion. If we add to this the massive deforestation by man, not the least by Western man, the picture emerges of man as a major ecological force on a global scale. Denuded forest lands accelerated runoff and reduced the share of water entering into plants for production.

In 1952 the then United States Secretary of Agriculture Charles F. Brannan gave a notable address titled "Till Taught by Pain." [1] He outlined American agriculture in terms of the needs to be encountered in the next quarter of a century—chiefly taking into account population and resources. He was most optimistic about the possibilities of filling the tremendously expanded needs in terms of grain, milk, meat, and eggs. He recognized there was a "land problem," but this, he said, could and would be tackled. The great limiting factor was water, to which, in his opinion "far too little attention" had been devoted, "becoming more and more a limiting factor to national progress" as well as to "future developments." Yet this whole analysis terminates the address and seems added as a kind of sobering afterthought, without being related to the first part of his talk and its exuberant promises of higher agricultural production in the future. Is America prepared to pay this huge extra cost in water? Is she capable of feeding further millions with dietary standards that demand in excess of 3,500 gallons per person a day for the raising of this food?

It can be truthfully established that mankind cannot afford this luxury, and still less can the globe. The total amount of water returned on the average to the entire globe each year would not suffice to raise food and feed, as required on the present United States level, for more than 2.7 billion people, almost 0.8 billion less than those now living on earth. On an extreme vegetarian diet the limit would be ten times larger. But this is merely futile academic exercise based on the absurd assumption that man could use all precipitation for the single purpose of raising crops.

Some rain falls on deserts or otherwise evaporates immediately; it cannot be captured for use by man. We certainly could not maintain sanitation without water for washing purposes, not to speak of our drinking and eating needs. Finally, it is highly unlikely we would forego industrial activities or accommodate to the gradual loss of our waterways. Still more crucial is the fact that

[1] *Journ. Association of Land Grant Colleges & Universities,* 1952, pp. 52–61.

no less than nine thousand cubic miles of rain per year falls on land where it evaporates immediately or within days or, at the most, returns in a few weeks to the oceans via runoff. Since modern rain sewers remove water efficiently and rapidly, and since growing areas of land are under concrete in cities, at airfields and roads, we have accelerated the bypassing of an effective utilization of rainwater for crops and other plant cover.

A realistic appraisal would seem to conclude that at the best we can expect to use one-fourth of the total available water. This leaves the world with the prospect of providing for around 500 million people on a United States dietary standard, and five billion on an extreme vegetarian diet. Man will surpass this latter number by the year 2000. Perhaps there is also a simple reason and deeper causal relationships explaining why hardly more than 450 million presently enjoy the United States standard of living in terms of food. It might therefore be quite symbolic that Mr. Brannan on the above occasion quoted Lord Byron (in *Don Juan*): "Till taught by pain Man really know not what good water's worth." Although presumably made inadvertently, the quotation was almost prophetic.

In Fairyland

THE EARTH'S WATER BALANCE
(The Hydrological Cycle)

EARTH SURFACE	LAND 29 PERCENT		SEA 71 PERCENT	
	mm.	*inches*	*mm.*	*inches*
Precipitation	670	26.8	820	32.8
Runoff	250	10	—	—
Evapotranspiration	420	16.8	930	37.2

Lackadaisically and gleefully, many technologists and engineers point to the almost stupendous fact that all but about 3 percent of the water of the globe is held in the oceans. There is no basic shortage of water as such. This can be further amplified by the equally astounding information that less than 3 percent of the fresh water is available; more than 97 percent is captured and bound in the ice caps and glaciers, which thus constitute another tremendous source of water. Yet man and his civilization is facing a water crisis. This will not be analyzed further in this context. We shall merely restate a few essential circumstances related to this shortage. First, we can be rather grateful that man has not been more successful than hitherto in tapping the ice caps or subterranean water reserves (it is not exactly known how vast they are, and they are not included in the table presented here). In both instances man could easily have raised ocean levels critically, to the point of jeopardizing life for hundreds of millions who now inhabit low-lying lands. Most capitals of the world could also easily have been inundated.

FRESHWATERS OF THE GLOBE

	Billion cubic meters	*Percent*	ANTICIPATED RAISED LEVEL OF OCEANS * *Meters*
1. Ice caps	16.8	97.74	50
2. Lakes and rivers	0.25	1.46	0.75
3. Groundwater (nonsaline and now accessible)	0.125	0.725	0.375
4. Atmosphere	0.013	0.075	0.04
Total	17.188	100	

* If released.

The removal of salt in ocean water would not create these hazards. But we here encounter a number of other fallacies, greatly circumventing the general application of such procedures. These will be analyzed in the next chapter.

It is time man takes cognizance of the known conditions of our own spaceship Earth and starts acting accordingly. Fairy tales constitute a treacherous basis for sound action. Catastrophe can certainly not be averted, unless we get back to the realities of our globe and show responsible and knowledgeable attitudes.

Water Requirements

On the basis of extensive studies in many countries the following figures can be said to indicate the amount of water major crops require to bring forth normal yields:

	MILLIMETERS	INCHES
Rice		
lowland types	1,650–2,200	66–88
highland types	550–650	22–26
Wheat		
winter wheat	600–800	24–32
spring wheat	300–500	12–20
Corn	410–820	16.4–32.8
Barley	365–760	14.6–30.4
Millet (kaoliang)	200–250	8–10
Citrue fruits	500–800	20–32
Sugar cane	450–1,200	18–48
Grasses	550–1,000	22–40
Sugar beet	700–900	28–36
Alfalfa	825–920	33–36.8
Willow, maple	1,200–1,500	48–60

To these requirements should be added the inevitable evaporative losses, also occurring during off-season. The figures above also reflect latitude effects in climate, not only the physiological needs of the various crops.

Sugar cane in southern Egypt requires 10,000 cbm/ha (0.9 million gallons/acre, *i.e.,* 1,000 mm.), while rice there uses 16,500 cbm/ha (1.5 million gallons/acre, *i.e.,* 1,670 mm.). To the layman these figures appear unbelievably high. This becomes still truer when relating the actual quantities of water involved in the making of our daily food as they emerge from extensive studies at our latitudes, which are less strenuous as regards evaporation than the hot countries. The following data give an idea of the heavy taxation that takes place in water to provide our food. (The figures also take into account the water needed to make the feed going into animal production.)

one egg—120–150 gallons	one pound of beef—3,500 gallons
one quart of milk—1,000 gallons	one 16-ounce loaf of bread—300 gallons

Once again, please remember that this water is lost to the hydrological cycle and cannot be subject to reuse!

Only when man clearly realizes these ominous relationships, and particularly when we in the rich wasteful world recognize that our daily life has similar tremendous cost accounts, can we expect a more realistic, meaningful, and constructive approach to world food issues. We will then better understand the imperative need for creating balance. We cannot continue to live on dwindling bank accounts, heading for catastrophe. The water crisis, consequently is far more than a calamity—it is the birth pains of a new civilization.

The Narrow Margins

Most of the rainfall received in southwestern Saskatchewan of Canada is soon returned to the atmosphere by evaporation from bare soil or by transpiration from crops. Only one-fifth of the precipitation is conserved in the soil during a twenty-one-month summer-fallow period. Wheat yield is here determined largely by the moisture stored in the soil at seeding time and by the subsequent rainfall.

When moisture supplied in the soil is deficient, wheat yields follow almost linearly with the total evapotranspiration (moisture evaporated from the soil surface plus that transpired by the crop). About five inches of water is required before any grain is produced, and above five inches the yield increases by about four bushels per acre for each additional inch of water used. Longtime averages show that stored moisture and rainfall received during the crop season (seasonal rainfall) had almost equal influence on the ultimate yield. When precipitation is short, only two alternatives remain open: traditional winter fallowing or irrigation (see p. 42).

(see p. 42)

The new grain basket of the U.S.S.R. in the Tselinnij region (southern part of west Siberia and northern part of Kazakhstan) on the average receives twelve inches in the core area. This amount is wholly required for normal yields. As drought is recurrent here and frequently gets serious this inevitably affects yield. Fertilizers can do little to improve the situation when water is limited. This explains why supplementary irrigation now is pushed with full force for this region.

Dew

An additional source of water is dew, but its significance is frequently overrated in crop production. Dew is condensed water but cannot always be traced as to its origin. It may not necessarily come from the atmosphere. Some is known to originate in the soil and ground, but few exact proportions are known.

NIGHTLY FALLOUT OF DEW
(*summertime*)

France — 0.4 mm. (0.016 inches)
Japan — 0.8 mm. (0.032 inches)
Israel — 0.9 mm. (0.036 inches)

On the basis of daily measurements annual totals have been calculated, *e.g.,* the following:

	MM.	INCHES
Florence (Italy)	8	0.32
Montpellier (France)	9.5	0.38
Dakar (Senegal, Africa) (dry season)	16	0.64
Essex (UK)	25	1.0
Israel	30–34	1.2–1.4

Dew is increased by expansion of the evaporating area, as for instance through greater leaf surfaces. Sugar beets get approximately six times the theoretical amount for an equivalent land area, and a potato plant seven times more.

Dew should not be confused with fog, which is generally registered as rain. In general, however, these figures bear clear evidence that dew is a minor factor in the water balance, some 2 to 5 percent; in very exceptional cases 10 to 15 percent. Under highly critical conditions created by desiccation, dew might avert death of crops but would rarely enhance production. Consequently food production can hardly ever be attributed to dew.

The Oasis Mechanism

Water can be made to condense on the inside surface of mulching paper or on the soil surface when subject to mulching. In this way it is protected from the direct heating effect of sunrays, which otherwise speeds evaporation. The air is more effectively "milked" of its water.

Oases may have drilled wells for the tapping of groundwater, but most commonly they are surrounded by sand dunes like ridges, within which temperatures in general are lower than in the immediate environment, particularly during morning hours. This results in massive condensation of water within these ridges, thus water is collected at their basis.

For a time it was thought that many pyramids were built to obtain water through such condensation "milking," in the cool interiors of these structures. Pyramids built as trials have, however, only given a fraction of anticipated yields.

Another Food Item in the Water Budget

Food enters into the water budget in yet another way than via agriculture. Considerable quantities of water have to be mobilized for the handling, preparation, and processing of foods. This is dictated both by technical and sanitary demands. For each quart of milk, 4 to 8 quarts are needed in the dairy; 4 to 5 gallons for the processing into sauce of each pound of apples; as for each can of peas, 1.5 to 2.5 quarts are involved in the cannery. Per slaughtered cattle, 150 to 375 gallons are consumed; similarly 50 to 100 gallons per hog. For each ton of sugar made in the refinery, no less than 60 to 70 tons of water have to be provided. For the manufacture of each quart of beer, 1.2 to 2.0 gallons of water are needed. Many more similar examples could be made.

The only point of consolation is the fact that a major part of this water falls within the category of nonconsumptive use and consequently belongs in a grouping quite distinct from that of the producing fields. It contributes greatly to withdrawal of water but far less to actual losses of water. Producing and growing crops return the water inescapably to the atmosphere, to become available again to man only upon return to the earth through the hydrological cycle. The processing plants either have their own retrieval system or rely on local waterworks for redelivery after purification. In several instances water may in this way be reused from ten to twenty times. Our present water economy has already forced the developed, highly industrialized Western world of Europe and the United States to reuse water in several river basins up to fifty times before it finally moves along toward the ocean.

Desalination of seawater, which in addition must be pumped up and out over the continents, belongs in the category of fancies when it comes to the raising of food crops. What this actually would mean is analyzed in more detail in the next chapter. It is high time that man returned to reality, at least in his strivings to secure daily food. Food is and will remain the largest item in the water budget for the very simple reason that man has very limited influence over the actual quantity needed by the food-producing plants other than a possible enlargement of this water-devouring account. His chances of economizing on this score are quite limited.

As clarified earlier, water to crops is a truly consumptive use, *i.e.,* a net loss which does not allow reuse until the water has passed through the distillation cycle of nature. Man may, however, exert influence on the amount wasted via direct evaporation from the fields, irrigation canals, and reservoir dams, as well as on what is lost through leaching to the groundwater. In this latter instance, however, he may in doing so increase the risks of hazardous salination—his operational margin is narrow.

Staggering Amounts

As indicated repeatedly, the most significant feature of water involved in the life processes of plants is the fact that almost all of this water returns as evaporated to the atmosphere and thus becomes part of the hydrologic cycle of nature. Only through rain, snow, or dew does it come back to earth. This kind of water consumption is designated *consumptive,* as against *nonconsumptive,* when the water after use still is available for repeat performances.

This makes food the key to the water issue almost everywhere. The amazing requirements of plants, measured by the so-called transpiration ratio, pushes the water budget to staggering heights, particularly in secondary production, as in animal raising, when it passes through two stages: first the plants then the livestock. As a consequence milk, meat, and eggs are extremely costly in terms of water, not so much on account of the water consumed by the producing animals, not even through the water employed in the dairies and slaughterhouses, but primarily by the water engaged in the raising of the feed crops to be consumed by these animals.

WATER REQUIRED FOR DAILY FOOD
PER DAY AND PERSON

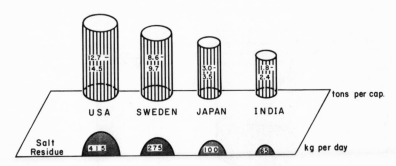

Fig. 27. Amount of water required to produce the daily food per individual and the amount of salt residue resulting, if desalinated water were used

On the basis of figures quoted on p. 148, the daily food of an American costs the almost unbelievable amount of 3,500 gallons. In the same vein, a woolen suit carries a water tag of no less than 225 to 250 thousand gallons, while if made from cotton it is ten to twenty times less. Intense high-yielding fruit and vegetable crops require around ten times more than wheat. This puts an orange (90 to 110 gallons) almost in the same class as an egg. These are facts of life, the cognizance and understanding of which would contribute to a sobering of the present glib water debate. Awareness of these matters would also make us better understand the true plight of the hungry world, forced to a parsimonious existence not the least due to its wavering water basis.

The Water Cost of Daily Food

How much water is then needed to secure daily food? With prevailing average diet the United States does, as just mentioned, need around 3,500 gallons of water daily in order to produce food for one single individual and at least 250 more gallons in

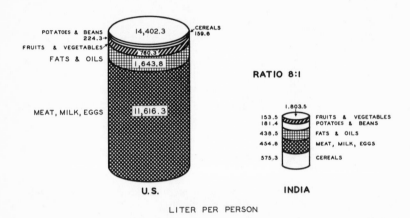

WATER FOR PRODUCING DAILY FOOD IN THE U.S. AND INDIA

POTATOES & BEANS 224.3
CEREALS 159.6
14,402.3
FRUITS & VEGETABLES 760.3
FATS & OILS 1,643.8

RATIO 8:1

MEAT, MILK, EGGS 11,616.3

1,803.5

153.5
181.4 FRUITS & VEGETABLES POTATOES & BEANS
438.5 FATS & OILS
454.8 MEAT, MILK, EGGS
575.3 CEREALS

U.S.

INDIA

LITER PER PERSON

Fig. 28. The production of daily food requires eight times more water per individual in the United States than in India. Graph shows the breakdown of this water by commodities (1 gallon = 3.785 liters).

order to make this crop storageable and nutritionally available. An extreme vegetarian diet (millet, cassava, and beans) may reach down to a water budget of approximately 350 gallons. Despite the vegetarian nature of the daily food of an average East Indian, no less than 500 gallons of water is needed for his normal daily intake, this primarily due to the high water needs of rice. Nevertheless meat takes twenty-five times more water than this water-demanding crop. Otherwise daily food of East Indians is only to a very limited degree subject to any water-wasting industrial processing. Such comparisons could be manifold.

It is no new wisdom that water is a prerequisite of our daily food. But it constitutes a basic fact that is often forgotten in our strivings to gain short-range benefits. And, even worse, it is not the only example in our management of basic resources of how we confuse capital outtake and productivity. It is to a considerable degree for this very reason that we now face a global water crisis, which in some ways is indeed more crucial than the food crisis and even more ominous. It is being felt not the least right in the midst of our own developed world, which in this respect stands out as becoming gravely overdeveloped. Therefore, the water requirements of our daily food constitute not only a key issue but a major neglected sector of our existence which we have taken for granted despite all indications of shortages and excesses.

CHAPTER VII

Is the Developed
World Threatened
by a Water Crisis?

WATER POLLUTION, THE CURSE OF AMERICA; THE THREATEN-
ING WATER CRISIS; WILL WE SUCCUMB FROM THIRST? THE COMING
WATER FAMINE; WATER SHORTAGE CREATING GHOST TOWNS; IS
U.S. RUNNING OUT OF USABLE WATER? This is a random sampling
of headlines from U.S. daily newspapers in recent years, and they
all refer to conditions in the United States, "America the beauti-
ful," where poets and writers have lauded the mighty Mississippi,
praised the wide Missouri, depicted in exuberant terms the eternal
roar of water in the great Niagara, and boasted of the tremendous
water reserves of the Great Lakes, containing one-third of the
world's fresh water in its gigantic basins. Is it seriously meant
that this continent ever could be faced with the risk of its civilization vanishing or even being hampered by lack of water? Most
people find this absurd.

Nevertheless the stark reality is that a water crisis is in the
offing, not only in our own continent but in all those parts of the
world that have employed the water-squandering technology
which has become a main feature of this century, as well as a
fantasy of our civilization based on the false assumption of inexhaustible resources, where one did not see any limitations or
problems but believed that man could persistently move on from

one technical advancement to another! Then suddenly we are faced with a reality which has been there all along but now with frightening clarity is pronouncing its warning: "Remember that you are mortal."

For some inscrutable reason—maybe simply due to our over-all flight from reality—we have believed our civilization would be the first in history that would carry the protective badge of immortality. Government commissions as well as studies by geologists and various such other specialists as hydrologists, biologists, and geographers have almost unanimously established that with present water consumption the water resources totally available to us via the precipitation on the land area of the United States would suffice for only fifty million additional people. A population growth of this magnitude will be reached long before the year 2000. A general water crisis is therefore clearly within sight for the United States and has already made itself felt in several crucial areas.

Against this background it is easier to understand why more than one-fourth of the United States population in recent years has been faced with water shortage difficulties, and in many instances has been forced to accept inferior drinking water. During 1957, a drought year, it was estimated that more than one-seventh of the nation had water rationing. In order to secure water for the nation during the next twenty years, investments in the range of from fifty to seventy billion dollars are required. Our situation does not differ in principle from that of Europe. What then has brought the developed world to this crisis situation? It is as much a major Soviet problem as a European and American one. It is encountered equally much in Canada, Australia, and South Africa. In the developing world water was a vexing matter long before the present-day worldwide crisis. Their industrialization efforts coupled with the population explosion have greatly aggravated the situation.

Underdevelopment is by no means synonymous with aridity; but semiarid and arid zones cover nearly one-third of the earth's land surface. Water is without question the key to their development, but capital used for investment in irrigation is a main burden and water usage has to be sharply circumvented. This frequently limits industrial as well as social activities, in particular when population starts pressing on scanty resources. In far too many cases water for irrigation of food crops is already too costly to food producers as well as to consumers. Such costs are frequently hidden in other accounts—compare p. 167.

Individual Consumption Mounting

Since water works were introduced to European and American cities in the latter part of the nineteenth century, and water became available largely to the urban population via the faucet, the quantities each citizen takes and consequently thinks he needs have constantly been mounting. From some ten gallons per day on the farm, when it had to be brought in from the well and largely carried manually, the individual consumption has soared in the United States to an average of 160 gallons per person per day. The ready accessibility has undoubtedly removed most restrictions in its use, even when obviously wasteful, but on the

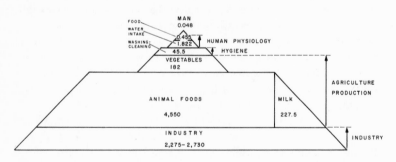

WATER PYRAMID
(1000 kg.)

Fig. 29. The water pyramid. Annual water needs (totaling about 16,000 pounds) per person in the United States broken down into (1) water content of man, (2) human physiological needs, (a) water contained in food, (b) liquid-water intake, (3) hygiene uses (washing, cleaning, and in sewage), (4) consumed in nature or in irrigation for agriculture production (inclusive of that used by feed crops and pastures) by (a) vegetables, (b) animal foods, (c) milk, and finally (5) water withdrawn by industrial activities. This is the total outtake of water, some of which may be reused. Nine-tenths of the consumptive losses are in the food sector.

other hand contributed to an improved sanitation. The United States average use of water per capita is currently almost three times that of western Europe, which is entirely adequate for reasonable hygienic needs, 160 gallons as against 60 gallons. The United States figure must, however, be judged against the fact that several major cities already have pushed their per capita figures to much higher values: about 250 gallons in Chicago and as much as 560 gallons in San Diego.

Formulated in another way, the United States is—with its increasing population and larger per capita withdrawals—currently using about 350 billion gallons per day (bgd) compared with 40 bgd in 1900, but it is anticipated on the basis of present trends that by 1980 a level of 500 bgd (billion gallons per day), and by the year 2000 a level of 700 bgd, will have been exceeded—see the table below, which was compiled by the author from several estimates used by different study groups. Some estimates reach figures exceeding 1,000 bgd in this century. What is essential, however, is the basic fact established by Congress (in 1963) that even with "optimum foreseeable developments in purification and engineering" not more than 650 bgd can be made available. Reuse will consequently have to be expanded considerably, and special measures will also have to be taken to mobilize *all* available water.

MAN-CONTROLLED DAILY DISPOSAL OF WATER IN U.S.A.
(gallons per person)

YEAR	1960	1975	2000
Population millions	190	220	320
Industry *	650	680	850
Irrigation †	700	1,000	1,200
Public supplies ‡	110	150	300
Total	1,460	1,830	2,350

* Reuses water on the average 5 to 10 times.

† 50 to 60 percent is possibly regained via seepage. This item does not include what agriculture normally uses for its crops, only what man willfully supplements.

‡ Reuses water 10 to 40 times.

The European Straitjacket

Many examples could be related from precipitation-rich Europe showing how its overpopulation is also clearly evidenced to be in the straitjacket created by water. Half the water of the city of Paris comes from wells, the remainder is extracted from the heavily polluted Seine, yet the average Parisian uses only seventy-five gallons per person—less than half as much as an American. There it has to be purified, but frequently this raises difficulty. The Paris of the year 2000 will need four times the flow of the Seine and seven times that of the Loire at the city of Orleans. New sources will then be urgently needed. Tapping of Lake Geneva currently stands out as the only recourse.

By the year 2000 England and Wales will need ten billion gallons of water a day, more than double the amount used now. Consumption is growing by about 5 percent a year. Plenty of rain falls on the British Isles every year to meet all foreseeable demands. But though the average rainfall is 36.5 inches a year, fifteen inches thereof are at present lost through evaporation, while another 18 flow down to the sea and only five or six inches are stored. Here lies the problem: Where should the extra water to meet rising consumption be stored? It is not easy to find acceptable places to put it.

The problem is national, but was never looked at nationally until the Water Resources Board was formed in 1965 and set about the monumental task of making a water inventory. Rain does not necessarily fall where it is needed, and though last year was wet enough for most water companies to get by without restrictions, it followed three unusually dry years. The driest part of England is the southeast, inclusive of the London area. The potential of several new population centers is hampered by below average rainfall.

A good deal of the southeast now relies on underground supplies rather than surface reservoirs, getting water from bored holes and wells. London used to rely almost entirely on these "aquifer" resources, but the water table has now fallen so low that it is practically useless as a source of future supply. Restrictions in water usage have become a regular feature of these parts of rainy England.

The Factories Surpass the Crops

In the previous chapter, "Water and Our Daily Bread," it was pointed out that the crops constitute the largest item in the water budget, both directly via nature's own operations—as when water passes through the plants to produce food and then returns to the hydrological cycle—and indirectly in the man-controlled sector of water use. Irrigation, especially in arid regions, actually constitutes the largest item in the United States water account, presently around 95 percent, measured as actual consumption and not merely as outtake.

There is, however, a new factor in the water equation: industry. In its modern apparition industry may not exceed crops as a water-gobbler, yet it is withdrawing immense quantities of water and in a growing volume, despite a strict economizing that has gradually been initiated. This is partly due to the enormous magnitude of the needs. Chemical plants for synthetic production of fibers, food processing units, paper and pulp factories, not to mention oil refineries and most recently the plants manufacturing nuclear fuel, have caused the water outtakes to skyrocket. Nevertheless this water is in several instances reused in the factories up to five, sometimes even ten times. The water consumption we are going to discuss here, however, is the net volume that is removed permanently from the natural water reserves, regardless of whether this water subsequently is used only once or several times. The fact remains that the lion's share of the water appropriated to industry does not constitute a true consumptive use in contrast to that utilized by the crops, where as mentioned above, the water evaporates and is returned to the atmosphere and to the hydrological cycle.

Industry Examples

When the first nuclear fuel plant, located at Savannah, Georgia, was in the planning stage, thoroughgoing investigations by the U.S. Geological Survey could find only one hundred locations supposedly capable of providing adequate amounts of water in the entire United States land area. After additional surveying of all these locations, the number of alternatives shrunk to four, the

only ones that could dependably offer the water quantities necessary for the enormous consumption of this single plant. Recently
a large brewery was started up in Milwaukee. This took so much
water that another sizable industry, located at a distance nine
miles (fourteen kilometers) away, was faced with a drop in the
groundwater level in its surroundings of no less than seventy-five
feet, and this in one single day.

In everyday life we give little thought to the copious quantities
of water—in many instances almost unreasonable—that our industrial civilization needs. In the making of an average-size car,
about 65,000 gallons of water are involved. More than 1,250
gallons of water are required to manufacture the fabric for one
man's suit made from synthetic fibers. A coal-driven electric
power plant takes 600 tons of water for each ton of coal burned.
This will be an increasingly major account in the water budget of
the United States. As early as in the thirties precipitation-rich
England was starting to feel the pinch of these large outtakes by
industry which resulted in shrinking groundwater reserves. The
many coal-fueled power stations, built in the fifties, further raised
the demand. In the United States it is estimated that the requirements merely for this single purpose will increase threefold before
the year 2000. In the total water budget of the nation these power
plants demand proportionately more water than other large-
scale water-gobblers, *e.g.,* organic synthetic plants, steel industries,
and oil refineries. Nuclear power reactors are almost limitless in
their water needs.

About 3.5 billion gallons of water was in 1955 withdrawn daily
for use by oil refineries in the United States. This was about 3
percent of the estimated daily withdrawal of industrial water at
that time. But surprisingly enough no less than 40 percent of the
intake, *i.e.,* 36 gallons per barrel, belonged in the category of
consumptive use: inevitable evaporation at all stages but in particular through air cooling. An average of 468 gallons of water
was required to refine a barrel of crude oil, and for this purpose
withdrawals ranged from 6.5 to 3,240 gallons per barrel.

Nine-tenths of the water requirements of the petroleum refineries is for cooling. Less than one-half of the refineries reuse
their cooling water from ten to more than fifty times. This has

improved considerably in the last two years, but refineries still remain major water consumers.

Major efforts have since 1955 been made to economize in the water account, but the trend has unmistakably been to reduce the intake of water by refineries, but largely by reducing waste water discharges. At the same time the losses through evaporation have increased.

About one-third of present water needs of industry is for cooling purposes. Reuse is in this case hampered by the obvious fact that cooling-water warms up when adequate time for recooling is not allowed. The turnover rate in this case becomes restricted. Many lakes and rivers in various parts of the United States and elsewhere show troublesome disruptions caused by temperature increases due to such inflow of heated cooling-water from industries—heat or thermal pollution. Furthermore, industrial water preferably needs to be cleansed, otherwise dirt and mineral salts accumulate in boilers and wands, and this in turn brings about rapid corrosion. The steel plant at Fontana, California, belonging to the Kaiser complex, experienced all these and many other inconveniences when water shortage forced this giant factory to resort to municipal sewage water. The huge English atomic power station at Windscale has at its disposal an entire lake in northern Wales, which is reused every ninth day, and the water temperature is continuously on the rise. The wildlife of this lake is now in jeopardy.

The intricacies and complexities of the water issue are rarely ever heeded in technical plans for developing countries. Nor is the narrow margin under which most of these countries already operate recognized. Finally we seem not to have well understood the dominant role played by water in providing ourselves with foods—in effect, widely overshadowing all other uses.

Plant Crops vs. Factories

There is yet another aspect to industry as a water consumer. In contrast to agriculture, most industry is nonseasonal. But nature's large hydrological cycle operates in periods. Even in the precipitation-rich East of the United States, water availability is on an average under one-tenth of the normal flow for no less than eighteen days of each year. The volume stability or continuity in the flow of the water is therefore a decisive factor, particularly when the pumps of industry operate on a high, sustained suction level without adjustment to seasonal fluctuations in water availability.

This large-scale industrial consumption of water has already had a decisive influence on Soviet industrial planning. Although the green plants utilize from between 300 to 1,000 times more water than the amount of dry matter they produce, they are in several instances less demanding on water resources than synthetic fibers are. It takes 400 to 550 times more water to produce one pound of nylon than one pound of cotton. Since water is a shortage commodity in the U.S.S.R., the decision was made to enlarge the cotton acreage in the irrigated regions of central Asia in lieu of building chemical factories for the making of artificial fibers, for which the water supply required is not available. Synthetic rubber removes the water burden from the Amazon basin of Brazil, richly endowed with water, and places it squarely on our own highly taxed water reserves. At the same time the water

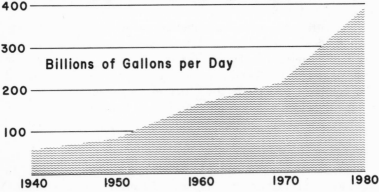

Fig. 30. Water requirements of United States industry at present and projected ahead to 1980

requirements are multiplied greatly when measured in terms of the weight of the final product.

Urbanization Inducing Huge Spot Outtakes

Urbanization coupled with industrialization has greatly contributed to the rapid upward spiraling of water consumption. A major factor is the serving of homes and individuals through faucets. The ready accessibility has inadvertently contributed to greater outtakes. In the United States the number of people served by faucets has more than trebled since 1900.

But there are still more revolutionizing trends. The agglomeration into cities tends to concentrate the outtake of water in areas very restricted in geographical terms. In many instances it may indeed seem justified to speak about spot outtakes. Twenty thousand families spread over the countryside can never constitute the same problem as an equal number of families settled within a limited suburban or urban area. When the cities become multimillion population establishments, frequently coupled with industries with additional huge water needs, they have the effect of gigantic suction pumps siphoning off both ground and surface water. Evidently this becomes most critical in dry regions.

In order to provide the water needs for the ever more thousands of people who each year move into the multimillion population center of Los Angeles, acre upon acre of California's orange groves and vegetable crops are being condemned to death by drought, if not straight out killed by the salt seawater seeping into the continent from the ocean, replacing the vacuum created by excessive outtakes of fresh water. Since World War II the citrus plantations have for this simple reason been reduced by one-fourth in acreage and one-sixth in production.

The Northeast Crisis

Even the rain-rich northeastern sections of the United States were in this very decade plagued by drought for five consecutive years (1962 to 1966). This brought about a crisis in several big cities including New York, which in 1965 was forced to take drastic rationing measures. The water outtakes for cities and industries in this general area have approached the ultimate limits for naturally available water in the large Hudson and Delaware river systems. Drought immediately makes itself felt, not only catastrophically on agriculture, but on the water supply of the cities.

Global Aspects

In big metropolises like London, Copenhagen, and Hamburg, the consequences of total water shortage are becoming critical. Huge investments are consequently needed for a replenishment of the underground reservoirs so that they do not run dry. A serious sustained lowering of the groundwater level has also been established in the Rhine Valley, at Basel in Switzerland, and in the Danube basin around Vienna.

The critical shortages discussed in this chapter are in no way

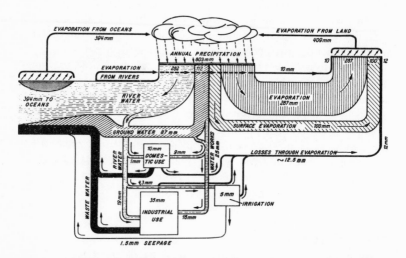

Fig. 31. The water balance of West Germany based on official data for annual average usage, losses and evaporation. The precipitation is 32.1 inches (803 mm); the evaporation originating from land areas is 16.4 inches (409 mm), and the evaporation emanating from oceans, rivers and lakes is 15.8 inches (394 mm).

limited to arid parts of the world. They are also seriously felt in regions where water never used to be an issue, or even where it was considered abundantly available, *e.g.,* in the southeast of England, in Hong Kong, and in Tokyo, all with an ample annual rainfall, but discrepancies in the pattern. Very grave situations developed in 1964 in both major Asian cities, jeopardizing many millions of people. A strict rationing was enforced with severe restrictions for industry. Precipitation in and around Tokyo fell to half normal between May and July. This practically emptied the city's water reservoirs. When rain finally came, there was literally no buffer left despite the severe rationing. A further prolonged drought period would have invoked a catastrophe.

In the spring of 1967 South American newspapers regularly carried tragic news about considerable numbers of children dying from thirst in Brazil, Colombia, and Peru. Most South American cities are seriously short of water and have severe lags in their implementation of water plans. In several instances the limit is reached for available water within reasonable distance. The groundwater level is in many instances down two hundred feet—uneconomic for pumping and with inadequate flow.

The Last Frontier

Over a number of years the U.S. Supreme Court has been forced to devote considerable time and effort to arbitrating the water takes as balanced out by the Rocky Mountain states and California. These wrangles have largely been focused around the Colorado, and in 1960 the Court handed down what amounted to a halt of any further aspirations by California for the allocations of the lower sections of this river. California is as a consequence faced with a reduction in its current outtake, particularly as since 1963 it has been realized that there is not enough water in the Colorado for all, and in particular not for the projected diversion (1.2 million cubic feet) for the development of central Arizona. This largely explains the almost desperate move to tap the border river to Oregon, the Klamath, a river that according to earlier plans did not need to be tapped until after 1990.

It is almost forgotten under the impact of the huge water transfer of California that the nineteenth-century West of North

America was won largely through a harsh adjustment to the strongly felt limitations of locally available water. There is a shrill contrast between these prime settlers and the excessively wasteful dwellers of our days. San Diego in California and Tucson in Arizona now hold almost the world record for per capita domestic use of water!! What a contrast to the nomads or oasis dwellers of the Old World with their careful husbandry of water.

Between 1950 and 1960 the seventeen western states emerged as the most highly urbanized region of the United States, and in the driest parts of these states. The withdrawals of water for municipal and industrial uses increased in this period almost three times, with a scanty 5 percent for irrigation. These cities are completely removed from reality, as manifested in their local resources. Increasingly they are fed from outside, yet irrigation accounts for 90 percent of all water actually consumed by man and returned to the hydrological cycle. It is by and large a question of gigantic mining of fossil waters (see p. 141) and rapid depletion of invaluable assets (supported by tax deductions for value depreciation). These western cities have not come to terms with their arid world, almost everywhere sustaining a level of water consumption far exceeding any natural stream flow.

Texas, having dangerously overutilized and irreversibly exploited its fossil groundwater, is now placing faith in a federal plan to amalgamate almost the total flow of the East Texas River into a half-billion-dollar canal, shunting these waters southward and westward.

Huge shale-oil resources, immeasurably large according to experts, are located in the western part of the state of Colorado and the state of Alberta in Canada. They have been described as the world's most important and largest fuel reserve for the future. It is, however, very much in doubt whether the mountain states will be in a position to utilize these riches fully without very costly water projects of continental dimensions. Already at the start of this century Colorado had emptied all its rivers with the exception of the Colorado River itself, which is now taxed to the limit. Alberta has very few adequate water resources within reach.

California has many grievous factors in its water equation. Four-fifths of its precipitation falls during the winter season, while the utilization is at its peak during the months from May to October. Two-thirds of the rain in California falls in the northern region, while three-fourths is used in the desert belt in the southern part with the Los Angeles metropolis and its industrial satellite cities. Water has consequently been transferred from the north to the south at great costs. Almost the last untapped reserve of the north is now being mobilized in the Feather River Project, a two-billion-dollar undertaking. This will involve fifteen dams, 618 miles of aqueducts, tunnels, and pipelines.

Partly as a result of the Supreme Court decision, California has taken another almost desperate step: Work has begun on tapping the Klamath, the border river with Oregon. It is no wonder that the inhabitants of this region now speak of "robbery" and view their own future in dark colors, since they would thereby be deprived of the future potential for both agricultural and industrial expansion. These facts are among other things behind the strivings to create a separate North Californian state. The total annual outtake from the groundwater reserves of California corresponds to a precipitation of 600 millimeters (eighteen inches). Only a fraction of this is restored. This is a measure of the speed with which the tapping takes place, or if we so prefer, of the intensity of the mining.

Similar drastic examples where the present generation is hitting the ceiling and yet does not hesitate to exhaust almost the last resources, can be related from a number of countries. Several cities and regions of central Europe are eyeing Lake Constance as their only resource. Paris is surveying the tapping of Lake Geneva, now supplying the city of Geneva, but the water along the French coast of the lake is severely contaminated. Lake Constance's water is also rapidly declining in general quality through pollution.

Northern Germany and even water-rich Holland and Denmark are in a corresponding way viewing the two big central lakes of Sweden as the only major water bodies from which to find future relief for their growing water demands. These two lakes, Vätter and Väner, are, however, small in the world of the giants, counting in the scale of millions of people.

Gigantic Proportions

The entire western United States, not to mention Mexico, is facing a day not so distant—in any case before the end of this century—when even larger water projects will be required if these regions are to be able to function. Most ambitious is the supergigantic plan for capturing the total head waters of the Columbia, the Fraser, the Peace River, the Athabaska, and other rivers of the Canadian Northwest as far north as the upper reaches of the Yukon and Alaska, the NAWAPA project (the North American Water and Power Alliance). These waters were to be channeled to an enormous storage reservoir in British Columbia, consisting of a nature-made trench in the Rocky Mountains. This 100-billion-dollar project with a time-span for construction exceeding thirty years has already encountered strong Canadian objections. Canada is simply not prepared to consider its waters as a continental resource. On the other hand, Mexico, in the throes of serious water shortage, is increasingly dreaming of its reincarnation through massive irrigation, the water for which by necessity has to come from far off sources—thousands of miles. From this majestic trench water is projected to be distributed not only toward the Gulf of California and the Great Lakes, but also south for replenishment of the Rio Grande water basin.

It is also being studied to create along the western coast an undersea aqueduct system which in addition could extend to northwest Mexico. Mexican planners are further eyeing the mobilization of their last water resource: the rivers of the humid southeast. When dammed en route to the Gulf of Mexico, they could be shunted north and to many areas now clamoring for water as food needs climb with human numbers—1.5 million added each year!

Other plans would cover the whole western part of the continent in a north-south direction with a huge network of pipelines to bring southward the water of the Yukon River and then at a later stage to tap the Mackenzie River, the mighty Canadian river now flowing northward. These plans are in direct conflict with other projects contemplating a transfer of some two hundred of the surplus millions of the world to precisely this river basin.

Even gigantic schemes dwindle when faced with meeting the gargantuan water demands of the new billions. Interbasin transfers raise many critical issues of a legal, technical, and social nature. All these will become more inflamed and tense the more mankind approaches the ultimate limits. Many decisions made are already highly arbitrary and not conducive to good economy, nor are they the result of sensible human planning. All these big transfer projects furthermore raise the pertinent question: At what point does it become more profitable to send people to water rather than water to people? But very soon even this option is lost, as total amounts of available water within feasible reach become inadequate. Man then really starts suffering thirst or worse: water famines, and this by not recognizing in time the obvious limitations of our globe and by moving far too close to the ultimate limits, not allowing for a reasonable operational margin.

South African Finale

South Africa faces a similar situation. Owing to the denudation caused by deforestation, coupled with the intensification of both agriculture and industry, practically all available water has been mobilized. Thousands of drilled wells dried up long ago in the early part of this century, as the groundwater resources were over-taxed. Only the Orange River in the northwest is now left to tap. In a thirty-year plan the total mobilization of this river has been outlined to obtain power as well as additional water for industry and agriculture. The dimensions of this huge undertaking can be understood by the mere fact that the dam's distributing system of canals will cover an area twice that of the British Isles. The project is estimated to cost close to 700 million dollars, but it is in line with the times that nobody is concerned with what to do next when this irrevocably last reserve has been marshaled.

The Two-way Lifeline

One consequence of people flocking into cities is the growing quantities of food that by necessity flow to these conglomerations, thereby tapping the soils of ever-growing amounts of minerals. This has created the need for a vast two-way traffic along this lifeline: not only food to the millions in the cities but also commercial fertilizers back to the soil. This has become a major task, requiring a constantly growing number of conveying vehicles and creating a mounting load, moving on highways and railroads. By and large this challenge has been met, but few realize the dimensions, which have now reached a point where seasonal deliveries to the farms are no longer possible. This has become a year-round routine operation, creating in addition huge storage demands, not only in industry but also on the farms.

We also have not managed to cope with the concomitant phenomenon of mounting sewage and waste. As late as the turn of the century human sewage from the cities could be disposed of in natural waters where it underwent degradation and entered the circulation of nature. But the quantities have become oversized and are greatly surpassing the cleansing capabilities of nature. This has now become a gigantic issue, and with each passing year we are lagging behind still more seriously in our countermeasures, as discussed in the chapter "Food and Microorganisms."

Fifty Billion Dollars

In the United States we have merely taken care of half of the current sewage load. More than fifty billion dollars are needed to restore balance and eliminate present inconveniences and hazards. These risks are now being compounded and threaten almost all major waters with overloading. This creates serious pollution, which in turn induces oxygen shortage and kills off fish and numerous other organisms. Behind these ominous developments lies not only a lack of foresight but rather widespread ignorance and unawareness of the true nature of this phenomenon. A tremendous overrating of the self-cleansing properties of nature is another factor for which many experts must share the blame. Even the huge Great Lakes are endangered. Lake Erie has been labelled a "dying water" and the southern part of Lake Michigan is almost a cesspool.

We commonly burden the waters with unreasonable amounts of organic substances in quantities far exceeding anything that our busy servants, the bacteria and fungi, are able to handle. At the same time we are depriving nature through growing outtakes of these vital water resources, and this at a frantically growing pace. Yet we are surprised at the calamities. No situation is more clearly man-made or man-induced than this. For some curious reason we expect that, simultaneously with our accelerated depletion of the water reserves, they will perform even greater magic tricks than ever before! This is the dilemma that has brought about the grave pollution crisis of today.

It was recently reported that a steel plant on the Ohio River, which had cost 5½ million dollars to build, was forced to invest another 2¼ million dollars in order to master its pollution problem and water supply. This is only one single evidence of our lack of coordinated planning, but it reflects our inability to grasp the causal interrelationships in our immediate environment. No wonder we fail to understand the critical dilemmas of the poor, hungry, and diseased world, which has a far more narrow margin than ours and much greater needs. In advocating and implementing our methods, how often do we take time out to ponder about the fact that of all men we constitute under 6 percent (of the world's population), 200 million? Yet many of our difficulties are overwhelming. Our methods are in effect not only inadequate but in several instances not advisable to implement.

Pollution

There are many other ways in which man has interfered in a disruptive way with his own water reserves. Soaps have largely been replaced by detergents, modern synthetic cleansing agents. These have several collateral effects. They interfere in the biological purification process of the sewage plants by killing the microorganisms that take care of the waste degradation. Mass water pollution has reached such dimensions that oils, detergents, sewage bacteria, and other contaminating microorganisms, spray-chemicals and several toxic compounds not only find their way to recipient surface waters but also filter down to groundwaters, causing many unpleasant surprises. A few years ago an entire housing development in Detroit was halted; the septic tanks were overflowing, spreading hepatitis and polio via trickling water.

Topsoil layers once provided a powerful cleansing filter, rendering fresh well water and the clear rivers of bygone times. But at many places in the developed world today natural water reserves constitute sources of danger. Even the fine Swiss Alp lakes have virtually been converted into sewage ponds.

The Great Water Steal of Chicago

One of the most sensational examples of where technological development has brought us is the Great Water Steal of Chicago.

The sewage works of this big city are in effect the world's largest industrial plant, a true technical marvel. This plant takes care of the sewage from three and a half million Chicagoans and one and a half million suburbanites, as well as the industrial waste which contributes an amount almost equal to that from the humans. All in all the sewage load is equivalent to a population of no less than eight million.[1] The enormous treatment plants are simply inadequate in capacity. Sewage from 800,000 people has to be channelled away via the Illinois River, a tributary of the Mississippi. Besides, the Illinois River needs the amount of liquid going with this load, in order to uphold its river traffic—this shows what a major water-consuming factor the sewage systems with water closets, one of the least ingenious of our inventions, have become.

The large sewage plant of Chicago is in effect returning several billion gallons of water daily to circulation via the water works. But the pollution load reached intolerable dimensions, and in order to avoid the risk of such excessive pollution, the sewage had to be further diluted with water before it was released into the Illinois River. The easiest way, one reasoned, to accomplish this was by resorting to the water resources of Lake Michigan, the world's third-largest lake. Two billion gallons per day are taken. After year-long negotiations Chicago authorities managed to persuade all the communities around the lake to agree to extra tapping, despite the appreciable losses it would mean for the power stations along the coast and the disruptions it would cause along the beaches, affecting hundreds of thousands of people. As a more distant effect, a deepening of major sectors of the famous St. Lawrence Seaway would have been required. Canada delivered, however, one of its strongest diplomatic protests ever to the Federal Government in Washington. This note simply amounted to a veto. (The request was for 650 million gallons extra.)

The sewage outlets into Lake Michigan from the innumerable communities along its coasts are already so many that because of prevailing currents the entire southern part of the lake is being converted into a major sewage recipient. What then was there to do? Faced with what amounted to an ultimatum, the United States retreated. So did Chicago. Canada possesses powerful counter-

[1] Sewage load is measured in terms of degree of pollution created by the average waste per human individual as a base unit.

vailing weapons. It is actually in a position to direct the upper flow of the Columbia River into the Fraser River. This would mean a death blow to the economy of the entire western region of the United States. Detailed plans for the full utilization of the waters of the Columbia River have actually been prepared by Canada. A compromise proposal was finally submitted which led to an agreement about a joint exploitation of these power resources.

As in the Chicago issue, the proposal has been put forward to reverse the flow of several smaller rivers, especially the Harricanow, now feeding into the Hudson Bay, and in this way attain a replenishment of the Great Lakes. Indirectly this would benefit Lake Michigan, but these water quantities would not go far toward meeting present and future needs. Far more fanciful projects have been presented, suggesting the installation of gigantic pumps combined with desalinization plants for a large scale use of the Arctic waters of the Hudson Bay—a project completely unrealistic from both the practical and the economic point of view. Chicago's great water steal dramatized to the public that there are clearly discernible limits even for a richly endowed nation like the United States.

Numerous examples could be cited from Europe and other continents of similar and maybe even worse complications caused by our unwillingness to face reality. The fact is that we have pushed our water frontier far beyond what is prudent. The communication lines to the rear threaten to break down. We are in many parts of the globe reaching a point of no return. Our wasteful extravagance and carelessness have beaten all records when it comes to water. It is sheer good fortune that, as far as we know, water is not lost to the globe, but recirculates in the hydrological cycle of nature, but unfortunately not as fast as we manage to use it. This explains why today on all continents, none excluded, an annual net loss of water can be registered. Furthermore, the quantity of this net loss is mounting with each passing year.

Lofty Speculations

Lengthy lists could be made of the innumerable projects that emerge as though on endless conveyor belts from the workshops of present-day scientific superstition, often in the disguise of science fiction. In many ways these prejudices and articles of faith take the place of the religious superstition of earlier days in human history. Proposals that normally would earn their protagonists the reputation of "nuts" gain credence because they are dressed up in scientific and technological terms. Even when they are thoroughly refuted by meteorologists, climatologists, geologists, geographers, and oceanographers through careful analyses, they continue their life or are resuscitated with almost ominous regularity in Sunday supplements and in the swelling flood of science fiction. Little does it seem to worry these writers that New York, London, and other big cities would be inundated if the atomic reactors were allowed to melt down the ice masses of the polar caps in order to give the world some additional acreage for food production, and that is only a fraction of the much larger losses that would be inflicted on homes and croplands. Nor do they worry about the fact that still more extensive areas of the dry tropics than is presently the case would then languish under a scorching sun. The towing of icebergs from these ice caps to New York or San Francisco is taken seriously by the news media.

Another fanciful project, the Markin Dam, which should close Bering Strait and unite Alaska with Siberia offers a little more qualified intellectual exercise, but it is certainly not to be taken seriously as a way of feeding the starving world. A prerequisite for this dam would be a large-scale expansion of the Lena and the Yenisey rivers, in order to pump water from the Pacific into the Arctic Sea via these rivers by means of gigantic installations in Kamchatka and on the Sea of Okhotsk. If these measures were carried through, major parts of Scandinavia would be inundated and the Arctic coast of Barents Sea would freeze, presumably permanently, together with the world's largest fishing port, Murmansk. Such major upsets do not worry the project writers or speculators.

The Sörgel Plan for irrigating the Sahara—damming the Mediterranean at Gibraltar and converting it into two large lakes, thereby uniting the European and African continents—is another such project, which supposedly is in a kind of planning stage. The enlarged version of the Lake of Chad in Africa, which would then become the new water reservoir of the Sahara Desert, would, according to this plan, be filled from the mighty Congo. The truth is that in the burning hot climate of the Sahara, more water would be lost through evaporation than even the entire Congo River could provide. Consequently the lake would never expand, and water would be lost at a faster rate than supplied, not to mention the loss of the enormous hydroelectric potential of this river and its function as a major waterway.

The only large-scale project seemingly founded on some realistic basis, and which appears to have a chance to create a favorable climatic effect, at least for Siberia, is the Davidov Plan. This involves the creation of a major Siberian Inland Sea by gradually turning the flow southward of the two large rivers, the Lena and the Yenisey, now feeding the Polar Sea. The first stage of this project seems to have been started, and this may introduce a new era for crop-raising in Siberia where the sun shines so abundantly from a predominantly cloud-free sky. But nobody knows for sure if, as a consequence, this Siberian high-pressure center will be affected. It is quite possible that the new inland sea will gradually exert influence on precipitation and air movements as far away as central Europe and North America. In other words, we have to be prepared for the possibility that undertakings of these major dimensions may have other consequences than regional, and consequences we can not even anticipate.

The large water resources of the oceans make many people take discussion about water shortages as fictitious or originating from a lack of imagination. Desalinization of sea water was mentioned in the previous chapter. To this we may add that desalinated sea-water will never in a decisive way improve the climate nor serve food production, save in a highly limited way, in coastal regions or on some islands.

As earlier discussed (p. 148), crops—whether for food or feed—need for each ton of organic matter produced approximately two thousand tons of water. This is measured in practical terms, taking into account such factors as varieties, inevitable losses, and the circumstances that man only harvests a fraction of the produced matter. If we are to do anything more than squirt along the edges of the continents; if we really want to provide food for the billions, such desalinated water would in most instances have to be pumped up and out over vast interior expanses. This energy account would be formidable, and in relative terms far exceed anything man has hitherto undertaken, inclusive of industrialization. Another consequence of the large water requirements is that pipelines would be wholly inadequate and huge subterranean tunnels would be demanded.

The size and number of salt-removing plants would be gigantic, even if man could manage to achieve an extra rapid flow and treatment procedure, and as a consequence attain almost inconceivable capacities. Most chemical plants of our day, even the big ones, look small in this context. This is a good example of the relativity concept as applied to that world of giants we are molding for ourselves through the demands created by the population billions—now almost an additional one per decade.

Subaquatic Cities

The alternative idea of shoving the human population into subaquatic cities on the ocean floor is certainly not dictated by the lack of space on land. It seems to be supported by some vague, ill-conceived notion of bringing man closer to water and to the "immense food resources of the oceans." Water will still have to be desalted, and the big cost item in the water budget will still be food production. The millions in such subaquatic cities will have to be fed from external sources, still demanding as much water as before. The living resources of the ocean will not be within closer reach of man in such a bottom bubble. The living mass of the oceans drops with depth. Catching from below is certainly not going to be easier than from above—rather the opposite—although you might be nose to nose with some fish down there. It goes without saying that the recycling of waste or any controlled photosynthesis within such a bottom-anchored spaceship in no way offers easier solutions than those devised for space travel.

The Developing Countries and the Water Luxury of Western Man

On an average, man today utilizes for his personal needs thirty-two times more water than around the turn of the century. But this figure merely reflects the excessive consumption of a few hundred million people, and yet it is still mounting, almost skyrocketing in this water-lavish world. One key factor is connected with modern industry, which by and large has been designed as to its procedures with little attention devoted to water.

Water has been taken for granted and looked upon almost as limitless or entirely reusable. This general attitude exhibits a high degree of irresponsibility with little recognition of other needs of society. This lack of a water economy has brought the Western world, led by its technology, to a situation where the water outtake for the daily bread, despite its immensity, is gradually being overshadowed by the excesses of industry. These two factors together provide the basis for the present water crisis. Europe and North America presently are using up more water than nature provides, thus practicing a large-scale mining of groundwater resources.

Consequently, the world is now faced not only with a Hunger Gap but also with the greater gap between those who live in water luxury and those who do not. Those of us who live in water luxury seem totally unaware of the plight of man, yet we endorse thoughtless procedures in projects and installations that supposedly aim to aid these countries that belong to a world that is not only hungry but likewise short of water and therefore in key areas desperately thirsty. We should not deceive ourselves by believing that a social order can remain where, as I have seen with my own eyes in Rio de Janeiro, poor people must stand in line for hours, furthermore often in vain, to try to get a couple of gallons of water for daily use, while a few hundred yards away, in the luxury resort of Copacabana, the hotels provide their guests showers without restrictions. But it is the irony of destiny as well as of history that the ghost of water shortage is now emerging right in the midst of the rich world and threatens the very food front itself. Daily bread is within this world already entering into direct competition with rockets, atom bombs, cars, and television sets.

Water as Holy

Water has been called holy, and holy it is in the sense that it is the basis for human existence. This is certainly no new wisdom, but it has often been forgotten in our Age of Technology, which preposterously assumed that it had placed man outside and above the unyielding laws of nature. This lack of foresight and economic planning becomes especially obnoxious when we proceed to give advice to what we arbitrarily choose to call the underdeveloped world. How could countries like Mexico, Brazil, and India allow themselves our water splash when food alone, in order to be adequate, would earmark all available resources and even require more? It is certainly of paramount urgency that we formulate completely new programs, taking water into account as a major cost factor. Above all, man must arrive at an industrial production far less wasteful with water, which already is in critically low supply.

In the United States we live with a civilization using daily between four and six times more water for other needs than for direct domestic and municipal purposes via the faucets. Even if this is primarily a question of withdrawal of water from natural resources and not of any significant loss to the hydrological cycle, these water quantities nevertheless have to be regionally provided. It is therefore basically absurd to place nuclear power reactors or oil refineries in countries where almost every drop of water is needed for producing food. So much water is, through such undertakings, channeled past the fields and ultimately never reaches forests or crops. In this way these peoples are deprived of the ultimate basis for their existence. Industrialization in these terms becomes not only a costly endeavor measured in water, but also a direct competitor to food (see p. 164). Even locating fertilizer plants in such overpopulated countries becomes a doubtful proposition. See further the chapter "Will Chemistry Offer Mankind the Third Freedom?"

The Water Scandal

Close to two and a half billion people live in the underdeveloped countries, no less than three-fourths of them in rural areas. But the population pressure there is becoming too great, and excess numbers are flocking to the city slums, and not due to the attraction of employment opportunities as in our own process of industrialization. The driving force in the hungry, developing world, is simply the super-pressure building up on the tiny farms and overcrowded countryside. In both city and village, and even on farms, the water supply is becoming ever more critical. According to World Health Organization (WHO) surveys, hardly 500 million people in the entire world enjoy the luxury of water from the faucet. More than nine-tenths of the population in the developing world does not have enough water, and furthermore its quality is generally unsatisfactory. This explains why annually 500 million humans are infected with water-borne diseases according to estimates also made by the World Health Organization.

A survey, comprising seventy-five underdeveloped countries with a total population of 1,300 million, recently established that only one-third of the city dwellers and less than one-tenth of the rural population had water faucets and water pipes.[2] Two-fifths of the urbanites and almost three-fourths of the entire population were without regular water supply. They were compelled to carry water from rivers, lakes, or wells, or buy from street peddlers.

Millions of people around the globe must walk for miles to pick up their daily water. Generous assurances that the earth has enough water and that there are few limitations in this respect sound rather shallow for all those numerous victims of critical water shortages. It is high time world politics does something about this water scandal, tries to make water available wherever possible, and mobilizes popular education in order to achieve a balance.

The grand water plans elaborated for South America and Africa are not only lagging behind the population growth and the mounting demands of industry, but most of these programs are from the start inadequate and do not recognize the true magnitude of the needs. Nor were they ever based on a realistic appraisal of resources, taking into account seasonal availability as well as fluctuations between years.

The Western World

It almost constitutes an irony of fate that Western man has chosen to look upon his water luxury as the acme of economic wisdom, and that in this respect he persists in confusing capital outtake with productivity. If a sound economizing with water were

[2] H. Dietrich, *Gas-und Wasserfach,* CV, 1334.

introduced, and a legal barrier put up for the sustained depletion of surface and ground water reserves, then a great many of our present cities, many other population centers, as well as industries would no longer be able to operate. This applies not merely to the United States but also to many parts of Europe, the U.S.S.R., New Zealand, South Africa, South America, Mexico, and Canada. Still more population centers would vanish, and industries would be closed down, if water pollution were legally limited to certain acceptable levels, in order to protect water resources. This would obviously be still more true if water pollution were entirely prohibited and penalized.

By and large, in few other respects have we been as careless and continued to indulge ourselves to such a formidable extent as in the water sector of our daily life. We persistently refuse to recognize how our joint water account is inexorably being emptied without returns or replenishment available within reasonable distance. San Diego in southern California, for instance, is now forced to bring in water from a distance of six hundred miles. Yet the absurd arrangement prevails in the southwest United States in which speedy depletion of water is given a premium. Tax deductions are permitted to compensate for the shrinking water reserves as is the case with oil. The more water that is squandered, the larger the profit the present owner can make by converting the limited resources, as long as they last, into crops or animal products. The youngster emptying his father's bank account was never looked upon as industrious or even socially acceptable; yet collectively we follow such perverted habits and even praise them as progressive and gainful.

The water crisis has already hit us, and there is a justice of history in the fact that the developed world has to take the first blow. The first victims are in effect the 400 to 500 million in the world's luxury club who have refused to see that there are limitations to their civilization and that their luxury rather stands out as an episode in history. The Golden Age, characterized by its supreme wastefulness exercised by a small minority of the human race, already lies behind us if we are not capable of formulating and developing new improved procedures for production and survival. I belong to those who believe that this would be possible, but it certainly cannot be done by continuing the frantic race downward to disaster. We must finally catch up with economy in its real sense and submit our action to long-range planning and to a clear recognition of the limits of our globe. The geologists count in billions of years, the geographers in millennia, the historians in centuries, but our generation is limiting itself to looking ahead a couple of decades, and yet most people seem to think that this is entirely satisfactory. Why worry about a distant future, when the perspective is narrowed down to a fraction of a century? Western man seems to have lost the notion of time completely, and many even refuse to look ahead at all. In this process we may very well deprive ourselves of both our future and our history.

CHAPTER VIII

Is Large-scale Irrigation Reaching an End?

Irrigation is as old as agriculture. It is quite possible that artificial supplementation with water dates further back than historical documents cover. There are several indications that irrigation was even practiced in primitive societies. Archaeology also gives evidence of numerous techniques for providing water, *e.g.,* from wells, storage ponds and canals, and through terracing combined with dams. There are many examples of even fairly large-scale irrigation projects built several hundred years ago, and in some instances some two thousand years ago. They are found in China, Egypt, India, Iraq, and Italy. Many of them are still in operative use.

Most widely known is the huge irrigation construction with storage dam attached to the Ninkiang River in China, built two thousand two hundred years ago. Egypt claims it has the oldest irrigation dam in the world. The Nile canal system originated 5,300 years back and played in those early days an important role in Egyptian agriculture. It is well documented that the irrigation systems serving the twin rivers Euphrates-Tigris constituted the foundation for the Sumerian, the Assyrian, and other civilizations which flourished in this region thousands of years ago.

The Irrigation Century

Not until during the latest hundred years was irrigation practiced on a truly big scale, however, and not until the middle of the nineteenth century did man venture the construction of huge irrigation dams serving hundreds of thousands of acres. Toward the end of the 1800s several large undertakings were in operation in Egypt, India, and other countries. During the nineteenth century the irrigated acreages of the world expanded from about twenty million acres in the beginning to about 112.5 million acres at the end, *i.e.,* an increase of 5.5 times.

These pioneering operations paved the way for the still more gigantic endeavors to come in the twentieth century, in which the irrigated acreage had more than four-folded already by 1965. The pace in building new dams has certainly not abated; on the contrary. Experts predict that the globe will probably exceed

DISPOSAL OF WATER DIVERTED FOR IRRIGATION
IN ACRE FEET

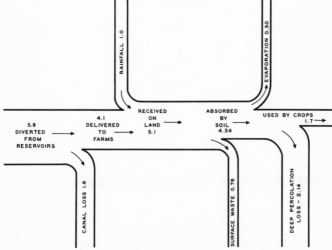

Fig. 32. Balance sheet for irrigation operations (based on California data). Note that only one-fourth of the water diverted from reservoirs for the purpose of irrigation enters into the production machinery of the crops.

600 million irrigated acres before the year 2000. With a certain justification the twentieth century may therefore be given the designation Irrigation Century.

Despite the enormous dimensions of present-day irrigation, only one-fifth of world food production can probably be credited to this account. More than half of this gain is due rather to local measures by individual farmers through small ponds, rivulets, and field ditches. The giant-size dams—created with the aid of the full arsenal of modern technology and involving complete control of entire river and lake systems, in other words large-scale irrigation —have not accomplished more than all the small-scale local measures added together have accomplished, when measured in total area served.

On a small as well as a big scale the ancient Chinese and Indian civilizations were pioneers in conquering the climate along this front. And throughout history China and India have maintained the lead in irrigation. They possess, even in this era of huge dams, more than half the irrigated acreage on the globe (see Figure 33). During this century and even in the fifties they have carried out irrigation projects which *in toto* amount to some of the largest undertakings in history. We in the Western world should speak in a lower key when we thoughtlessly classify these countries as

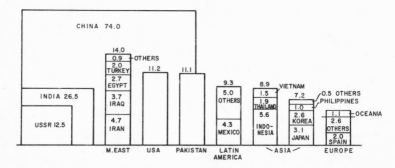

IRRIGATED LAND
(mill. ha)
1963-65

Fig. 33. The irrigated acreages of the globe in the 1960s, showing the dominance for China and India sustained through the centuries

underdeveloped, disregarding their impressive technological feats carried out long before any Western technical aid appeared on the horizon. Aside from Spain, Europe has an irrigated acreage only one-sixtieth that of China. Spain, which also has a lengthy history of irrigation, accounts for three-fifths of Europe's irrigated lands.

Impressive Wonders

In the fifties China created irrigation on another hundred million acres (forty million hectares). This corresponds to about the total tilled acreage of Canada, and this has been carried out in less than a decade! Today more than two-fifths of all irrigated land on the earth is located in China. The seven wonders of the antique world and anything accomplished in technical terms in latter centuries dwindle and seem dwarfish when confronted with the dimensions of the large-scale irrigation projects brought to fulfillment in China and India during the postwar period. For each one of these new projects overwhelming quantities of concrete, coal, oil, and timber have been required. This has, if nothing else, brought into distinct focus the priority of food in the present stage of world development.

Reportedly, in constructing the huge dams of China during the fifties 450 times as much dirt was removed as for the construction of the Panama Canal. At least three of India's projects are much larger than this famous canal in magnitude, when measured in terms of soil transport. Yet all these impressive technological achievements fall pathetically short of man's feeding needs as they now emerge, unduly expanded by a veritable tide of excess people. The catastrophic crop failures in China around 1959–1960 give some reason to believe that in this case man may have overexerted himself, basically by overestimating the amount of available water, this in turn leading to a serious overtaxing of the water resources.[1] The failure to acknowledge obvious limitations facing man within our spaceship leads to foolish and aggravated calamities.

Many more examples could be reviewed illustrating the fact

[1] G. Borgstrom, *The Hungry Planet* (New York: The Macmillan Company, 1967), p. 111.

that in effect man is operating in two distinct worlds of completely different dimensions. On one hand we describe and implement our technical wonders. On the other hand we encounter the tremendous inadequacies and shortages as they evolve when measured against the avalanche of the billions.

The Aswan Dam is in technical terms an indisputably masterful achievement, which will create one of the largest artificial lakes of the globe. In its final stage it will serve an acreage corresponding to one-twentieth of that of the United States (about the cultivated land of New York State). This will augment the cultivated lands of Egypt by about 15 percent. The dam will be in operation by 1975. But at that time the population of Egypt will have grown by nearly 35 percent. If, later on, it would be possible to double the irrigated acreage to five million acres, one would still not catch up with the population increase. During the six years 1962–1967, Egypt's population grew by ten million.

The Mexican Government announced in 1960, with justified pride, that it was planning to increase irrigation by more than 2½ million acres (one million hectares). This would involve, however, the building of several dams, the total serving acreage of which would not surpass that of the Aswan Dam. These big watering plans, if and when carried through, would be an impressive feat, but not overly reassuring when the annual population growth exceeds one million! The large-scale projects of North Pakistan involving the two big life-giving rivers of Indus and Ganges reached, in terms of irrigated acreage, similar imposing figures from a purely technical point of view. The Sutlej Dam alone serves 2½ million acres and the Sukkur Dam twice as much.

In the Near East serious efforts are being made to restore the Euphrates-Tigris irrigated region of earlier centuries. Present plans would bring another ten million acres (four million hectares) under irrigation in this general area, which corresponds to one-tenth of Canada's tilled land. Knowing that Iraq is counted upon as a granary for the Middle East, which has a total population of some 125 million and is currently growing by 3.5 million annually, one finds that the irrigation projects, though impressive as such, shrink considerably in relative significance when projected into the future. If the entire newly irrigated acreage could be used exclusively to the benefit of Iraq, the effect would naturally be considerable. But what is this key area going to do when within a decade or so the present irrigation projects are completed? Only one major potential reserve then remains in the entire Middle East: the upper Euphrates region in Syria. At the most, maybe 100 million acres (some thirty to forty million hectares) of desert can be made to flourish—not much of an increase for an area that is rapidly moving toward a quarter of a billion people in the year 2000. The U.S.S.R. will be concentrating on this Syrian project when the Aswan Dam is finished, and it is furthermore providing monetary aid to pay half the costs (fifty million dollars) of the first major dam.

The Reverse Side of the Medal

Parallel with all these magnificent achievements and with the general advances in hydraulic engineering, awesome complications—some with wide repercussions—have arisen. Unfortunately not even the experts have paid due attention to these ramifications. This is one of many clearcut examples of how specialization dims the view of other fundamental relationships. A saying, often repeated, is that technology has created more problems than it has solved. We are prone to revel in our successes and look to the end results, bypassing failures in silence, or minimizing them. We avoid discussing difficulties, and above all, we are little inclined to give a true accounting of our costs. In far too many instances they are entirely forgotten. The pressure from the mounting tide of billions of humans is too overwhelming to allow attention to such trifles for very long.

Along with the growth of world population, activities on the human supply front, including the irrigation sector, have gradually been intensified. With the prospect of most available land, reasonably fertile, being for all practical purposes taken, and having pulled down the forests, frequently far beyond obvious risk limits, man has ever more desperately turned to the use of water to overcome aridity. But in these very areas the difficulties are compounded and quite crucial. For this very simple reason most irrigated acreages of the world are not—as pointed out in the previous chapter—located in arid regions but in areas with a fairly generous precipitation. In this category fall large parts of the rice fields of the world, primarily in Southeast Asia, China, and India.

But even under favorable circumstances, *i.e.,* in relatively rainy regions, irrigation does not easily yield a net profit. The amount of required capital is high, and so are costs for building and maintenance. Dams and distribution canals furthermore require space and take a considerable share of the productive soil, normally one-fourth. In addition, the imposing dam constructions are not permanent installations. They have an ephemeral existence, and most of the large-scale dams in the world get filled with silt within the relatively short time of 200 to 300 years (see further p. 203). Particularly in South America dams are found in many places which man was forced to abandon after ten years of operation as they were filled with silt and sand and surrounded by marshlands.

The collapse of irrigation systems has in effect brought about the decline of several previous civilizations. But frequently this has been attributed to other causes, labeled by historians short-comings due to cultural, political, or economic conditions. The engineers have on their side been unwilling to admit that their creations have a time-limited duration. The big new dam in the Zambesi River of Africa, the Kariba Dam, is probably unique in that the experts estimate its lifespan as exceeding one thousand years, due to the low particle load of the river. It remains an open question if these predictions can be sustained when the watershed of the dam becomes cultivated to a greater extent and the forests reduced with ensuing erosion, removing soils and sand.

Salinization

The complications arising from extended irrigation on a global scale are most conspicuous in arid regions. It came as a shocking surprise to progressive United States when in the thirties it was suddenly discovered that the flourishing irrigated valleys of California in large parts showed deterioration. The paradoxical happened that marshlands developed right in the midst of the tilled irrigated lands, which previously were desert. In other irrigated areas, particularly in Utah, the surface gradually evolved a whitish tone resulting from salt deposits. In both instances a major tribute was exacted in destroyed soils where nothing any longer grew.

Those who tend to potted plants in the desert climate of modern heated homes undoubtedly have noticed that the soil surface frequently turns whitish. This is due to the very same phenomenon: salt gradually being deposited on the surface through rich watering accompanied by excessive evaporation. The plants do not manage to consume all the water and are not able to dispose of its minerals through growth. Around the globe there are millions of acres of tilled land which in this way has been turned into marshlands or where all vegetation has been killed off through salinization.

Irrigation technology, which aimed at providing water in the right place, at the right time, and in sufficient quantities, had overlooked the intricate water movements in the soils as well as their not less complex salt accumulations. On top of all, man had grossly underrated the hecatombs of water which in the deserts of the world are catapulted into the atmosphere through evaporation. At the same time he had overestimated the ability of the soil to swallow water. As soon as more water is brought in than the vegetation utilizes, or when the air is so hot that the water evaporates before it reaches the roots of the plants, it leaves large amounts of salt behind. The end result is so detrimental to the plants that the vegetation is simply killed. Millions of acres in Pakistan and Egypt, Greece, and South America have become salt deserts due to such salinization. Historical records describe how Mesopotamian soils gradually turned whitish, and this as far back as nineteen hundred years ago. Early documents from India tell the same story. China, when pressing on with irrigation in recent years, has also been forcefully reminded of these limitations. Salt destruction of tilled land set in when permanent irrigation was introduced in lieu of seasonal. In Pakistan the gains made by opening up new lands in recent years were practically canceled out through acreage losses due to salinization.

Disturbance Phenomena

The big annual inundations by the Nile, the Euphrates-Tigris, the Hwang Ho, and the Yangtze Kiang rivers were great revitalizing forces. The water drenched the soil over hundreds of thousands of acres, also providing it with indispensable nutrients through the silt, which was left behind. It was, however, only natural that man early got the idea to save part of these abundant water quantities through storage in dams for use in the subsequent dry season, thereby safeguarding the annual crop. As long as this procedure was allowed to function without disturbances, the risks were minor. But faced with the mounting needs for food, it was demanded with ever greater insistence that *all* dry seasons should be eliminated, and wherever possible, two or more harvests should be taken from the soils. It was therefore decided to save still more water and prevent it from being lost to the sea. More and larger storage dams were constructed. It was only then that really serious complications arose. The dams caught the silt, which in this way was removed, in turn resulting in the need for large compensating quantities of commercial fertilizers in order to maintain soil fertility. Furthermore, through this double-cropping, the soil was deprived of its important rest periods. Water trickled continuously through the soil carrying in addition silt particles and a heavy excess of mineral salts. Billions of small particles were soon caught in the fine mesh of the topsoil, were laid to rest, and gradually a compact hardpan layer developed, next to impenetrable for water, but usually beneath the root zone of the plants.

Drillings at Ur in Chaldea, the birth place of Abraham, demonstrated the existence of such an impervious layer beneath the root zone of the vegetation. Similar hardpan structures have been found in the irrigation terraces of the Incas, high up in the Andes, and in many other parts of the globe where longtime irrigation had been practiced. In the Imperial Valley of southern California, after ten years of permanent irrigation, it became noticeable that region after region was being converted into marshland. A similar compact hardpan layer was found. The same phenomenon was observed in the Rio Grande Valley. In this way the explanation was found to this paradox of man-created marshlands in the deserts. Presumably it also offered an indication to the causal relationships behind the many breakdowns of irrigation systems which have been recorded throughout history. These occurred in many different civilizations but were invariably interpreted as the result of invasions by savage peoples or evidence of moral or cultural decline. Actually, the soil simply fell victim to a salting disease, and overexertion lay behind the marshes.

The causal mechanism behind the salt cover of the soil and the marshes is slightly more complicated than so far indicated. Through capillary suction within the fine soil pores, water is actively lifted toward the surface where the evaporation is particularly intense, creating another suction. So there are two forces driving the water to the surface. Dissolved mineral salts are left behind and precipitate as a whitish coating. This soon becomes fatal to the vegetation. This salinization process is in fact the Achilles heel of permanent irrigation. Salt may in this context not only mean common table salt (sodium chloride) but frequently such other mineral salts as magnesium, carbonates, sulphates, etc.

Some of the disturbances reviewed above as typical of desert irrigation, particularly when permanent in the form of a year-round operation, have started to make themselves felt even in regions with adequate rainfall, where permanent irrigation has been introduced in order to procure two or three crops instead of one per growing season as was traditionally the case. The yield increases from Taiwan, Japan, and certain parts of India during recent years are in effect due to double-cropping, *i.e.,* more than one crop per year is taken from the same acreage. But the soil needs rest, among other things in order to make it possible for the myriads of soil organisms to carry out their loosening activities. What is gained by two or more crops is therefore often lost through these disturbances. There is also a limit for what the soil can accomplish. A second crop usually gives lower yields than the first one, and gradually this may result in mineral depletion unless corresponding artificial fertilization compensates for these losses.

A Costly Illusion

The very idea of making the deserts bloom is dubious from the basic point of view of water economy alone. With a limited quantity of water at disposal to produce food, it is evidently most prudent to reduce the losses through evaporation and seepage as much as possible. The goal is to produce the largest possible amount of food from a given amount of water. Therefore, the mere thought of going out into the deserts or other arid regions, where the evaporation is most intense, is hardly reasonable. In the oases of the Sahara desert 20,000 to 30,000 cubic meters are required per hectare, *i.e.,* five to ten times as much water as in Morocco and Tunisia and thirty to fifty times more than in southern Italy.

The huge losses taking place through direct evaporation from man-made reservoirs in hot regions are in most instances many times larger than the amount of water utilized in direct organic production of food in the plant. Such irrigation projects have therefore little to do with economic common sense. In the hot regions of the world the lion's share of the water disappears in the atmosphere before it has a chance to serve plant production and pass through the water-carrying systems (the vascular strands) of the plant crops and get involved in metabolism and transpiration.

The Shrinkage of Desert Rivers

Those peoples and nations that have the privilege of living in regions with ample precipitation have some difficulty getting a good picture of these relationships. We are accustomed to rivers which become larger and more powerful the closer they get to the oceans. They collect water from ever-expanding watersheds, carried also by tributaries. Such rivers get wider and are as a rule quite large at the mouth when emptying into the ocean. Desert rivers usually show an opposite picture. Most of them never reach the sea; they have long before dried up and vanished. Their water in the meantime, due to excessive evaporation, frequently becomes critically saline and in this way unusable for crop-raising. Basically it is true that only desert rivers that receive melted snow from neighboring mountains manage to provide a fairly dependable water supply.

Among the many spectacular examples of such river shrinkage are the world-famous twin rivers Euphrates and Tigris. The water that passes the city of Baghdad has only one chance in twenty to reach the sea. Only forty miles below Baghdad the water quantity has been reduced to one-tenth. The average precipitation of Iraq is between 0.5 and 0.6 inches (125–150 mm.). The total evaporation from the land surface of the country, including what the vegetation cover throws into the air via transportation, amounts to ten times the annual rainfall. Water must consequently be brought into the Euphrates-Tigris river system from Turkey, Syria, and Iran. This large-scale evaporation explains why Iraq constitutes a tremendous natural salt-making plant, presumably at the present time the world's largest. From the tilled acreage approximately thirty-seven cubic kilometers of water is lost annually, but at the same time twenty-two million metric tons of salt is left behind. This and many similar examples can be presented in order to eluci-

date the desperate battle which man must carry on against the
salt.

The Drainage Paradox

Confronted with the need for such extensive drainage to remove water with excess salinity, the hydraulic engineers are with
increasing vigor discussing drainage as an imperative supplement
to irrigation. South of Baghdad the famous Dujaila Project is
located. One-tenth of the tilled land has there been taken for the
digging of huge drainage ditches 0.5 to 1.0 meters (yards) deep,
in order to dispose of the water after it has passed through the
root zone. This drainage water has a salt content exceeding that of
ocean water. If not removed, it would have a direct killing effect
on all vegetation.

Massachusetts Institute of Technology (MIT) has made up
plans for the control of the salt situation in Iran, which steadily
has been aggravated. The plans involve the construction of gigantic draining culverts at about half a mile (1 km.) distance from
each other, through which the water is to be drained. Such continuous drainage is, however, not sufficient. Too saline water
must, furthermore, be kept away permanently, so that it is not
absorbed anew by the soil. Nobody seems to have considered seriously the risks of more long-range effects on the steady salinization of the groundwater. The largest part of this salt has no way
out. It remains. In the economically important Imperial Valley
in southern California the salt concentration has reached such
dimensions that eighteen hundred miles of open drainage canals
have had to be built in order to channel away the "brine" coming
from the fields.

The Colorado River received worldwide attention in 1962
when the Mexican Government, through its President, complained
to the United States President about the salinity of the water supplied to Mexico via this river. It carried so much salt that about
one-third of the cotton fields in the Mexicali district on the Peninsula of Baja California had already been taken out of cultivation
due to salt damages. The Colorado River chiefly transports water
to the Pacific, originating with the melting snow in the Rocky
Mountains. This river serves in part Los Angeles, as well as the
cotton fields of Baja California in Mexico. When everybody in
the watershed region and along the southward course of the river

has satisfied his needs, the water gradually becomes so loaded with salt (due to evaporation) that when it reaches the Mexicali Plains it has a killing effect on the crops.

Hundreds of thousands of tons of salt are transported there annually with the river water. Drainage canals were built at a feverish pace in the years from 1952 to 1958 to transport water away as soon as its salt content reached too high a level. These canals presently have a total length of 750 miles (1200 kilometers). The salt also goes up in the air in the form of brine spray. The corrosion on agricultural machinery is ferocious. Machines used in the cotton plantations must be greased anew every second hour to avoid their rapid destruction by corrosion. It is of little avail that the United States President promises his Mexican colleague to improve the quality of the water. When water is not available in adequate quantity, politicians are powerless. The city of Tijuana on the Mexican side of the California border is on the verge of becoming a ghost town, due to water shortage. The Tijuana River was long ago used up and has vanished. Water is now brought to the city in cans and bottles and costs from one to two cents a quart.

Evaporation Losses

There remains another basic aspect of the irrigation of desert lands: The mere idea of storing water above ground is dubious because of evaporation losses. The impressive large-scale dams have, figuratively speaking, a very shaky foundation. The big new Aswan Dam, so widely publicized, is in fact Egypt's fifth Aswan Dam. According to estimates, it will have an annual evaporation loss, measured in water, that is larger than the entire dam it is planned to replace, namely the third Aswan Dam.

The transfer to permanent irrigation in the Nile Valley has furthermore meant that more than one-third of the current water use has to be employed in eliminating salt. This actually means that more water is utilized in the battle against salt than is devoted to direct irrigation. This represents an enormous waste item in any kind of balance sheet. In ancient Egypt the Nile water did not carry this burden of eliminating salt. This development belongs to modern times and is a direct consequence of the intensified water use that has taken place during the last hundred years. The magnitude of the interference in the Nile valley water balance system may be best illustrated by the fact that during approximately three to four months of the year the Nile no longer supplies the Mediterranean with any water. Early in this century this forced the British to construct huge locks at the entrance to the delta region in order to prevent saline Mediterranean water from penetrating into this key area of Egyptian agricultural production. Nevertheless, hydraulic engineers seriously contemplate the total mobilization of the Nile water and storage in the upper regions of the remainder, now being lost to the Mediterranean.

With the Aswan Dam being completed, the floodwaters of the Nile River are contained for the first time in Egypt's, as well as the Nile's, history. However, many drastic changes will be the result. In the absence of the annual deposit of silt from the upper reaches of the Nile, heavy applications of fertilizer will be needed on farmlands along the banks. This effect has also been noticeable through earlier dams, and nowhere have artificial fertilizers rendered the level of nature's annual complementary contribution. Furthermore, few farmers can afford such quantities; a serious matter in itself.

Degradation of the river channel downstream from the dam is expected, and will require construction of a series of minor control dams, costing almost half as much as the Aswan Dam itself. The effect of the project on groundwater and seawater intrusion in the delta may well be disastrous. A marine famine in the eastern Mediterranean was anticipated, since organic matter and mineral nutrients formerly supplied in great quantities by the Nile flood would no longer reach the sea. This would reduce the eastern Mediterranean fisheries which were an important source of food, particularly for Israel.

This has already happened and has also deprived Egypt of desperately needed fish for their daily food. Special countermeasures have been taken, and fishing has been forced into greater depths, away from the coast. For this purpose special large fishing vessels were loaned to Egypt by the U.S.S.R.

Underground Water Storage

In the future, storage of water in arid regions will probably have to be organized in other ways than hitherto. Primarily an expanded replenishment of overtaxed underground resources is needed. But also in this respect there are obvious risks of salinization due to extensive underground pockets of saline water, particularly in such regions.

In the previous chapter the excessive tapping of underground water reserves was discussed, with its resulting intrusion of sea water into the aquifers of critical coastal regions, as with the Pacific Ocean into California, the Gulf of Mexico into Texas, the Atlantic Ocean into Holland and into Long Island. Rinse from evaporation pits of oil wells in the Southwest and Midwest is seeping down into the water table.

The growing depletion has also led to the pumping of water from clearly uneconomical depths. Pumping costs increase quickly with depth. Besides, the deeper one goes, the greater are the risks of obtaining saline water. Not only has this been experienced in the arid sections of the United States, but this phenomenon has put an almost complete stop to continued deep-well pumping in major parts of Australia and Africa, especially South Africa. If man had not had such salt-tolerant crops as barley and dates to save himself, and such salt-resistant animals as the Spanish Merino sheep, large parts of the irrigated arid regions of the earth would never have yielded any food. But it is to be noted that these hazards normally do not apply to irrigated wet regions where the salinization problem as outlined above is of an entirely different nature and becomes a serious matter only when transferring to permanent irrigation almost on a year-round basis—that is, irrigation extended throughout the dry season.

Before man ventures into underground storage of water on a grand scale, he needs to know a great deal more about the subterranean water movements, again a task much more urgent than moon rockets and other space adventures. One of the many paradoxes in this field is that when the colonizers moved into South Africa, Australia, and many other arid regions of the globe, they could report plenty of water when, through drilling, the richly gushing artesian wells were opened. Even scientists hardly suspected that these represented long-time buildups of underground water stores, in many cases accumulated over thousands of years. Even in areas where probably not a drop of rain had fallen in several thousands of years one had little forethought. Obviously man in this case believed in miracles! The saga of the artesian wells became a short one, often briefer than that of the large underground water domes, which have been mined recklessly in various parts of the globe. In an improvident escapism from reality, man continues to do so, as the examples from Arizona and Texas, mentioned in the previous chapter, testify.

After World War II Saudi Arabia was invaded by hydraulic experts happily replacing the eternally trodding donkeys around the wells with oil-driven pumps. A brief flourishing took place both in agriculture and horticulture rendering substantially increased production. But after five years the water began to diminish. What had been accumulated over the centuries in large underground basins had been rapidly depleted. The performance of the donkeys seems to have been evenly balanced with the average replenishment of these subterranean resources, primarily through the daily condensation. Geologists and geographers, who were called in too late, soon established that the groundwater level, despite natural replenishments, was located more than one thousand yards beneath the surface, and further that water at reasonably accessible levels was only to be found several miles away.

Man, in his strivings to compensate to some degree for the huge evaporative water losses connected with desert irrigation, soon established that any vegetation—particularly the wild one, which thrived in the shadow of irrigation—was robbing far too much water. These consumers, also call phreatophytes, partly feeding on excess irrigation water, leaching into adjacent soils, had to be removed. When this is done, and such "natural" vegetation is eradicated, the desert expands. The tamarisk and other plants are in this way doomed to extinction. There are numerous publications giving estimates of how much water such plants are robbing through their saboteuring activities against man. In several instances they consume more water than irrigated agricultural crops on corresponding acreages. Such schemes become in effect part of the history of man-made deserts. These already exceed in acreages many times what irrigation has created in terms of tilled land in the last hundred years. Even today man is creating more deserts than he is building up plant cover via irrigation.

Evaporative Film Obstacle

Popular articles have glowingly described how the evaporation from water surfaces may be reduced by means of chemicals such as cetyl alcohol, hexadecanol, and other compounds which have been studied and have proved useful for this purpose. Pilot scale experiments have also been run. But few among these writers have probed into the economic side of these ventures. The costs are considerable. A one-time spraying of the water surface is not enough. This surface layer, inhibiting evaporation, is gradually dispersed and has to be renewed.

Furthermore, few studies have been conducted on such indirect effects as the buildup of disease agents induced by the radical change of the oxygen and temperature conditions in huge water masses through such measures. The dams would obviously be deprived of their cooling effect resulting from the persistent evaporation. Sewage water with accelerated temperatures which now is being allowed to enter into many natural waters on the globe causes annoying disturbances in microbial populations; besides making the natural waters lose their value as cooling water. Fish growth may occasionally be enhanced in the initial phase—in cool regions of the world—but later, when passing optimum, it is detrimental to fish production.

Seepage

Some underground water reserves seem to originate in seepage from river beds or lakes, over the centuries or maybe millenia. It has gradually been discovered that most large rivers in the world probably have a counterpart in huge underground rivers. This has been studied especially in the Nile basin where a sizable underground river is encountered in deeper-lying layers but moving toward the Mediterranean at a very slow speed. Beneath the land surface of the dry Australian continent there are huge underground lakes. The same is true in the Central Asiatic regions of Siberia. These subterranean water reserves have, however, been tapped quite efficiently in California, Arizona, Egypt, and Australia. Central Asia is in the beginning phase of this exploitation of underground water resources.

A seepage similar to that from natural waters constitutes a

serious drawback, both economically and technologically, to large-scale irrigation projects around the world. Close to ten million acres have in this way been converted into marshlands through seepage from the many canals, several miles in total length, in the irrigation districts of Punjab and Sind in Pakistan. Energetic efforts have gone into developing economically feasible methods for waterproofing such canals, but so far the costs have exceeded what anyone, even technical gamblers, was willing to underwrite.

The Soviet Union is at present, in the hot Central Asiatic deserts, testing a method of distributing water to the fields in elevated aqueducts, resting on supports. In this way seepage losses are eliminted, possibly evaporation is also reduced. Nothing, however, has been revealed about the costs of these devices.

Health Hazards

It is a well-known fact that malaria in several instances is man-made and induced by the massive accumulations of water man has created. Malaria has in this way been spread even to once uncontaminated regions. Approximately one-fourth of all malaria cases in India can be labeled man-induced, as they have their origin in malaria-infested mosquitoes, raised in reservoirs, dams, and ponds created by man. It was discussed earlier how the much more unmanageable bilharzia, today often called schistosomiasis, with even greater justification can be blamed on expanded irrigation. The afflicted percentage of the population in the rural villages of Egypt has risen dramatically, in several cases now exceeding two-thirds. This fact alone is estimated to have caused a decline of at least one-third in the total productivity of Egypt.

Schistosomiasis is carried by a flukeworm. Its larvae (cercarie) penetrate the skin and move via the blood into several vital organs of the body and develop there. The eggs are distributed through water and are dependent for their hatching on certain snails as intermediary hosts. The natural desiccation which during the dry season regularly used to take its solid tribute of the dangerous host—a snail species—was eliminated through permanent irrigation. The soil never dries out, and the mollusks thrive the year around. They are no longer decimated in a natural way through seasonal drought.

Man's fumbling with even high-potency chemicals appears less efficient on a major scale both as regards space and time. All prospective hideouts for the snails can simply not be kept under relentless chemical bombardment, especially since these marauders advance with several new generations each year. From 150 to 200 million people are now estimated to be suffering from schistosomiasis, which has expanded so largely due to the irrigation advances.

The same ecological changes as described above are also conducive to the spread of river blindness (see further p. 111). It may soon be added to the long list of diseases clearly favored through measures taken by man in his desperate fight for food.

It is further reported that the massive Chinese extension of irrigation in the fifties, mentioned above, has given unprecedented spread to bilharzia, taking major tolls in humans, affecting health as well as working efficiency in all inflicted regions. Strong countermeasures have reportedly been taken, but great concern is frequently expressed about the dimensions of this menace.

Recently, the discovery of an efficient remedy for this debilitating illness was reported, which eliminates the disease agents in the body. But our experiences so far, not the least in regard to malaria, point to the fact that such evildoers learn to deal with our toxic substances. In any case, we must contend with this risk. The modern synthetic malaria remedies, which performed miracles during World War II, and even the insecticides, have been partly circumvented today through resistant strains of malaria-spreading mosquitoes. These circumstances have been of serious concern in Vietnam and have caused many complications.

Land Robbery

The biblical vision of how man goes out to make the deserts bloom—a vision born out of the desert environment where the Christian religion originated—is thus in many ways a false mirage. Popular textbook presentations of the conquests due to expanded irrigation and its glorious achievements are hardly ever supplemented with an account for the true or total costs or for the obstacles and complications. Yet, every layman doubtless understands that the multitude of canals, wells, and dams are not only expensive in construction and maintenance but also land robbers.

We rarely realize, however, that today one-fourth of Egypt's invaluable land is used for canals and other water distribution measures. In addition, one-tenth is now being taken out of cultivation in order to supplement with an expensive and complicated drainage system.

Hydroelectric Fallacies

Hydroelectric plants belong in a special category and are frequently presented as the great bonus of irrigation. There is a great deal of talk about the multipurpose use of water, hydroelectric plants being almost as important as irrigation in the utilization of water resources. This overlooks the basic geographical prerequisite for such an arrangement being that the power outtake takes place *prior* to the watering of the crops. Many crucial regions of the world do not lend themselves to this kind of arrangement. The vast tilled acreages are on the highland plateaus and slopes, while they are critically limited in proportion on the narrow coastal shelves where the water, after delivering its energy to power stations above, can be used for irrigation. This is by and large the situation in tropical Africa (particularly in the east), in Mexico, in Spain, and in many other places.

There is another critical fallacy attached to hydroelectric development. Such plants are thought to be permanent sources of energy, *i.e.,* unlike those based on fossil-fuel energy, they can be counted upon for all time. The heavy load of soil and sand carried annually by flood waters into the reservoirs behind the dams settles, however, in these areas and gradually deprives the reservoirs of their storage capacity. Even the clearest of rivers will in time carry enough silt into a reservoir to fill it up—not to mention the notoriously muddy ones. The capacity of any dam is therefore gradually reduced and finally lost, with all that this means to irrigation, flood control, and navigation. Some of the power generation may remain, but the water stagnation gives added evaporation losses and gradually lowers the power potential.

The storage life of dams differs depending on soil types and general topography. Many dams in Latin America have filled in less than ten years. The Columbia River, however, carries relatively little silt. Hence the dams at Grand Coulee and Bonneville will have long lives—as far as storage capacity is concerned—possibly a thousand years. On the other hand, Lake Mead with the Hoover Dam (in Arizona), according to the U.S. Geological Survey, is good only to the year 2225 or possibly to 2300. Some estimates give this lake only one hundred years more. This assumes no change in the rate of silt influx, as would be caused by construction of dams above this dam, or alteration in the rate of erosion in the Colorado River basin, effected either by nature or by man.

The Guernsey Reservoir, on the North Platte River in Wyoming, has lost one-third of its capacity in twenty years. In little more than another generation, assuming no change in conditions, this reservoir will be filled with mud. On the other hand, the Elephant Butte Dam, on the Rio Grande in southern New Mexico, has lost one-sixth of its capacity in thirty-two years. It should, with unchanged conditions, have a total useful life of two hundred years.

The filling of reservoirs with sand and mud can thus be taken as having no early effect in the energy supply. However, it does underscore the dire need for attention to strict control of soil erosion. Furthermore, it greatly limits the lifetime of hydroelectric investments—making amortization a far more short-range business than generally is recognized.

Irrigation—an Efficient Climate Control?

It can be concluded that man has been eminently successful in eclipsing the climate through his large scale redistribution of water. The magnitude of these achievements has taken on ever greater proportions, but the effect on world food production has in relative terms become less and less noticeable. The needs are so exorbitant that our technology, even when operating on a huge scale, is grossly inadequate. Hydrologists estimate that it would be a masterful achievement, especially from the technological point of view, if before the end of this century additional food could be provided through further irrigation projects for 150 to 200 million people, yet this is only the present population growth over a period of two to three years, or one-twentieth of the growth anticipated before the year 2000.

But this is not all. Man has concomitantly been expanding other sectors of his activities, and this to a degree that is far more difficult to assess, but he has thereby accelerated the evaporation and increased the water outtake in nature to a level where even conventional agriculture, depending as it does on the regular natural water flow, is being threatened for its very existence. Man as a water robber is, due to the efficiency of modern technology and the magnitude of the industrial development, on his way to becoming the main obstacle to a wise water economy.

Water Storage vs. Food Storage

Finally, as a food technologist I feel obliged to point out that it is considerably cheaper from almost every viewpoint to store and transport foods than to store and transport water for the production of foods. As discussed in the previous chapter, each ton of food raised through crops requires a hundred times more water, frequently even one thousand times more. In desert irrigation, taking into account the losses in evaporated water and seepage, ten to fifty thousand times more water is needed.

Unfortunately the earth is already overpopulated to such a degree that it is hardly any longer feasible to revert to wise planning. If man—in order to procure oil, metals, and other products—is compelled to go out into the arid regions of the world, it would be much more practical to bring in foods—as is now being done for the millions of industrial workers in Siberia. World trade, which brought foods and raw materials from regions economically most suitable for their production to those less fitted for this purpose, as envisioned in the nineteenth century, unfortunately by and large belongs to history. Mankind has not been willing to draw a reasonable line for its growth and show the maturity which lies in prudent planning, in moderation and economy. With regard to irrigation man has already gone far beyond the limits for what is technically justifiable and economically sound. Irrigation has been proclaimed a great and glorious adventure of technology. In this statement one can wholeheartedly concur, but it ought to be underlined that it has been and remains an adventure where the hazardous aspects with each decade take on ever more frightening dimensions.

CHAPTER IX

Water in
International Politics

In the beginning of the sixties Bolivian students in La Paz, their capital, gathered and marched on the Chilean Embassy, which was completely demolished by stone and brick throwing. It was basically not an outburst of political discontent. It was water that caused the riot. The Lauca, one of the few rivers that constitute an important water resource for the high-altitude country, originates in Chilean territory, flows into Bolivia, and disappears finally in the deserts. This river system had for years been developed by the Chileans despite loud protests from neighboring Bolivia. The hydroelectric plant with its attached irrigation system was now completed, the newly constructed dam disposed of a considerable part of the available river water, to which Bolivians lay claim, based both on traditional usage and on the indispensability of this water to the future development of their country.

This might have been the first time water caused the demolition of an embassy, but it will most likely not be the last such incident. All around the world tensions are mounting over the most efficient and wise utilization of water reserves, and this tension grows in pace with the population explosion.

Water and the right to the taking of water constitute, since far back in history, a common cause of conflict in the civil courts of many countries. Ancient documents like the Koran and others contain detailed stipulations regarding water rights. Theft of water used to bring capital punishment in many parts of the world. Earlier such tensions were limited to water-short regions, but with rising water consumption legal suits have become increasingly numerous and are today not uncommon even in the most water-rich regions of the globe.

Water wrote world history when the Mongolian hordes time and time again swarmed into new areas whenever droughts deprived them of food and feed in their homelands. Successively they invaded the Chinese, Roman, and Russian empires. But water is now causing permanent tension between many countries and has consequently become an integral part of international politics. Some examples of such acute conflicts will be given below.

The Indus

Ever since India reached independence and the Indian subcontinent was divided into three political units, *viz.,* India proper, East and West Pakistan, water has been the outstanding bone of contention and cause for unrest. For thousands of years the Indus River provided the stage for large-scale rivalry between various empires. In the fourth century B.C., when Alexander the Great of Greece on his wide-ranging conquests reached these regions, he encountered a flourishing culture around the mighty Indus, one of the largest rivers of the world. In its drainage area civilization started 2,500 years ago, and for nearly 5,000 years the population of these regions has been totally dependent for its existence on the Indus and its many tributaries. Even today three-fourths of all the people that live in the Indus basin rely for food production on irrigation systems based on these rivers. Rain falls only during a short summer season when the southwest monsoon sweeps in over land from the Arabian Sea. Practically all crops are dependent on irrigation. In 1947, when England abandoned its rule over the Indian continent, there were no less than 10.5 million hectares (26.25 million acres) of irrigated land, one of the largest irrigated regions of the world. This area was later expanded to cover about 25 million hectares (62.5 million acres). Some of the world's largest reservoirs are located here, and additional ones are under construction.

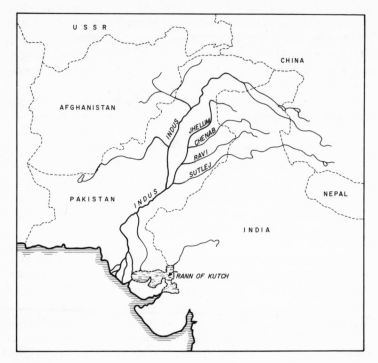

Fig. 34. The Indus

With the political partition of the continent, borders were drawn straight across this indispensable irrigation net with its thousands of canals—the vast areas between the mother river, Indus, and its five most important tributaries as well as the land between the tributaries. This functioning entity was thus disrupted. In connection with the partition, millions of people passed across the new borders in both directions with intolerable sufferings—a large amount of blood flowed—in order to accomodate to the seemingly arbitrary boundaries dividing peoples and religions. Six million Muhammadans from all over the continent emigrated to the newly created Muslim state of Pakistan. Four million Sikhs and Hindus went eastward away from Pakistan and the Indus. The worst aspect of the partition was the fact that this complex and highly developed irrigation system was cut transversely. Large cultivated regions lost their water resources. The head river fell to Pakistan, while the upper reaches of the five main tributaries became a part of India. The world-famous jute crops were cut off from water. The political tension reached the boiling point and made any kind of reasonable adjustment or agreement impossible. It was at least three years before the water supply was to some degree restored and could feed the channels.

The Punjab Confrontation

This battle has been raging with particular ferocity around the central portion of the Indus basin in the Punjab region. In the old local Urdu tongue *Punjab* actually means *the land of the five rivers*. Repeated efforts, some with the aid of international arbitration, failed to achieve an agreement on the utilization of these five important tributaries. India, in which the upper reaches of these rivers were located, did not waste time developing long-range comprehensive plans for the use of these water treasures, which—if put into effect—would have caused serious economic havoc to Pakistan. Most resented by the Pakistanis was the proposal to tap the Sutlej—one of the major tributaries—almost entirely through a huge subterranean channel, with the aim of irrigating the immense Radjastan desert, an area almost equivalent in size to the entire cultivated acreage of West Pakistan. At this stage the World Bank entered the scene and managed to open up channels for an international arbitration of this major water conflict.

After more than a decade of delays and unceasing debates, common sense finally prevailed, and both sides accepted a treaty whereby India got the right to the total water resources of the three eastern tributaries, the Sutlej, the Beas, and the Ravi; and this regardless of whether the rivers in some instances happen to flow through Pakistani territory. The Beas is in effect a tributary to the Sutlej and has its origin in the Indian Himalayas. Pakistan on the other hand gained the right to the three western rivers: the Indus itself, the Chenab, and its subsidiary the Jhelum. The treaty also provided for emptying the many irrigation canals that carried water to Pakistan from the rivers allotted to India. In compensation, constructions were supported by the World Bank for a transfer from the western rivers to meet those needs that used to be served from what then became Indian resources. In return, India was obliged to aid in building these dikes serving Pakistan, which were created so as not to interfere with Indian water rights.

The agreement amounted to an immense surgical operation, requiring drastic cuts in a whole network of arteries and minor water vessels. The bitter controversy over the water of the Indus was reduced in dimensions, but as we will see, other aspects remained unsettled. To Pakistan a question of life and death had been resolved, and that country was given a breathing spell. This agreement adjusted crucial conditions and removed most major causes of fiery confrontation.

The Kashmir Issue

The battle continued, however, in a new phase in the well-known Kashmir dispute, where many eminent diplomats have tried, so far in vain, to reach an acceptable compromise. In 1965 war actually broke out between India and Pakistan over the Kashmir issue. This was successfully arbitrated by the U.S.S.R. but without eliminating the root cause of the conflict. That this area, located on the borderline of the gigantic Himalayan mountain range, could be the subject of such deep controversy may seem puzzling. But the waters allotted to Pakistan are from two tributaries of the Indus that actually originate in Kashmir. Sovereignty over Kashmir therefore brings control over water reserves vital to Pakistan, the use of which has consequences reaching far beyond the debated province. The Pakistanis speak in the Kashmir issue with great apprehension about the supposed plans of India, their arch-enemy, to tap these rivers for irrigation and other purposes high up in the Kashmir mountain valleys and long before they reach Pakistan territory. But behind this an even larger complex looms. Most of this water originates in the Himalayan mountains with their eternal snow. From year to year the snow-clad mountaintops show fluctuations of more than thirty yards in the thickness of the snow layer. The volume of snow in these distant mountain regions decides, more than anything else, the annual water flow of the Indus. What is added later through precipitation, when the river passes through the vast basin, is quite insignificant in comparison with this original contribution to the river.

But the Indus also reaches far into Tibetan territory, where China now is making large-scale efforts to extract additional food for its numerous people. One prerequisite to such a goal is, in effect, irrigation of the Tibetan high plateaus. To what degree the competition for the water of the Indus will later become another cause of conflict between the two Asiatic giants, China and India, is hard to foresee. But such a development is certainly not inconceivable, since water is becoming an increasingly scarce commodity and is the key to the food issue, which already is emerging as the focal point of world politics.

The Nile

When the Indus reaches the Arabian Sea, it has traversed a distance of no less than 3,600 kilometers (2,250 miles). This is, however, only half the long journey of the Nile, though the water flow of the Indus is much larger, more than twice that of the Nile. The Nile waters today are heavily taxed. As pointed out in the previous chapter, that river is now developed and utilized to the degree that the delta lands must be protected against the influx of highly saline Mediterranean water by means of an elaborate system of locks, which hinder the salt water from seeping into this fertile land, which is indispensable to the feeding of the Egyptian people. Egypt is in effect entirely dependent on the Nile for its existence and is now looking southward for more water. This constitutes Egypt's only chance to procure additional water. The enormous watershed area of the mighty Nile stretches deep down into the heartland of Africa.

The Nile has two principal upper branches above Khartoum. One is the White Nile (Bahr-el-Abyad), taking this name only in its lower stretch. This branch flows in a straight northward course from the huge Lake Victoria in Central Africa, passes through Lake Albert, and then flows as the Albert Nile through northwest Uganda. It then crosses into Sudan under yet another name, Bahr-el-Jebel, and there forms a large inland swamp. After picking up a tributary, the White Nile is then born, and when finally approaching Khartoum, it has a stable water flow amounting to between 30,000 and 50,000 cubic feet per second.

The second major branch is called the Blue Nile (Bahr-el-

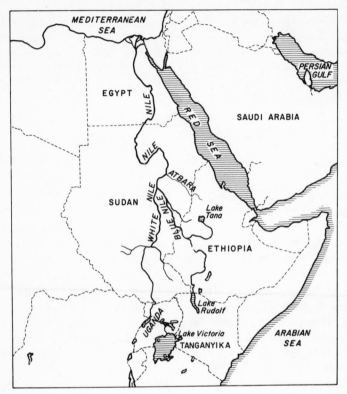

Fig. 35. The Nile

Araq). It originates in the Ethiopian highlands and flows via Lake Tana in a general easterly direction, joining the White Nile at Khartoum, located in the Republic of Sudan, now a sovereign state. The waterflow of the Blue Nile varies considerably, from about 7,000 cubic feet per second during the dry season to 20,000 cubic feet a second during the rainy season. The two united branch rivers flow almost 3,000 kilometers (1,800 miles) through northern Sudan. After 200 miles it picks up the Atbara, also originating in the Ethiopian Lake Tana. The Nile flows through Egypt without receiving any additional water.

Until a few years ago Egypt assumed the role of sole owner of the Nile. The Fifth Aswan Dam, which will replace the Third Aswan Dam and which is now under construction with Soviet economic and technical aid, will—though located on Egyptian territory—have its effect also on Sudan. About 60,000 Nubian peasants in Sudan will see their land flooded. Since becoming an independent nation in January, 1956, as the Republic of Sudan, Sudan has tried to safeguard its interest, and in the final agreement on the Fifth Aswan Dam it obtained concessions for considerably increased water outtakes within its own borders. Sudan has in mind its own Gezira region, which has been made to flourish by means of irrigation and which brings in valuable foreign currency through the exportation of cotton, but in direct competition with Egypt. As pointed out in the previous chapter, from the point of view of good water management, it stands naturally more reasonable to exploit the water in Sudan than to bring it down into the scorching heat of the Egyptian desert. These adjustments include the evaporative losses in the flow from Sudan to Egypt. There is simply more water to be had higher up the river.

Central Africa in the Conflict-ridden Sphere of the Nile

Naguib, the now forgotten predecessor to Nasser, and the apparent instigator of the revolutionary period of Egypt, unsuccessfully tried a simple annexation of Sudan, obviously aiming at a tighter hold on the Nile, the basic life-giver of the Egyptian nation. Since then a great deal of water has flowed down the Nile, and the nationalistic waves have run high in the entire African continent. The tension is still latent, and the higher the population figures zoom in Ethiopia, Sudan, and Egypt, the more intense the battle for water will become. As in the case of India and Pakistan, far-reaching water regulations under international supervision emerge as the most sensible solution and the only way to stave off the risks of war over water rights.

With certain farsightedness, Egypt has developed plans for new reservoirs far up in Uganda in order to safeguard additional quantities of water from the rainy season and thereby increase the irrigation potential of the Nile, though primarily for their own benefit. The Nile monopoly of Egypt is taken for granted in these plans. Unfortunately, they do not take into account other inhabitants of these regions who equally need to utilize these water reserves. Sudan has already presented claims that far supersede what this country now receives, and the needs of Egypt itself mount with an uncontrolled population growth (ten million in the past six years). The enormous Fifth Aswan Dam, the world's largest, will therefore only mark another episode on the road toward misery of still more millions.

East Africa, represented by countries such as Kenya, Uganda, and Tanganyika, all three in great need of additional water, has made many plans for irrigation, and several of these have been executed. Even the northeastern parts of the former Belgian Congo fall within the magic circle of the Nile. Even Ethiopia, which like so many other African nations views industrialization as its hope for the future, is now surveying its hydroelectric and irrigation potential, based on the waters of the Nile River system as a primary resource. Most of the few large-size African lakes would be affected, since they all belong to the watershed of the Nile, even the Albert Lake in the former Belgian Congo. Whatever happens to one system would thus have repercussions on the other.

Man does not want to recognize that there are obvious limitations, that in particular the natural water reserves are quite restricted, and that even giant rivers like the Nile and the Indus dwindle when facing the needs of insatiable human hordes. The closer man gets to the end of the total reserves, the sharper these water-induced conflicts will become. It should be obvious to anyone who has given these issues some serious thought that water will become an ever more central question in international politics. Undoubtedly, this fact lies behind the intense interest that Egypt devotes to African affairs, particularly those concerning the heartland of the continent. Egypt, together with other Arab countries in the Near and Middle East, is in turn feeling the pressure of the newly created state of Israel—which finds itself in still more desperate need of water.

The Jordan

This makes the Near East another tension-ridden region where water plays the crucial role, maybe in an even more ominous vein. Despite the fact that the Jordan River, known from the New

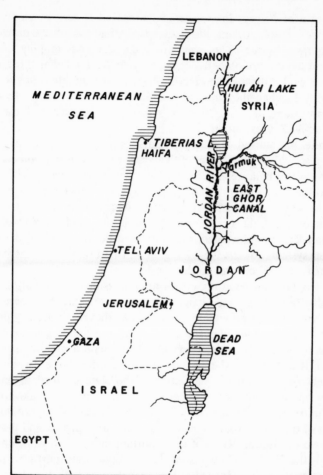

Fig. 36. The Jordan

Testament, is considerably smaller than those rivers discussed above, the conflict is far more fierce. Jordan is actually a dwarf among rivers. The water flow is less than one-hundredth that of the Nile or the Euphrates-Tigris. Furthermore this river only has one tributary of any significance, *viz.*, the Yarmuk. Israel's water resources are located in the northern part of the country, but its arable land is in the coastal regions in the south including the province of Negev. In this arrangement Israel very much resembles California. Among the many plans that have been drawn to bring more water to its southern area, the final tapping of the Jordan figures prominently. It is easily understood that those who inhabit and cultivate the river valley become agitated, not to say infuriated, when they hear about plans to bring in salty Mediterranean water in order to gain hydroelectric power and use the Jordan Valley as outlet.

Israel has started to drain the marshes north of the Sea of Galilee, also called the Lake of Tiberias. This directly affects the Syrian water balance and deprives that country of water. The state of Jordan has presented complaints against Israel for having cut off the water reserves for that part of their country located to the south of the Lake of Tiberias. Even if the total tapping of the Jordan River is prevented, the continued development of the irrigation systems for the Negev region will naturally mean increased water outtake from the Jordan basin.

The world has good reason for apprehension—what will happen the day these large-scale irrigation systems are put into operation, depriving both Syria and Jordan of water that these densely populated countries equally desperately need! The tensions in these regions have made fruitless every effort to obtain a more reasonable water distribution, whereby the entire Jordan River would be subject to international regulations. The state of Jordan, on the other hand, threatens to put into effect its own large-scale project to build a canal parallel with the Jordan River, which would tap most of the water from its important tributary Yarmuk and thereby deprive the Jordan River of an important influx. The work on this canal, the Eastern Ghor Canal, is also underway, partly with international capital. In 1966 Jordan celebrated its twentieth anniversary by starting work on the Mokheiba Dam to catch the water of the Yarmuk. When this dam is finished, and operation of the Ghor canal starts, this will by and large nullify the value of the central and lower Jordan. By reducing the influx of fresh water via the Yarmuk, the salinity of the water of the Jordan has already started to rise to such a degree that is has become hazardous to the crops.

The Jordan River is, amazing as it might seem, another of those rivers that via several rivulets is fed from melting snow, in this case from the massive Mount Hermon. Additional water does not seem obtainable through artificial melting, but the moisture-laden air around the mountain range could possibly be "milked" by crystal sowing. This constitutes, however, a rather fragile basis for permanent cultivation; it is rather an emergency measure to resort to when grave drought periods occur. The ultimate is clearly in sight. However, none of the parties involved wishes to face reality: There simply is not enough water available for all these needs, and the question is who grabs the assets first. Water is indeed an explosive commodity in these arid lands, and it is high time that some kind of arbitration is implemented. Four countries are involved: Lebanon, Jordan, Syria, and Israel. All four can rightly claim that their existence depends on the water of the River Jordan. Syria is affected not only by these many water projects. It is also entangled on another front: the Euphrates River of Iraq receives its inflow from Syrian territory.

The Euphrates-Tigris

The Koran gives priority to rights of water taken upstream, and this provides the basic tenet in Muslim water law. Such a rule, applied to the Tigris, gives priority to Turkey and then to Iraq the second rank, since the water reserves are larger before they have reached the intensely evaporating two-river land of Mesopotamia, the core of Iraq. A couple of years ago Iraq became quite concerned when it received notice about Syrian plans to exploit the waters of the Euphrates River before they reached Iraqi soils. Both the Euphrates and the Tigris originate in Turkey, which has so far been rather slow laying claim to its share of the water of these rivers, but is now moving to mobilize these waters for its economic development. The United States and the World Bank are in that order aiding Turkey in the creation of the Kaban Dam near Elazig in the eastern part of the country. This coincides with a counterpart project in Syria, aided by the U.S.S.R. This latter dam would be constructed near Tabaga and provide irrigation to no less than 1.5 million acres and render 0.8 million kilowatt of hydroelectric power. Iran has already taken a considerable part of the only tributary feeding the Shatt-al-Arab, formed by the confluence of the Tigris and Euphrates rivers, the Karun. These

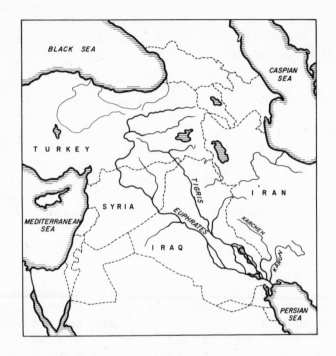

Fig. 37. The Euphrates-Tigris Symplex

circumstances will unquestionably affect the traditional irrigation potential of Iraq—a country that is entirely dependent on these rivers for its survival. This explains why the atmosphere in the entire Middle East gets so agitated when water is discussed, as for instance when West Germany in 1963 gave Syria a huge loan for the construction of a power plant in combination with an irrigation system along the Euphrates.

The Mekong River

The Mekong River has a rich delta, and in its watershed area there is still new land to be broken and expanses to irrigate. The twenty-five million inhabitants of these regions belong to no less than four different nations: Cambodia, Laos, Thailand, and Viet-

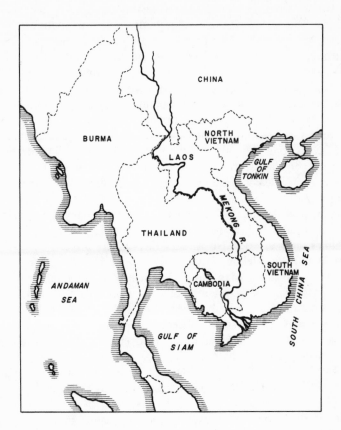

Fig. 38. The Mekong

nam. Cooperation between them is difficult in every field due to political instability and the Vietnam war. This deplorable spectacle goes on while the population figure for Southeast Asia (twenty-five million in 1966) rapidly mounts, and according to conservative estimates will approach ninety million before the end of the century. At least fifty million of these people will then be residing within the magic circle of the Mekong River.

At the present time experts from no less than fourteen nations cooperate in planning for the total mobilization of this river. By and large the comprehensive plans are being copied, which the

Japanese occupation authorities worked out during the Second World War. They included hundreds of power stations, water reservoirs, and fish cultivation establishments. But large-scale warfare, guerrilla fighting, government crises, ruling-house rivalries, etc., do not provide an appropriate atmosphere for such peaceful development programs. Besides, all plans suffer from the absence of any coordinating supranational administrative bodies. Even worse, all plans have so far been made without taking into account the most important power of the Asian sphere, China.

The Mekong is another of the many rivers that originate in the Tibetan highlands. It belongs to the giants among the world's rivers. After leaving Chinese territory, it drains an area much larger than the twin rivers of Euphrates-Tigris taken together. As to transported water volumes, the Mekong is many times the size of the Indus. It also supersedes the Hwang Ho River, one of China's main arteries. No wonder the Chinese are attracted to the potential of the Mekong River, the more so since its major portion remains unbridled. Man has so for disturbed this river very little. No single dam is as yet arresting its main flow. But the city of Pa-Mong on the border between Laos and Thailand will, according to international plans, become the seat of a major dam, larger still than Lake Mead or the Hoover Dam, both in the Colorado River of the United States.

Most writings about the Mekong River Project underestimate the technical difficulties connected with its realization, but over-estimate its future importance. The time factor is in most cases completely ignored. The experts generally agree that it will take about thirty years to carry out the plans after peace has been restored to the area. The new acreages obtained through irrigation will not suffice to feed the natural growth in population in those regions during that period. Finally, several soil experts have pointed out that in many key areas of the river basin there are numerous indications that the jungle soil cannot stand breaking and permanent irrigation.

Other Tension Areas

Another startling example of how international politics may have a retarding influence upon progress is the Amur River. All the proud plans the two main partners, China and the U.S.S.R.,

worked out for power stations, irrigation systems, and fish cultivation to the benefit of these regions of the Far East have ap-
parently come to a halt, despite the fact that, as far as is known,
the Seven-Year Plan was based upon the realization of these more
or less impressive projects. The tributary Sungari with its warm
water serves China by irrigating the Heilungkiang, the key region
in the former Manchukuo state.

Similar analyses could be made of other major rivers and their
watershed areas, particularly in Europe, where both the Rhine and
the Danube are in the center of great campaigns for more water.
Recently, Hungary took another of numerous initiatives throughout the centuries for a multinational control of the Danube and
the full mobilization of this major river, primarily for irrigation
of the many rich agricultural regions of eastern Europe where
drought constantly jeopardizes the crops.

All major rivers have one trait in common: complete unawareness of sovereign rights and political boundaries. They all supersede such fragile human constructions, created without any basic
understanding of fundamental geographical relationships. This
constitutes a major argument for bringing such rivers with their
watersheds under international or other coordinated management,
for the common benefit of the surrounding lands or of mankind.
Such large African rivers as the Niger, the Congo, and the Zambesi belong to this category, as well as many others. Water as a
limiting factor is also reflected in the fluctuations of the crop
yields of the U.S.S.R., and it constitutes a seemingly overex-
ploited natural resource in China, which loomed greatly in the
food crisis following the overdone "Great Leap Forward" of 1958.
It could further be maintained that basically it is water shortage
which has created the misery and poverty of southern Italy and
Sicily. It is also a permanent feature of Spanish poverty, and this
in spite of the many irrigation measures taken by that country.

This also applies historically. Much law took its origin from
disputes reflecting the early need for mediation in this vital area.
Sumerian tablets from 2400 B.C. relate ferocious struggles between cities of the Euphrates-Tigris basin. Historians have attributed the development of administration and strong governments
(dictatorships) to the basic need of coordinated water management. The valleys of the Nile, the Euphrates-Tigris, the Indus,
the Mekong, the Yangtze, and the Hwang Ho were all cradles of

civilizations. So were Jaxartes (Syr Darya) and the Oxus (Amu Darya), not to mention the role of the mighty Siberian river systems to their many early peoples.

The Hydraulic Explosion

With modern days came the mass transportation of water through big energy inputs. Man had gradually extricated himself from the bondage of water, he believed. Los Angeles stands out as the epitomy of this grandeur. There was nothing wrong in this, but man forgot the limitations and transgressed the boundaries dictated by prudence. Arrogantly man is strutting ahead, oblivious of his true situation, and following a course of disaster. Thirst and famine, in effect a Siamese-twin relationship, are closing in on mankind and at a rapid pace, and this despite the fact that no century in history has seen such glorious accomplishments as the present one, with regard to gigantic irrigation projects, huge reservoirs, and hydraulic structures. In all these respects what has been accomplished in this century in terms of both water quantities and irrigated acreage surpasses in totality what has been done in the entire previous history of the human race. There is no doubt that this majestic hydraulic explosion is a mighty corollary to the population explosion. Yet in no other area does it seem more important than with water that man regains control of his destiny and recognizes the crucial limitations of our spaceship Earth.

Tensions are now mounting everywhere (North America, central Europe, the Middle East, China, India, etc.) in pace with the dwindling water reserves, as many nations desperately try to fill the rising needs of their growing populations and the expanding demands dictated by a technology unaware of the water dimension of daily life. These tensions also reflect on the municipal and regional level. In peaceful Wales some dam installations, intended to provide the growing population of the city of Liverpool with water, were in 1961 blown up through sabotage. This was an act of protest against water robbery, highly resented by the local population. It was reported even in the American provincial press. Both central Europe and North America are eyeing the tapping of their last major surface bodies. Lake Constance, Lake Geneva, and the few major lakes of Sweden figure in most plannings for the future. As previously mentioned, the tapping of the Great Lakes has already started in North America and caused diplomatic incidents between Canada and the United States. Man and cotton are jeopardized in Mexicali, since the Colorado delivers its dwindling, saline waters into neighboring Mexico.

Wherever we look, we encounter the water crisis. The examples presented above clearly indicate how intimately this issue now influences day-to-day politics. The closer we get to the limits of totally available water reserves, the more severe these tensions will become in both courts and government agencies all around the globe. The despair of the nations involved, fighting for their survival, coupled with the teeming millions of humans, may even bring these issues to the boiling point. We have refused to see in time that there are limitations for human expansion, and when we now suddenly, almost violently, are confronted with these obstinate facts, we continue as hitherto, instead of making an effort to regain control and trying to steer the vessel of mankind into more navigable and safer waters. The examples analyzed above are most likely only the beginning of a highly ominous development, which can only be brought under control through increased international cooperation or by supranational bodies with coordinating powers. Fisheries and water management are two major areas where the contours of a world government can already be discerned, and where man has perhaps the best chances to initiate a new era of human history, in which we shall regard the globe as our great common resource, one which we must manage wisely and to the benefit of the entire human race. The present rapacious exploitation under the aegis of nationalism will inexorably lead to war and disaster.

Finally, it constitutes food for thought that large-scale control of water systems since the dawn of history has brought about concentration of political power. There is serious reason to raise the pertinent question whether efficient irrigation possibly does not have dictatorship as an ultimate precondition—in itself a paradox. More food has too often been identified with a larger measure of freedom and increase of human happiness. This may be seriously challenged when the margin dwindles and we begin to feel the limitations of our spaceship Earth.

CHAPTER X

Better Utilization
of World
Food Resources

As late as a century ago fresh milk was brought to Stockholm, the capital of Sweden, by rowing boats from the farms in the vicinity. During summertime this milk got sour before reaching the city. This is a reminder of how close in time to our days is the revolutionary development of modern refrigeration and preserving techniques, which provide the Western world with unspoilt foods all year round, regardless of season and distance from the source. Earlier days had such characteristic features as ship biscuits laden with insect larvae, fruit with mold or rotten sections, or worm-infested meat, mold-damaged grain, rancid butter, mite-ravaged or moldy cheeses, moldy bread, and dried fish or meat, also infested (carrying insect larvae). All these phenomena have almost completely disappeared from the horizon of developed countries.

For very much the same reasons overpopulated Europe came into a position to supplement its inadequate food production with perishable foods from transoceanic sources. The heat girdle of the tropics was penetrated with what might be described as a refrigerated tunnel, created by a whole fleet of ships with refrigerated holds. As far back as the nineteenth century they started to carry meat, butter, eggs, fruit, etc., to European ports from Argentina,

Australia, and New Zealand. A less demanding and also less strident flow came from the North American prairies, *e.g.,* Canadian butter and cheese and United States meat. At this early stage canning and freezing plants could be counted in the thousands. The volume of refrigerated space has been rapidly expanded in pace with technical progress and demands on transport volume. Modern storage and preservation technology is therefore part of the Western standard of living and in effect constitutes an indispensable prerequisite for the type of society we have created in the West. The wish to extend these blessings to all peoples on earth is only natural and logical. Professional journals, technological investigations and surveys, as well as the press contain eloquent predictions of how a more general application of these processing techniques would benefit the malnourished and starving of the world.

There is no question that the spoilage of grain, beans, and oilseeds through insects, mites, rodents, and molds, which is most severe in the tropical and subtropical areas of Asia, Africa, and Latin America, reaches staggering amounts in volume as well as value. The estimates vary, but it is generally agreed that one-fifth to one-third of what agriculture is producing never reaches the human consumer; in hungry countries it often exceeds 50 percent. In extreme cases the losses have been total. Unfortunately, statistics on these matters are notoriously defective. A real effort to establish in irrefutable statistical terms the magnitude and true nature of the waste and spoilage in the common household of mankind would in itself be a monumental task which might have worldwide repercussions. The present lack of reliable data is explained partly by the reluctance of both local and national bodies to admit shortcomings, which might easily be interpreted as negligence. It is further explained by the fact that the Food and Agricultural Organization of the United Nations (FAO), like most departments of agriculture around the world, is dominated by producers' organizations, whether farmers or fishermen. Their main task as they see it—it might even be called an obsession—is to maximize production. As a consequence they are little inclined to bother about losses or admit mismanagement in handling and storage. In most instances other links in the distribution chain take the beatings. Commerce and industry take most of the brunt.

The appraisal of actual losses of food and feed due to waste, weeds, insects, and microorganisms is seriously overdue. Only then can truly rational control measures be developed and applied. Such an undertaking would also have a considerable educational value. It would lead to improved procedures and awaken the public to a keener perception of the significance of this important dimension of food—taking better care of what is being produced—which is as vital to the future of mankind as is producing more food.

It is not sufficient, however, only to measure the actual losses in quantity and quality. This whole phenomenon has far broader implications. In some regions of the world it is not possible to grow certain crops and raise certain animals simply because of looming diseases. This kind of loss is difficult to assess. The expense required to maintain an alerting and control service is another cost item not always considered but vital to a complete accounting.

It is easy to prove that the productional gains in world agriculture over a quarter century or more are by and large canceled out by these tolls. At least 500 million people are deprived of their daily food due to this blind spot in the handling of world food affairs. So far the economists have not paid real attention to the Gross National Waste of countries in their concern with the Gross National Product. It would be much more rewarding to direct our efforts toward improved care of the crops that are presently being produced than, as is now the case, to stake all resources and almost all our prestige on producing more, much of which goes to the support of still more pests and spoilage agents. The tilled lands are forced through various devices to yield more, but the humans do not benefit in proportion. Storage, distribution, and processing fail or even collapse because these links in the chain are too weak.

From this point of view it can in all earnestness be argued whether the World Bank and other such money-providing bodies would not have been far better advised to appropriate the billions that are currently involved in costly large-scale irrigation projects —of dubious long-range significance—to storage facilities and processing factories. Such undertakings may not have been equally spectacular, but they would presumably have served the involved regions and their peoples far more effectively. One could almost place this paradoxical situation in the same category as the classic Roman antithesis, bread or circus. It becomes almost tragicomical in view of the fact that in favoring circus one believes that bread will be the winner. The chapter about large-scale irrigation makes it clear that this is far from always the case.

The immediate task ahead of us is consequently to break off the unfortunate spiral: higher yields . . . increased spoilage . . . demands for still higher yields. We must replace this vicious cycle with a less miserable state of affairs: an arrangement where the middle link between production and consumption is strengthened by drastically reducing losses and spoilage. In this way more food would become available even without higher yields. It appears unlikely, however, that this goal could be reached without the creation of a new organization, independent of FAO and clearly disengaged from narrow agricultural interests around the world. Its function should be to take the lead in a radical improvement of conditions for transporting, storing, and processing food. The time is certainly ripe for world commerce and industry to enter the world arena and shoulder their part of world responsibility. For far too long these essential tasks have been monopolized by the vested interests of agriculture and to some degree of fisheries.

It is rather telling and quite indicative of the actual state of affairs that the only field where this is being done to some essential degree is within the Fisheries Division of FAO. Such wider planning was in this case necessary from the start, since fish are highly susceptible to spoilage. Probably it can also be attributed to the fact that the fisheries industry possesses far less organizational and political power than agriculture. It is furthermore evident that the global upsurge of the Japanese and Soviet fishing fleets on the oceans, discussed later in this chapter, has brought about new thinking in broader and more rational terms.

Nobody should be induced to believe that losses can ever be eliminated altogether. Unfortunately, we are here again facing one of those myopic viewpoints that mark the debate on the part of far too many specialists. Large gains can be made by taking better care of what is being produced, thus averting or at any rate reducing waste and spoilage. But even in this case there is a limit, set by biological and climatic realities and also by what is economically feasible. Complete elimination of waste may in itself easily become too costly a proposition. Yet a better utilization of the world's food resources is one of the most urgent tasks now facing mankind, but this is in a regrettable way seriously overlooked in most appropriations. Most billions still go to the further perfection of already ridiculously overdeveloped military weapons of annihilation or to interests at the fringes of real need, for instance our costly space adventures, which can do little to aid a hungry and impoverished world.

The Testimony of History

The history of food preservation is actually that of mankind. Most civilizations, after having passed the most primitive stages, depended upon storage and preservation of its food. In most instances they resorted to quite ingenious devices. Strictly speaking, canning is the only preservation method that can be wholly attributed to the applications of science and technology in the modern sense. All other methods are ancient and the result of empirical findings. Drying, salting, freezing, and curing, as well as combinations of these methods, have all been in practical use for many centuries. The dried buffalo meat of the prairie Indians, the freeze-dried potatoes of the Andean Indians, the frozen meat of the Eskimoes, the Laplanders, and the Samoyeds, the dried meat (*xarque*) of the Brazilian Indians, the dried curds and butter of the Tartars, the melted butter fat (*ghee*) of the East Indians, and many other preserved products all constituted essential ingredients in the everyday diet of these peoples. Without these items they would hardly have been able to survive.

We know what the salted herring meant to the medieval European household and the dried cod to the Caribbean and the Mediterranean regions. Both products have in effect written world history, and well into our days they are still a mainstay in the protein supply of both tropical Africa and Latin America in the shape of dried codfish from Canada, Norway, and France. This is being shipped to the Caribbean Islands, to South America, tropical Africa, and parts of Asia. The dried fish industry on the Maldive Islands is indispensable, for instance, to the survival of Ceylon. Dried nonfatty fish constitutes the most concentrated protein in world trade, containing by weight two and a half times more protein than nonfat milk solids, *i.e.,* dried skim milk. This explains why fish—although the world production of protein through fisheries is smaller than through milk—plays a larger role than does milk in providing relief protein to the malnourished people.

The conclusion is obvious: Simple preservation methods such as drying and salting certainly offer greater possibilities to a hungry world than the more complicated and costly ones, such as canning and freezing. Our "Western" methods are in effect far too expensive in terms of capital and equipment and simply cannot be applied on a global scale at this stage of technical and economic development.

The Privileges of the Luxury World

It is quite telling that canning only to a minor degree has been utilized in world feeding. Admittedly, canned foods are important in world food trade, but they move almost exclusively between the luxury nations of the world, primarily to broaden their range of taste sensations. Parenthetically it may be underlined that most cheese in world trade channels has this highly limited function of feeding the well-fed. The canned Alaska salmon, the peaches and pears of California and Australia, the canned king crab packed by the U.S.S.R. and Japan, the herring delicatessen of Scandinavia, the sardines of France, Norway, and Portugal, and Japan's mandarin oranges are available around the world—but only to that small minority of the world's billions who can afford them. Canned hams fill the shelves in the well-stocked supermarkets of the United States. They come from Poland, Canada, Holland, and Denmark. Most of the corned beef packed by Argentina originates primarily in Brazil. It is also exported to the United States and western Europe.

Canned food is certainly no component of the diet in hungry nations. The president of the Association of Fish Canners in Morocco once told me that a cheap Moroccan canned fish, developed for the Middle East markets, primarily Egypt, brought a higher price when sold to the United States as cat food. One third of the canned fish of the United States is in effect pet food. An equally large portion of the British output of canned fish is devoted to the same purpose. In most instances this constitutes food which would be very much in demand if offered to the protein-needy and malnourished around the globe.

The Mobilization of the Oceans

The present race for food explains the large-scale mobilization in the postwar period of the fish resources of the seas. But this is almost entirely based on resorting to one or another kind of preservation. Without preservation soon after catch, this large-scale exploitation would not be feasible. The United States initiated this development as early as the thirties, when the catching expeditions for tuna were extended from the national Pacific waters southwards toward Chile. These vessels were equipped with freezing installments for preservation upon catch and subsequent canning in California industries. This tuna empire is today of impressive dimensions and has been steadily enlarged in order to satisfy the needs of the rapidly growing population in the United States, but also to meet increasing demands due to the persistently increasing uniformity of the United States diet, resulting in tuna becoming a standard item. The United States consumption is at present more than two pounds per person per year. The Pacific waters no longer yield sufficient quantities, despite considerable purchase of packs and raw material from Japan and despite canneries in American Samoa. With Puerto Rico as a new base the United States has developed fisheries in the tropical parts of the Atlantic Ocean, partly with contributions from Japanese and French catching units supplementing the catches of United States ships. A fourth base has been created in Boston, to which tuna is brought from adjacent Atlantic waters.

The most sensational happening on the fishery scene is, however, the emergence of the Soviet land giant as one of the world's leading fishing nations. The buildup of an impressive modern fishing fleet supported by newly constructed floating factory ships of various types and dimensions has made Soviet working cities out at sea, with 10,000 to 30,000 people on each major fishing ground, almost permanent phenomena on the oceans of the world. In the Davis Straits at Greenland, the Sverdlovsk Bank at Newfoundland, the St. George Bank off the New England coast; in Norwegian waters; at the Faeroe Islands, the Shetland Islands, and the Hebrides; off the coast of Africa, from Cape Etienne in Mauritania via the Gulf of Guinea all the way down to Cape

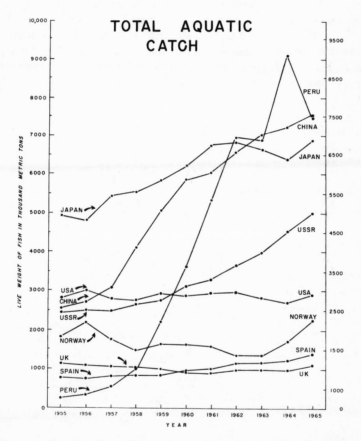

Fig. 39. Growth of world's total aquatic catch, 1955–65, in thousand metric tons. Some six million tons refer to freshwaters. Note the stagnation of fisheries in the United States and western Europe (excluding Scandinavia). The postwar mobilization of the oceans has been led by the U.S.S.R. and Japan. Peru has developed a huge fish-meal industry in the Peruvian Current, also called the Humboldt Current. China has in a remarkable way marshaled its freshwaters for its enormous feeding task.

Town; in the Red Sea, in the Arabian Sea, in the Indian Ocean; in Bering Sea and passing through the Aleutians into the Gulf of Alaska Soviet fishing fleets, small and large, are encountered. But they are not there to procure food for the hungry in the poor countries. Until quite recently (1963) almost everything captured and landed was brought back to the homeland bases in the Black Sea and in the Baltic, as well as to the port of Murmansk (in the west Arctic flank) and to Sakhalin, Kamchatka, and the Far East mainland. Here the fish is canned, salted, and smoked or merely unloaded and shipped inland by rail to be prepared directly to ready-made food in the continuous processing lines of central

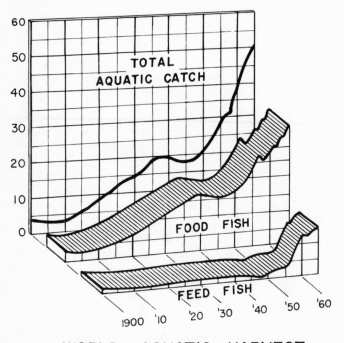

WORLD AQUATIC HARVEST

Fig. 40. World aquatic catch (in million metric tons), broken down as to basic utilization. Note the increasingly growing percentage of feed fish moving into reduction plants for the manufacturing of feedingstuffs (meal) and oil.

kitchens in cities and institutions. The frozen blocks of fish (twenty-five to fifty pounds) from the ocean expanses reach the major cities almost everywhere in the U.S.S.R. and provide a welcome addition to a protein supply that used to be perfunctory, in large part due to the precarious climatic conditions adversely affecting agriculture.

This worldwide aquatic harvesting, coupled with an immediate preservation on the fishing grounds, must be recognized as an impressive accomplishment in terms of planning and management. The U.S.S.R. persists in pursuing these efforts. Soviet shipyards employ at least one million men engaged in building additional fishing vessels and floating factories, transport and service units, base ships or mother vessels. Processing facilities are installed in individual fishing vessels—small and big trawlers—for salting, freezing, etc., but also in specialized ships designed as base ships or mother vessels, sometimes combined with transporting duties. Ships are also built exclusively for this latter purpose.

The U.S.S.R. furthermore has on order at least 150 new ships of various kinds: from Denmark, the United Kingdom, France, Holland, Japan, Sweden, and West Germany, not to mention continuous deliveries from the shipyards in Poland and East Germany. A leading East German shipyard with large Soviet orders recently reported the launching of its eighty-seventh ship in the "Tropik" series (designed for fishing and processing in tropical waters) and the start of a new order for no less than 104 vessels of the "Atlantik" series (designed for fishing in the North Atlantic).

East Germany, Poland, Romania, Bulgaria, and Yugoslavia are rapidly following suit, by creating fishing fleets of their own with processing units allowing long distance fishing. Similar trends have come to dominate, but on a more modest scale, in western Europe during the sixties: in West Germany, the United Kingdom, France, Italy, Spain, Portugal, and Greece. Shipyards all over the world are busy filling orders for floating processing factories of highly varying types, the majority for freezing, but some for salting and canning. They are all equipped to take care of the oil and the vitamins in the fish liver and also for full utilization of fish wastes, converting them into meal and oil. From the point of view of efficient economizing with food resources, this development is highly commendable.

Japanese vessels today are also fishing in all oceans. Since 1965 they have taken part in operations in waters as distant as those off Iceland and Greenland in the North Atlantic. The catches from Japan's own coastal waters are far from adequate. The Soviet Union further forced Japan, through quotas set at annual meetings of a joint fisheries commission, to reduce significantly her catches in the Sea of Okhotsk and the Bering Sea. The United States has tried to restrain Japanese intrusion upon traditional United States catching grounds in the Bering Sea and the Gulf of Alaska.

China, too, is beginning to take to the sea and is descending with large fleets upon the Yellow Sea and the East China and South China seas. These waters constitute some of the richest fishing waters in the world and have been regularly visited by the Japanese for fishing but they are no longer freely available to them, as Mao's China jealously guards her waters. So does South Korea, in addition engendering a very expansive phase of its own fishing. Japan was therefore, after the wartime restrictions were lifted in 1952, virtually forced to launch evermore extending operations to supplement the inadequate catches from coastal areas and from waters possible to reach from homeland ports. Distant fishing of a new kind entered the Japanese scene. Early in history the cries for food drove them to a major endeavor to develop fishing on the Far East mainland in Kamchatka and Sakhalin and in some of the Siberian rivers. The last outpost of this fishing empire, south Sakhalin (Karafuto), was lost through World War II, and Japanese high-sea fishing got its start. These ventures not only swept over major parts of the North Pacific, inclusive of the waters of Alaska, but gradually they went to all parts of the Pacific and developed several new fishing grounds in that ocean. Particularly rich fishing grounds were further discovered and exploited by the Japanese in the Indian Ocean and off the east coast of Africa.

But Japan developed a pattern that differs from that of the Soviet Union. Instead of investing in floating processing factories, Japanese fishing companies made agreements with their counterparts in a great number of countries. In this way a broad network of fishing bases was created, provided with refrigerated warehouses, freezing factories, and in some instances also canneries. Practically in every country around the Mediterranean basin such bilateral arrangements exist with Japanese companies, even in Egypt and Israel, the two mutual arch-enemies. Similar Japanese bases are found on the Fiji Islands, on the Philippines, on Madagascar, in Ghana, the West Indies, the Dominican Republic, etc. Besides, Japan has managed to take an almost monopolistic lead in the development of the fisheries of Brazil and those of Argentina. Japanese fishing has also entered the North Atlantic scene. Its catching vessels are seen at Iceland, Newfoundland, Ireland, etc. They have also acquired bases of support on Ireland, Newfoundland, and on the French islands of St. Pierre and Miquelon, off Newfoundland. A key base is the Canary Islands, where special storages have been built for transit trade with eastern Europe via Hamburg. Agreement has been reached with Portugal about bases on the Cape Verde Islands and in the Azores. Again, food preservation is writing world history, but primarily to fill Japan's own needs and in order to sell to those who already have enough to eat. So far the undernourished and starving peoples get an insignificant share. (Compare my book, *Japan's Success in World Fishing* [1964], listed in the bibliography to this chapter.)

The Soviet Union has started to copy Japan by creating the first operational bases for its fishing fleets outside the homeland. This happened in Cuba and was widely reported by the United States press. This base located close to the port of Havana is to be the focal point for Soviet trawlers operating in the middle and south Atlantic. It is dimensioned to accomodate some 110 trawlers. This arrangement was soon followed by a second one in Alexandria of Egypt (to serve Indian Ocean and Arabian Sea fishing) together with a third smaller one (Ras Banas) in the Red Sea.

Peru, a Giant Protein Bastion

The third remarkable event in fish utilization is the creation of the big fish meal industries, primarily in Peru and Chile, and a similar cluster in southwest Africa and on the Atlantic coast of South Africa. With the aid of west European and United States capital Peru has grossly expanded its fisheries into the rich Peruvian Current (tradionally called the Humboldt Current) off the Pacific coast of South America. It now almost surpasses in volume Europe's entire sea catch (9.8 million metric tons in 1967).

Chile is following suit, rapidly expanding its fish-meal industry, but on a more modest scale. Most of the invested capital is west European or American; some is national. Close to half of the protein taken from the Pacific (1966–68) emanates from these new fisheries in Peru and Chile—quite a remarkable accomplishment. Practically the entire catch is converted to animal feed in fish-meal factories. A major part (80 percent) of the fish riches of the African Benguela Current is in a similar way channeled into reduction.

In both cases almost the entire output of meal and oil goes to western Europe (approximately two-thirds) and the United States (slightly less than one-third) with a minor part to Japan, where it constitutes a significant base for the budding animal production. The oil serves the European margarine industry. The impressive increase of animal production in postwar Europe is to a substantial degree due to this gigantic influx of first-rate animal protein, which enters into agricultural production almost through the back door. The agriculturists of Europe seem to realize little that they are so heavily indebted to the sea for their magic tricks, or they

SOUTH AMERICA
FISH PROTEIN DELIVERIES
1963-65

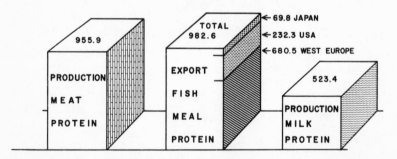

Fig. 41. The Peruvian-Chilean fish-meal export deprived South America (1964–66) of more protein than that contained in the total South American production of meat and almost twice that of the milk output. The 1966–68 average has boosted this delivery to 1.5 million metric tons, *i.e.,* one half above the 1963–65 level.

may not like to admit this in priding themselves on their flourishing animal production. In effect, this constitutes a new phase in the history of commercial colonialism. Its beginning was in the food sector through the exploitation of the world's grasslands in the South African veld, the Argentine pampas, the North American prairie, and the grasslands of Australia.

We are now repeating this trick, this time on the basis of the drifting plankton pastures of the oceans. No doubt everyone realizes how preposterous it is that the two most protein-needy continents, Africa and South America, are the main suppliers of the largest quantities of animal protein feed moving in world trade— and they provide those who already have plenty. This constitutes political dynamite. The supremacy of the white race was lost *after* World War II. This was the period when more than 1.5 billion people gained national independence, and it will without a doubt be judged as one of the great dividing lines between historical epochs. The earlier we in the Western world make adjustment to this new reality, the better. Nobody should expect that in the future the malnourished peoples of South America and tropical Africa will not make their well-founded claims heard and demand that appropriate action be taken. The Peruvian catches alone would suffice to raise the nutritional standard with respect to protein for the undernourished on the entire South American continent to southern European level. The amount of protein extracted (1966–68) exceeds by one half the meat protein produced in South America and is three times the milk protein raised. The corresponding fish meal coming from Africa would be enough to reduce by at least 50 percent the present protein shortage of that continent. Technically it is simple to convert these fish riches into human food, either by way of drying the fish directly or through extraction of the protein for the manufacture of fish powder or simply through minor improvements in the present meal production. Such a measure would at the same time render a major contribution to economizing with world food resources.

Historically such a switch in utilization can be viewed in the following way. There was a time when excessive fish were scooped up to be used as fertilizer in the fields: herring from Scandinavian fjords and along the shores of Hokkaido, the northernmost of Japan's main islands, salmon from the New England waters by Indians living there. It was a great step toward better utilization when these resources were used directly as animal feed; we are now in the next phase of this development, when they must become human food.

Anachronisms

We can look forward to similar radical changes on two other crucial points. One is with regard to skim or buttermilk. This remainder after the fat has been removed is of far too high nutritional value, in particular with respect to protein, to serve merely as feed to hogs and poultry. The second case refers to oilseeds, the presscakes of which by and large move as cattle feed to the rich and well-fed nations. These residues from the pressing of sunflower seeds, soybeans, etc., will increasingly be processed into a kind of flour, which is added as extender to regular flour or used directly as food, often mixed with quite a number of other foods. This is particularly essential to peanut-producing nations, like India and Nigeria, or cottonseed producers, like Egypt or Central America. As late as 1939 ships fully loaded with peanuts went in a steady stream from malnourished and starving India to England, largely to feed its cattle and provide the working classes with cheap fat. The oil went into margarine and the presscakes were used as feed for the dairy cattle. Of the oilseed cakes currently moving into world trade, no less than 95 percent go to western Europe, primarily England (U.K.), West Germany, Denmark, and Holland. This is the second artificial leg upon which the current food abundance in western Europe rests: 1.5 million metric tons of protein, enough to raise by 50 percent the protein-content in the poor diet of the malnourished of the globe. Denmark has the world record in protein importation, in excess of 240 pounds per person (!), *i.e.*, three times its intake per person. Surprisingly enough, the Netherlands comes second, with no less than 170 pounds, and Israel third, with 132 pounds, on the world list of protein grabbers on a per capita basis (these figures are annual averages for the five-year period 1961–1965 but are since then still larger).

Added together, the oilseed cakes of the world contain more protein than the total catch of food fish, enough to double the protein consumption of the underdeveloped countries. The food scientists in the world are now experimenting to make this plant-

PORTION OF WORLD TRADE IMPORTATION THAT GOES
TO WESTERN EUROPE (1963–1965)
(*In percentage of total world trade*)

	PORTION OF WORLD TRADE IMPORT	PORTION FROM COUNTRIES OUTSIDE WESTERN EUROPE		PORTION OF WORLD TRADE IMPORT	PORTION FROM COUNTRIES OUTSIDE WESTERN EUROPE
Frozen eggs	97.5	96.1	Wool	64.5	57.9
Oilseed cakes			Barley	61.8	23.0
and meal	93.0	78.9	Copra	56.4	56.4
Bacon, ham	92.8	9.3	Meat extract	56.2	31.0
Fish oils	80.6	52.0	Sunflower seed	54.6	54.3
Oats	78.6	58.6	Egg powder	54.5	26.3
Poultry meat	78.0	10.0	Soybeans	53.5	53.5
Cheese and			Bran, etc.	52.8	45.5
curd	77.3	7.6	Peas, beans	51.6	37.2
Butter	77.0	39.4	Meat meal	44.4	23.9
Fish meal	72.7	51.4	Non-fat milk		
Peanuts	71.6	70.2	solids	44.0	8.2
Corn (maize)	68.8	60.7	Cottonseed	37.7	37.7
Eggs	68.6	12.5	Sugar	28.6	18.7
Meat	66.5	82.5	Wheat	22.3	13.5

JAPAN'S PORTION OF ASIAN TRADE
IMPORTATION (1963–1965)
(*In percentage—rank in parentheses*)

Meat meal	81.8 (1)	Meat	58.0 (1)	Cheese	31.8 (1)
Cottonseed	80.0 (1)	Bran, etc.	56.7 (1)	Dried milk	30.8 (1)
Soybean	78.4 (1)	Oilseed cakes	55.1 (1)	Peanuts	19.5 (1)
Corn (maize)	75.2 (1)	Barley	46.5 (1)	Wheat	18.7 (3)
Fish meal	66.7 (1)	Peas, beans	37.9 (1)	Rice	10.9 (4)

bound protein fully accessible to the human stomach, thereby
giving their aid to a better utilization of the world's nutritive re-

UNITED STATES' PORTION OF WORLD TRADE
IMPORTATION (1963–1965)
(*In percentage—world rank in parentheses*)

Shrimp	71.9 (1)	Bananas	34.7 (1)	Beef	23.8 (1)
Coffee	46.5 (1)	Cocoa	27.7 (1)	Canned meat	23.5 (1)
Tuna	45.4 (1)	Fish (raw)	26.8 (1)	Sugar	20.5 (1)

sources. This could become a major asset in the world's food balance—on the assumption that the well-fed world could find substitute feedstuffs or contribute to a reduction in the current imbalances of the world, which have created the grave Hunger Gap. In retrospect it seems absurd that for a long time span the oil was the only substance of these oilseed riches the Western world deigned to utilize fully, while the press residues, containing the vital protein, were looked upon more or less as waste products. This is undoubtedly a consequence of the historical fact that in recent centuries the well-fed nations have been in charge of the exploitation and utilization of these resources. Other people with more parsimonious conditions for their existence did otherwise, and developed completely different patterns. Two examples may be chosen to illustrate this.

The Soybean in East and West

The soybean, which is original in east Asia, has for centuries been utilized there almost exclusively for human food. It was made into cheeselike curds, into milk and a whole series of fermented products, mostly without first removing the fats. The milk of China has for thousands of years been made out of soybeans. This plant reached the outside world only in the nineteenth century. It came to the United States as late as 1872 via Georgia and was then called the oriental bean. It spread, and it was generally believed that it would soon find its place in the United States diet. This happened, however, only with the oil. Nine-tenths of this goes to margarine production and the making of other fats for direct human consumption. The press residues, originally a great nuisance, were used as fertilizers, and only gradually were they recognized as a protein-rich by-product with a key place in feed production. The volume was not adequate, however, to sustain the high-level animal production of the United States. Additional sources were sought in other oilseed cakes, partly imported from Argentina and other countries. The menhaden fisheries were then expanded, but despite huge catches this fish could not fill in the protein gap in United States feed production. Increasing quantities of fish meal had to be purchased on the world market.

But the serious food shortage in the world is increasingly making itself felt on the world scene. The demand for high-quality soybean protein is day by day becoming more acute. This is reflected also in the price quotations; so for instance the price for soybean oil has steadily been declining while that of protein has gone up—as it ought to do. But still only one-tenth of the soybean protein consumed on the United States domestic scene enters into human food, primarily via milk and meat substitutes, but also as toasted soybean protein.

The happenings on the soybean market of the United States give a clear indication of the trends. Large-scale efforts are now being launched to make these protein riches directly available as human food, regardless of whether they come from soybean, sunflower, cottonseed, rapeseed, or coconut. Mobilizing the oilseed cakes, and still better, the oilseeds directly as human food is therefore a significant "New Deal" in nutrition with many intriguing aspects. All over the world—in the Soviet Union, in India, and in Nigeria to mention but a few examples—toasted soybean protein has already become a staple in the food market. In the United States it is being stored by Civil Defense as an all-purpose food, with vitamins and minerals added, under the name Multi-Purpose Food. This product is used for relief purposes by a world-embracing private United States organization called Meals for Millions.

The protein potential of the oilseeds produced around the globe exceeds twenty million tons—approximately equivalent to what terrestrial animal products provide, *i.e.,* exclusive of proteins from aquatic sources. The mobilization of these resources, largely untapped as direct human food, would make a major contribution to improving the over-all nutritive conditions in the world household. They would actually fill in half the present protein gap. It goes without saying that this would have profound repercussions on the fat and protein provisions of the well-fed world, which in this respect largely enjoys a false—one might even say artificial—standard, which amounts to nothing else than an almost parasitic existence at the behest and to the obvious detriment of the hungry world.

Trade Dominance

Outside the area of cereal grains most food and feed of the world market moves between the well fed and, still more surprisingly, from the hungry to the rich countries. This is particularly conspicuous in regard to protein, with the well-fed countries on balance making a net gain exceeding one million tons. Western Europe (see table, p. 239) is buyer number-one, followed by the United States (see p. 240); Japan dominates Asian trade in a similar way (see p. 239).

Copra

French nutritional scientists found through studies in tropical west Africa that the protein of the coconut is surprisingly potent in its amino acid composition (aminogram). Instead of drying the coconuts to copra and selling this product for the manufacturing of oil and feedcakes in the United States and western Europe, this source of food ought to be channeled directly into the human larder. Despite recognition of such fundamental facts, the distribution pattern still remains the same. Within the framework of the Freedom-from-Hunger campaign almost no effort or even study has been made to implement an economic or technical readjustment.

Indonesia and the Philippines, both seriously undernourished nations, still provide the world market with the largest quantities of copra, thereby making significant contributions to the luxurious food standards of West Germany, Holland, and the United States.

Skim Milk

Still more preposterous, however, is the fact that a few countries, among them Scandinavia, the U.S.S.R., the United States, and Australia, can allow themselves the wastefulness of feeding skim milk to hogs. In the Chinese household the pig always had the function of being a scavenger, a refuse and waste converter. He used to live off the waste from man's society and still does. This is feasible for the very simple reason that his nutritive needs are almost identical to those of man. In the Western world the hog has become a competitor to man, sharing his food, not only grain, potato etc., but also milk! We can still afford to give him this standard close to our own valuable diet. These strange conditions will, however, soon vanish under the mounting pressures from a world in rapidly growing distress due to food shortages, in particular proteins.

Until quite recently, skim milk was regarded by farmers and dairies with annoyance as a cumbersome by-product. The whey was looked upon in the same light. This is another such aberration in the utilization patterns of our food. As in the case of oilseeds, the milk-producing farm was so one-sidedly set on extracting or processing one single ingredient, *viz.,* highly coveted butter fat, and succeeded so well that all remainders were categorized as "waste," even when they constituted much more valuable nutrition, as is the case with buttermilk, *i.e.,* milk from which the fat has been removed by making butter. Significant progress in economizing with milk protein has since taken place, but there is a long road ahead before we get to a satisfactory and complete saving of the proteins, invaluable both nationally and globally.

We put up an astonished face when the hungry world maintains that they cannot afford to buy our butter, but at the most purchase the dried skim milk, which they supplement with cheap vegetable fats to produce "filled milk," a rather inadequate term which has been applied to this kind of milk. In effect, "fat-substituted milk" would be a more correct designation. To the fat-free milk powder (nonfat milk solids) is added coconut fat, safflower oil, corn oil, cottonseed oil, or rapeseed oil, in replacement of the milk fat. It would, however, be a task of prime importance for the food scientists to find cheap and more satisfactory methods for the drying of whole milk which in turn would allow cheaper packaging. We would thereby disassociate ourselves from the not very clever sport of manufacturing butter, which millions of people cannot afford even in the well-fed countries. This is a rather questionable economy, especially when, on top of that, tax money is used for the long-time storage of these rather dubious butter surpluses. Obesity is a luxury disease of the West, while hundreds of millions of undernourished people in the world are plagued by a damaging fat shortage and would need the extracted butterfat to go with their purchases of powdered milk.

In Australia, New Zealand, and Scandinavia, and presumably also in the U.S.S.R., more milk protein is channeled past human consumption into feed or simply lost as waste than the total amount of meat protein consumed by these countries. It would be far more advantageous to explore further the possibilities of making new kinds of hard cheeses that are readily stored. The traditional rennet technique leaves one-fourth of the total milk protein in the whey, and they are the two proteins most valuable for human nutrition because of their aminogram. Soviet scientists pursuing research on milk coprecipitates, however, have obtained curds carrying the entire protein outfit of milk. This curd renders cheeses of a slightly different type, but no protein waste is left in the whey. This more economic and less wasteful procedure has been further developed in modern Soviet dairies as well as in Australia. No part of modern food science could be more necessary than this.

The United States has pioneered the full utilization of both skim milk and whey, and it has presumably advanced further than any other country in this respect. Yet waste and losses remain large. On the world scene this situation is atrocious. Today no less than four million tons of milk protein are still annually bypassing the human household either by being used as fodder or simply by being discarded as waste.

Waste as Feed

Current meat production in Florida is to a considerable degree based upon feed the orange juice factories continuously provide and which is largely composed of the squeeze remainders, including the peel. Brazil and Ghana feed their cattle the residues from coffee and cacao beans. In Central America, Brazil, and tropical Africa a whole range of industries have emerged for the manufacturing of banana powder and other banana products. Banana peels, orange peels, and spent ground coffee will in the future probably not add to the contents of the garbage cans in Western countries. They contain too much valuable nutrition to be disposed of in this wasteful and costly way. Processing factories for concentrates of coffee, orange juice, etc., and banana products are gradually becoming important industries in all those countries that produce the actual raw products. This is the more likely pattern of the future, since besides coveted animal feed, these plants provide added employment opportunities. Furthermore, rational logistics speak strongly in favor of this kind of arrangement.

The Nutritional Privileges of the Well-fed Approaching an End

The traditional classification of the world into raw-material-producing countries on one hand and industrialized countries on the other is gradually becoming an anachronism. A completely new economic pattern is taking shape. It is deplorable that so far there has been no true recognition of the fact that the food issues constitute significant pieces in this new mosaic. The food shortage and world hunger seem in some queer way to be overlooked in most plans for industrialization and investments. The nutritional needs of the afflicted peoples and their own interests must be taken into account. The economists must somehow be taught to calculate with the capital asset of a healthy and well-fed nation. In a series of hungry countries around the world all these preposterous deliveries of food and feed to the Western world are recorded with considerable satisfaction and as a sign of a flourishing economy. It is certainly not indicative of a sound economy that southern Rhodesia up to the present crisis furnished the luxury markets of London (Smithfield) and Madrid with meat that brought money into the pockets of a few white colonizers, while at the same time 95 percent of the Rhodesian population suffered various degrees of malnutrition and certainly could not afford meat in their diet. The Peruvian fish meal deliveries are by no means the only example of a seriously irrational management of world food resources. The United States is at present being provided with shrimp from more than sixty countries, among them Hong Kong, India, Surinam, Panama, and Mexico. In all these countries this shrimp would fill a crying need.

A radically new way of thinking is demanded. This will lead to

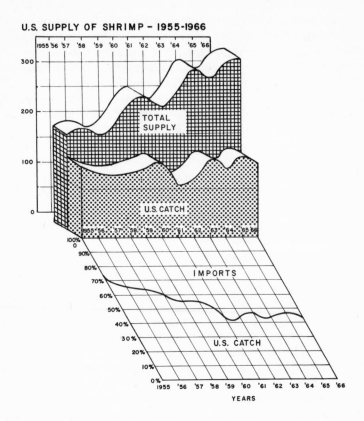

Fig. 42. United States shrimp balance, 1955–66 (in million pounds)

a new world order, developed along sounder economic lines. A nutritional council encompassing the entire globe could constitute a far more effective step toward world peace than the futile disarmament squabbles. The hungry and destitute in the world are moving close to the limits of their patience and endurance. They have been waiting far too long for the multibillion-dollar expenditures for arms to be reduced and the world's resources utilized in a more rational way, serving the whole of mankind. To channel the enormous military outlays into a large-scale war against Global Misery would be a constructive contribution toward a better world. Trouble is brewing among the impoverished and undernourished when they witness the present astounding irresponsibility toward the world instigated by the two superpowers and in turn supported by their allies.

For far too long the rich world has either refused to listen to the clamorings of the poor or lived under the grave fallacy that charity and ambulance services in the form of relief deliveries were all that was needed. With increasing frequency the demand is now heard for justice, and this with no little justification. It is certainly not political realism to behave like the well-fed rich world did at the first United Nations Conference on Trade and Development (UNCTAD), held in Geneva in 1964. Each group on the two sides of the Hunger Gap spoke its mind, but no meaningful interchange took place—not a vestige of an action program was formulated. The whole matter was buried in commissions. When the second UNCTAD conference (with 139 nations represented) was held early in 1968 in New Delhi (India), this most important postwar conference was hardly mentioned and far less covered in the United States press and other mass media. The Indian Prime Minister Indhira Gandhi in her keynote speech warned the world and in particular the rich nations that the gap must be narrowed with the underdeveloped countries through urgent action or "men and women will be impelled to revolt."

To behave like this is unwise, almost inexcusable. These conferences could equally well have been held on two different planets, so infinitesimal was the interchange. The longer we persist in believing that mankind can continue to live in two separate worlds, the greater are the risks that the Western world will join the cavalcade of vanished civilizations. Whether we like it or not we have to recognize that it no longer remains empty rhetoric that the World Is One. We need revival of the basic Christian creed of Universal Brotherhood of Man, far too little heard in recent decades.

In a paper I gave at the World Affairs Institute at the University of California in Los Angeles some years ago, I pointed to these conditions and concluded among other things: "We will witness a nutritional revolution, the consequences of which will be more worldwide and deeper than those of the French, the American, or the Russian revolutions."

We should certainly not believe that we can remain seated in the first row, unperturbed by the great human tragedy unfolding on the world scene: two billion hungry and destitute rapidly growing to four billion. When the chips are down, we the privileged may well feel the consequences far more profoundly than these others, already pressed down to a least common denominator. The repercussions may well be considerable when we will be forced to adjust to a reality in which we no longer are the most favored party and furthermore will have to share our abundance. I disregard here the fact that the white race from the outset had at its disposal such a disproportionate share of the world's resources in land, forest, and water. More significant is that we in addition have persisted in grabbing from the entire globe whatever we can lay our hands on (admittedly with payment, but mostly on our terms) and with overt neglect of the needs of other people. A better utilization of the world's food resources will mean, not only the end to the nutritional monopoly of the West, but also an end to the era of commercial colonialism to which most Western nations have been and are addicted, regardless of whether they have been colonial powers in the political sense or not. We can clearly discern the end of these nutritional privileges of ours, when the other nations in the world increasingly raise their legitimate demands for a better utilization of total resources and also claim a more equitable distribution of the world's food resources and other prerequisites. One third of the world's population can simply not expect that it will be allowed to continue to gulp down two-thirds of the world's food, whether it comes from land or sea.

CHAPTER XI

Lakes and Dams
for Fish Cultivation

Lakes, rivers, and other freshwaters have poorly withstood the blessing of human civilization. Almost everywhere man has leaned upon these waters not only as the great life givers, but also as cleansers. They have served as recipients for the major part of human waste both directly and indirectly, wastes which frequently became excessive wherever people concentrated in cities and densely populated areas. Even at an early stage Europe felt the consequences of this large-scale pollution of nature; North America followed suit. The waters became overburdened with organic matter; the oxygen content became depleted, accumulations in the bottom started fermenting, malodorous substances surfaced, and diseases spread. The initially favorable effect for fish and other living organisms of the added nutritive substances soon had the reverse influence, inducing death by suffocation to all animal life inclusive of fish. Then modern industry emerged, adding immensely to the pollution load, frequently aggravated by toxic matter. In many regions fish management as a kind of repair and maintenance service had to be organized, later followed by water protection measures. Both North America and Europe are now in the midst of this second stage.

From the point of view of food, water pollution meant less to eat. The fish yields diminished drastically, in many instances to zero. Fish species of such high food value as salmon, trout, sturgeon, and pike-perch yielded to such less palatable species as whitefish, pike, loach, and others. Lakes, rivers, and other fresh waters gradually lost their importance as food resources, and paradoxically enough, in pace with desperate and costly efforts to save the stock. These efforts, however, were principally in vain, as the pollution mounted when the numbers of humans to feed grew.

Industrialization and Population Centers

The same chain of events led to stagnation and decline in the inland fisheries of the enormous Soviet Union. Despite a series of almost desperate measures, such large inland waters as the Caspian Sea, the Black Sea, the Sea of Azov, and numerous other larger and smaller lakes, among them the often praised Lake Baikal in far-off Siberia, show steadily decreasing catches. In the Caspian Sea they are down to two-thirds of those of the thirties, and a large portion of the fish caught are less suitable as direct human food and goes into the manufacturing of feed. In view of the vast expanses of the Soviet empire, which encompasses one-sixth of the globe, this development is startling, to say the least. But the growth of the cities and the industrialization process follow exactly the European and North American pattern: The waters are forced to serve as recipients for mounting volumes of waste of various kinds and are simultaneously tapped at an accelerating pace to fill the water needs of population centers, of irrigation, and of industrial production. Besides, large hydroelectric plants, several with huge dams, whether under construction or in operation, interfere with water distribution and induce increased evaporation losses, and this frequently in key areas already short of water. The pollution crisis has hit the Soviet Union much faster than Europe and North America, mainly due to the fact that its water reserves are infinitely more scarce, the further one moves eastward into the land mass of this giant. Soviet scientists recently presented an ardent appeal to the government to take measures to save Lake Baikal, with its unique flora and fauna. Among the latter is the omul, a special salmonid fish indigenous to the lake, which has often been described and praised. Its very future is now in jeopardy.

The Role of Freshwater Fish

How important, then, is freshwater fish in the world household? Judged on the over-all scene, it is certainly not as significant as one would be inclined to imagine. To a large extent, due to the adverse effects of industrialization just mentioned, drastic declines have been registered in catches from freshwaters in most such industrialized countries as Japan, the U.S.S.R., western Europe, and the United States. One-ninth of the total global catch comes from freshwaters, *i.e.,* around 6.4 million metric tons annually. More than two-thirds of this take is attributed to China. This corresponds to about one-sixth of the ocean fish catch used as human food. In addition there exists a widespread freshwater subsistence fishery, for which catch records are scanty. Its volume has been estimated at approximately the same figure or around six million tons. (All figures quoted are the annual average 1965–67.)

Fish cultivation is of far greater importance than freshwater fisheries, relatively speaking. This may best be illustrated with an example from East Germany. The "natural" waters yield about the same amount of fish in volume as the fish ponds, but the latter cover merely one-eleventh of the area of the natural waters. Pond yields are consequently as a rule higher per acreage unit. The annual yield of fish obtained through cultivation, in this strict sense of the term, amounts to about 700,000 metric tons with yields around 100 to 150 pounds per acre in temperate regions and two times that figure in the tropics. More than half of this cultivated fish is produced in China, which country has nearly half a million acres of fish ponds and thus has retained its global leadership in this field. The fish pond acreage of the Soviet Union is almost twice as large, but due to the northern location, the total yield is only one half that of China's. About one-third of all cultivated fish on earth is harvested from lagoons along the ocean coasts in Indonesia, the Philippines, and in the brackish Po delta of Italy and other places.

Fish cultivation is of crucial importance not only to China but in large parts of Southeast Asia and central Africa. In Hong Kong, for instance, it is much cheaper to raise fish in ponds than to invest in long-distance fishing, and in China fish-raising is an indispensible source of first-rate protein. Without this resource many millions would get an insufficient amount of protein in a country where the transportation of fish, be it by air, by rail, or by road, is still too complicated and costly. In the future a mounting number of millions will bless the raising of fish as the key to their survival.

Fish Conservation

For most parts of the world the primary task has been to safeguard the productivity of natural waters as food producers. This used to be true in pre-Columbian North America for all Indians living at fish-carrying waters. Salmon was the mainstay in Alaska and the Northwest.

On a world scale man has seriously jeopardized fish yields, and large-scale fish management has become a must. Such endeavors are pursued with increasing fervor and are rapidly becoming a matter of key importance as hundreds of millions of additional people demand their share of food. Protective measures thus are imperative, but so far the record of the industrialized world is rather miserable. Very few clear advances can be registered. Man has by and large been fighting a rear guard battle in this field of endeavor. We the well-fed have reconciled ourselves to this very fact and are mostly inclined to believe that these steps primarily favor sports fishing and serve to keep the fish biologists busy and happy.

China was the first empire in history that felt the damaging effects of population congestion upon water resources. It is undoubtedly no mere coincidence that China actually became the birthplace of fish cultivation. China also initiated large-scale utilization of natural waters for food production and developed methods for the hatching of fish eggs and the raising of fish fry as well as the collection of young fish during spawning seasons for home ponds. Through all these measures the foundation was laid for the monopoly China still enjoys in the exportation of fingerlings and young fish. She supplies, via Singapore, the entire Asiatic *lebensraum* with fish fry both for implantation in natural waters and for fish ponds.

For decades a lively debate has gone on among fish experts regarding the value of artificial stocking of fish. It was once looked upon as a rather self-evident cultivation measure comparable to the seeding of fields. This notion overlooked that the procreative capability of fish, the number of eggs laid by each female, is so enormous that the small contribution man can make is picayunish. Nature works with an extremely high waste percentage. The West has furthermore neglected a series of other factors, which the Chinese have so far felt very little, but which might become serious in that country's present industrialization drive. It is of little avail to plant young fish in waters which are so strongly polluted that the oxygen supply is too low to enable the fish to breathe. Such steps become even more futile if the waters are poisoned. Fish conservation is useless when the optimum ecological requirements are not met, let alone the basic conditions for simple survival. To this might be added that adverse biological factors other than man's chemicals and wastes might induce drastic cuts in the stock of some fish. To pursue a man-led implantation policy then becomes foolish obstinacy and is doomed under the strict ecological framework prevailing.

The Production Machinery of Lakes

Lakes and dams have a highly complicated production machinery. As in the oceans, the surface layers that are penetrated by light—the photic zone—determine wholly the productional capacity of fresh waters. It is in these layers that the planktonic algae via photosynthesis manufacture food. That portion of this basic feed which is not eaten by fish and other animals gradually reaches the bottom, either as a rain of dead organisms or via animals in undefined side links of the main food chains and via microorganisms reconverting this organic matter. Finally the living organisms on the bottom, benthos, are reached by the feed they need—literally "manna from heaven." This bottom fauna sustains fish. But the primary source is under all circumstances the organic matter formed via photosynthesis, taking place in a rather shallow surface layer. In a true sense this is the only productive part of the water—as in the sea (discussed in my previous book, *The Hungry Planet*). All life, even in lakes of great depth, thus depends on this life-supporting surface layer. Consequently,

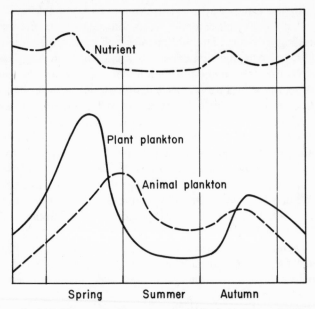

PLANKTON POPULATION IN TEMPERATE WATERS
(with nutrient fluctuations)

Fig. 43. Seasons in lakes. In the spring, lake waters of temperate regions
are well mixed. Nutrients are at a peak (top curve). Plant plankton spurts,
followed by a certain lag period caused by the upsurge of grazing tiny
crustaceans and other organisms such as animal plankton. In the fall, as the
thermocline breaks, new mixing occurs. A second increase then takes place
in the nutrient content of the photic layer, resulting in greater plant plankton growth.

bottom fish and deep-sea fish feed on what reaches them from
above or via predators. These complex relationships were known
to the Chinese of old, and they bred many types of carps, which
in the ponds could feed either from the excess reaching the bottom and feeding its fauna of benthic organisms, *e.g.*, worms, star-
fish, echinoderms, etc., or from what was available at different
levels, but primarily in the photic zone.

Modern fish cultivation has been forced to copy agriculture in one fundamental respect, fertilizing the waters. In shallow areas this boosts the production of aquatic plants such as grasses and seaweeds. But primarily the phytoplankton abounds, in turn affecting the zooplankton crop. The whole feed basis is thus enlarged. This improves coastal fish productivity as well as the production of bottom fish via benthos, in the way indicated above. Nevertheless, if this initial bloom of the phytoplankton is not matched with a corresponding expansion of the grazing animals, whether small or big, the balance is upset. This upsurge in phytoplankton raises the load of organic matter tremendously. If not consumed, it starts decomposing and its content of organic matter is released into the water. There it induces pollution and initiates fermentation. Instead of producing oxygen through photosynthesis, the surface layer starts consuming oxygen in order to eliminate this organic matter through decomposition. High fish mortality ensues. Man has toppled the producing machinery. This risk is particularly large in temperate regions, *i.e.,* the farther north or south of the equator, the slower the rate of growth and the less are the chances of rapid buildup of grazers. This is further the same mechanism that regularly upsets the balance in tropical waters, spurted through monsoon runoffs to water blooms from which mass mortality of fish ensues. The red tides in Florida waters and the Arabian Sea are caused by such processes.

Large-scale Mixing

In spring and fall, lakes of temperate regions experience a thorough water-mixing period, a kind of large-scale blending of otherwise highly stratified water. In fall, when the surface water cools down, it becomes heavier, reaching its peak in specific weight at 40°F (4°C). Water has many unique features, this being one, namely that of having its greatest density at such an odd point. This cooling above 40°F induces a downward movement of water. Conversely, a stratification is created when surface water is heated. This causes expansion and a reduced specific weight, separating the top layer from denser, colder water below through a so-called thermocline, a kind of temperature barrier. In spring the brief warming spell from 32°F (0°C) up to this critical point of 40°F (4°C) causes a corresponding but smaller downward movement of surface water, then becoming heavier than the water below.

The disappearance of the thermocline and the thorough mixing of all water are the clue to the explosive development that all living matter in temperate lakes exhibits in the spring, showing

SEASONAL TEMPERATURE CHANGES IN LAKES

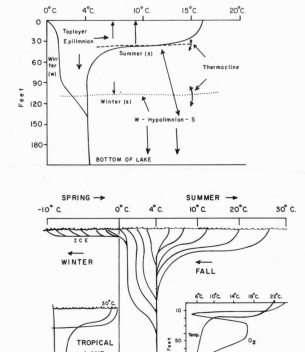

Fig. 44. The thermocline in lakes. As the water warms up in spring, a temperature discrepancy develops between a surface layer separated from a colder, more dense sublayer through a thermocline. This vanishes in the fall cooling. When lakes are deep, this discrepancy is in tropical regions almost permanent in character.

a sudden outburst of growth, initially in phytoplankton. This same favorable upwelling—a kind of major spring cleaning and rejuvenation process—does not take place in the lakes of the tropics. Here the surface layer rests all year round as a kind of lid on the colder, heavier water layer below. The exchange of matter between the two layers is quite restricted. Suggestions have been put forward to install huge pumping and mixing devices with the aim of breaking up this persistent thermocline, blocking regular interchange of water between the surface layer and the water below. Tests to this effect have given no conclusive results, and such methods are not economically justifiable.

Fish cultivation in warmer regions is mostly practiced in rather shallow dams where the water moves perpetually from the surface to the bottom. Due to the thermal stratification described above, deep tropical lakes are usually poor producers. For the same reason it is hard to obtain a reasonable level of production in big power dams located on warm latitudes. Production becomes limited to a rather shallow layer, blanketing the top surface and by and large stiffling active life in deeper layers.

Production Limitations

The production machinery of lakes reveals clearly the rather stringent limits set for organic production in water. In effect, the amount of soluble oxygen is the chief limiting factor in most waters. It is true that fish succumb in air on land, but it is equally true that an inadequate amount of oxygen in the aquatic environment stifles respiration and eliminates life through suffocation. Oxygen is required to allow fish and other aquatic animals to breathe, and its solubility in water is the factor that decides the upper limits for production. Any excess oxygen produced by the photosynthesis of the plants is lost to the atmosphere. In this light it becomes of paramount importance to create optimal conditions for oxygen production, and avoid conditions conducive to oxygen depletion through pollution due to an overloading of the waters with organic matter emanating from sewage or other waste.

Under scientifically controlled conditions, ponds in tropical and some temperate regions nevertheless yield more than tilled land when under intensive production. There are no indications that

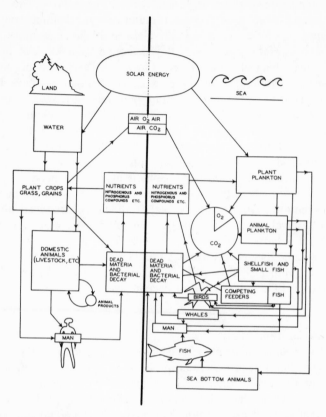

Fig. 45. Food chains in water are complex compared to those on land. Conditions in freshwaters resemble those of the oceans.

man can get much further than this. This might in one way be a blessing. If all factors adverse to productivity were eliminated, and a massive surplus of organic matter accumulated on land as well as in waters, global suffocation would gradually be the result. Man is here confronted with a highly important limitation, which almost has the character of a law of nature. Technical advances seem to have little chance to sidestep this limit.

There are other complications. The more ideal the cultivation conditions are in water, the more favorable are the conditions for the development of fungi and bacteria, many of which are deleterious to such aquatic food-producing organisms as fish and shellfish. Under these conditions fish diseases get good opportunities to abound. Man must prepare to meet this particular threat, and in order to do so, he is forced to keep up an unrelenting vigil, defending the frontiers for human existence. Fortunately, several fish species, especially carp, possess a protective mechanism of their own, so that when the microbial load of the water is at its peak—in temperate latitudes culminating as a general rule in late summer—the fish happens to exhibit the greatest resistance to these invaders. The carp is capable of immunizing himself. Diseases become a serious menace to the carp only when the lake and pond waters begin to get cold. As man in this way approaches the climatic limits for carp, maladies become difficult to keep under control in cultivated ponds. This is why the disease frequency mounts when moving farther into the Eurasian continent, the closer the ponds are located to the northern and eastern limit for fish cultivation.

Mineral Nutrients

Fish production is in many instances limited by the availability of mineral nutrients. This is actually already the case in the oceans but is still more conspicuous in inland waters. In lakes as well as rivers the mineral content of the waters and thereby the nutritional basis for the fish population is indirectly controlled by the mineral content of the adjacent soils, *i.e.,* their runoff.

The early floods of the Niger River are in the beginning very rich in nutrients, since the water, when it initially wells forward, is carrying along all the minerals collected in the runoff from stripped areas in the forest—together with nutrients from dung and other organic matter which have accumulated during the dry period and moved down in the rainy period. In the next stage the natural paucity of minerals in these soils becomes decisive. The Niger flows partly through regions of granite rock, which hardly yields any water-soluble nutrients at all. The fish catches from this river are correspondingly small.

Long stretches of the Amazon and its tributaries are naturally poor in nutrients due either to the lack of mineral salts in the surrounding rock or to its special structure, which does not release anything to the water. By and large it holds true that the richer the waterflow of rivers is in minerals, the higher is their productivity. But, as pointed out earlier, this does not necessarily mean that the productivity of fresh waters can be pushed further upward merely by fertilizing. The stage is soon reached when additional mineral nutrients only induce excessive plant production. Inland waters may easily become completely overgrown and thereby lose value as fish producers. They may not only become affected in a detrimental way through abnormal loads of organic matter, also a source of contamination, but when excessive, it accumulates on the bottom. Even the huge Great Lakes of North America are now in various stages of "dying" due to such overloading, causing oxygen depletion.

Large-scale Fertilization

In the postwar period it has been reported that most of the world's large rivers have fallen victim to a mass invasion of a floating flowering lilylike plant called water hyacinth. This plant, of South American origin, has been called the scourge of our days. It was discussed more fully in the chapter "Man's Competitors for Food." It might here be added that it has spread all around the warm belt of the globe. It raises havoc with the shipping on the Congo River, the Nile, the Magdalena, the Mississippi, and several other huge rivers. It is rather typical that in most places the water hyacinth is looked upon as a weed and attacked with chemicals. With this procedure large carpets of organic matter sink into the depth, where they gradually start fermenting, depleting oxygen resources.

This basic ecological relationship poses the question: What causes this excessive organic production? The spread of artificial fertilizing to tropical soils with their high degree of leaching has raised the influx of mineral matter (nutrients) to these natural waters. Extensive cutting of forests with ensuing denudation has magnified the runoff and its mineral content. All this is carried directly into the rivers, spurring plant growth. The massive development of water hyacinth as an aquatic pest is therefore most likely the indirect result of such development conditions. Modern transportation and increased mobility with a growing population have furthermore facilitated the spread of the pest from one waterway to another.

Several suggestions have been made about how to dispose of

this cumbersome weed, *e.g.*, employing it as hog feed. This would require harvesting operations on a major scale. Others have proposed the making of composts or the manufacture of methane gas to be used for fuel purposes. Finally, the proposal has been made to extract the protein from the leaves to be used as a food or possibly food supplement in hungry countries, largely located in these same general areas. All these operations would be quite costly; to raise fish or turtles on water hyacinth appears to be a more promising alternative.

Fish Cultivation

The only radical way of mastering the vagaries induced by man to natural waters and of obtaining a maximum of food production is in all likelihood to place fish production under planned management through direct cultivation. The Chinese probably found this out as early as 2000 B.C. A voluminous textbook on this subject, by an author named Fan-Li, was issued in the year 850 B.C.; the manuscript may still be seen in the British Museum of London.

Organized fish cultivation may be compared with the raising of livestock animals in agriculture. The misconception unfortunately prevails that the fish farmer produces from nothing. As long as a pond functions solely on the basis of what the light produces in the surface layer through photosynthesis, it is in principle operating as a natural water. Consequently it is also subject to the same limitations with regard to productivity. It is, however, possible to go one step further in ponds than in lakes: regulate the size of the fish stocks. If the level of the primary productivity of the water is elevated by fertilizing, the number of fish can be artificially adjusted from hatcheries or propagation ponds, and it becomes possible to utilize at a maximum the green matter produced.

As the Chinese also discovered quite early, it is possible to implant different species of fish in the same pond, if they are so chosen as to depend on different categories of available feed. This is accomplished by avoiding too heavy competition and by selecting species which concentrate on feed available at different depths of the pond. This is called multilevel fish-cropping. There may be one species that feeds upon the plankton in the photic surface layer, another that grazes along the rims of the pond, and finally bottom species which get their nourishment from that which precipitates through the water via bottom organisms feeding on such debris. Whatever measures are taken in order to obtain maximum production, a surplus of nutrients finally accumulates on the bottom. In most ponds higher productivity therefore results, if they are drained intermittently and allowed to dry. A mineralization of the nutritive matter on the bottom then takes place so that, when the pond is subsequently refilled, this emerges in the water as mineral nutrients, boosting production.

Carp

In the history of fish cultivation two species have played such an important role that they may be categorized as livestock animals. Carp is one, the other is tilapia. In some regions ide is raised, but not as commonly. Carp appears in several species and subspecies, of which the Chinese have bred the majority. Carp cultivation is presumed to have emerged originally as a sideline to silkworm production. The cocoons and other waste from the raising of these worms were used as feed. The Chinese not only taught the cultivation of carp to the Japanese but spread the techniques over Southeast Asia. It never seems to have reached India, a fact of particular historical significance. Yet large-scale cultivation of carp was common in Europe in the Middle Ages, primarily in the monasteries, which were on the whole centers of advanced food production. The first carp ponds appear to have been located in Poland. The Soviet planners, despite the promotion of deep-sea fishing on a large scale, count increasingly on carp as a locally available cheap fish. The raising of carp is flourishing all the way from central Europe deep into Siberia. As in animal husbandry on land, a constant battle is raging against diseases, in particular belly-burn, a common bacterial disease. It is difficult to keep under control at the northern climatic boundary for the carp, and it often gets the upper hand in the ponds. Under these strenuous conditions carp are far more susceptible than otherwise. Man is here confronted with another limit. Despite the use of a considerable arsenal of antibiotics and other chemicals, he has to fight rather hard to protect his carp at these northernmost latitudes.

Tilapia

Tilapia may be said to be one of the few new domesticated animals which man has acquired in modern times. This fish and its prolific nature reportedly was discovered during the Second World War in Africa. Biologists noticed its rapid growth and its abundance in some African lakes. It was later established that tilapia was well suited for mass cultivation. Today there are thousands of tilapia ponds in the Republic of Congo, in the whole of East Africa, on Madagascar, in India, Ceylon, and Indonesia, and in the central American republics. Tilapia renders valuable protein food for millions of people; how many depends on how the estimate is made, but probably in the range of ten million. The carp without question provides protein for ten times as many people.

Other Cultivation

Oyster and clam cultivation has been known since far back. The cultivation of certain mountain snails (French: *escargots*) is a central European specialty for vineyards. These activities also date back to the monasteries of the Middle Ages. A new accomplishment, however, is the raising of shrimp in China and Japan. In special hatcheries the young ones (two million eggs from each female) are released into tanks of special construction for feeding and growth. Japan has a great number of shrimperies in operation. The goal is an annual production of 2,000 metric tons.

Japan has no less than 760 eel farms, a further development of the cultivation of this fish by the Moors in Albufera's wet rice fields near Valencia in Spain. The Japanese also raise salmon, trout, ayu, and carp. Furthermore Japan has, like the United States, establishments for the raising of edible frogs. Soft-shell turtles, in Japanese *suppon*, are raised in six establishments as a culinary specialty.

Mariculture

The production of the oceans was, as mentioned above, discussed in my previous book, *The Hungry Planet*. Nevertheless, a word should be said about the new forms of marine fish cultivation currently being developed in Japan, the U.S.S.R., China, and elsewhere.

Concerted efforts are being made to extend cultivation from coastal lagoons to large-scale sea-farming. So far only initial steps have been taken on this intricate road to realization of the great vision of cultivating the ocean expanses in a way comparable to that practiced in agriculture on land—mariculture or aquaculture. Primarily this could be a kind of animal husbandry involving grazing herds of turtles, sea cows, and whales.

The key operations in mariculture would be huge pens in which fish populations are raised and given supplementary feed, treated against diseases, and protected against predators or competitors. One important step toward this visionary goal has been the inculcation in fish of conditioned reflexes as they gather on sonic impulses for feeding. This has been accomplished with cod by Soviet scientists (at the Murman Coast) and with trout by the Japanese (in the Inland Sea).

The way, however, is long to such controlled sea-farming. Reducing the living space and operational sphere for such fish is further conducive to an easy spread of diseases. To halt contamination and control diseases therefore becomes a major task when living conditions, through these procedures, get congested.

In 1966 the United Kingdom resumed its experimentation, first begun during World War II, with the raising of flatfish in Scottish fjords closed off for this purpose. They are stocked with young fish and the waters are fertilized. Growth is considerably enhanced, but an accumulation of phosphate and organic matter takes place on the sea bottom. No results from the recent studies are available. This kind of mariculture resembles the lagoon cultivation of Italy and the tabak ponds for milkfish in Indonesia and the Philippines.

Feeding

To achieve through cultivation additional production of real significance for the feeding of the urban millions, one has to take a step beyond the productivity limitations set by nature and supply additional feed in the same way as is done in animal husbandry. Fish as livestock then immediately becomes a more doubtful proposition. So far man has not found fish species that can compete with poultry and hogs in conversion efficiency of feed. In other words it costs much more to produce the same amount of protein via fish. Such production pays off only under one condition, namely when the feed is cheap and can not be used by land animals. It never pays to feed fish flour and oilseed cakes to carp. High fish yields per hectare are therefore sometimes drastically reduced when the "ghost acreage" required to produce the feed that is utilized is taken into account. Only genuine waste utilization is profitable. Normally it does not pay to raise crops on agricultural land to be used for fish farming. This has been tried in various places on the globe with poor economic return. In the chapter "Food and Microorganisms" the utilization of sewage and other city waste in the raising of fish was discussed. In this case the feed is obtained at low cost and also in concentrated form. Besides, transportation is already paid. Alternate ways to use the waste profitably are furthermore quite limited—one possibility could be for insect farms (*cf.* p. 282).

One of the reasons that Southeast Asia holds the world record in yields from fish ponds is the fact that various Chinese carps are being used together with the leaf-eating species *gourami,* the latter a phytophagous (plant-eating) fish with good conversion efficiency. Banana leaves, discarded tea leaves, and many kinds of waste from the jungle go into these ponds and are directly consumed by the fish. Congolese tilapia dams have registered record yields even surpassing five metric tons of fish per hectare, but this species shows one of the best conversion factors in existence. Almost anything is converted into fish flesh, such as leaf wastes, coffee residues, flour mill dockage, spent brewery yeast and malt, oilseed cakes, etc. Tilapia feeds uninterruptedly all year round in the warm climate. The limitations set by climate may be most clearly illustrated by the fact that a five-hectare fish farm in the tropics is looked upon as large and yields almost as much under intense cultivation as a ten times larger fish farm located in temperate regions.

The Marauders of Fish Cultivation

The ingenious combination of rice cultivation and fish raising practiced by the Chinese and Southeast Asians for centuries is often presented as well worth copying. By and large this system functions quite well, and it has been successfully introduced in the rice paddies of Arkansas. But the difficulties are rarely mentioned in these writings. Many rice paddies in Southeast Asia and India are infested by both sea and land crabs, which operate in quite a devastating way, especially during the young stages of the rice plants. The crabs themselves drill into the walls of the dams and cause rapid deterioration and serious damage. In Burma the crab menace is so serious that the replanting of rice has to be postponed until the marauders depart for the sea after spawning in the end of July. Efforts to eradicate these pests have so far been of little avail despite energetic tries.

The raising of fish in rice fields has entered into a new, almost critical phase, due to the urgent need of maximizing rice yields, which makes spraying against insects and fungi almost indispensable. This spraying excludes fish-raising because of the toxicity of the chemicals used. Such joint cultivation has been practiced in Japan for centuries, but it is now reportedly vanishing for this very reason. Nevertheless, treatises and popular reviews elaborate on the enormous potentialities of rice fields for fish-raising and on the advisability of introducing the age-old Chinese and Japanese procedures to all rice-growing areas. Millions of tons of fish are anticipated, but it is not always recognized that only one-third of the world's total rice fields are paddies sown with wet-land rice— and it is only in such rice fields that fish can be cultivated.

A Soviet book devoted to the damage and havoc created by birds attacking fish populations, particularly when concentrated in dams and ponds, also contains a special chapter on a species of cormorants the Chinese and Japanese have trained to fish in lamplight at night. A ring is fastened around the neck so the birds cannot swallow their prey. These fisheries are not very productive. But this cormorant is not the only bird that specializes in using fish as feed. Seagulls, other cormorants, and several other species do the same thing.

Birds sometimes constitute a menace to fish populations in lakes and rivers. But it becomes much more serious in the case of pond cultivation, where the fish stock is much denser. The economic losses may reach considerable proportions, and eradication of this additional group of man's competitors may become necessary in the future. The higher man pushes yields, *i.e.,* the more lavish tables he spreads in nature, the more serious the attacks that can be expected from his competitors, another limitation to which a special chapter, "Man's Competitors for Food," is devoted in this book.

A great deal has been written not only about how man taps and pollutes natural waters but also how he creates new waters by such means as storage dams for hydroelectric plants and for irrigation. In particular, Soviet fishing journals have carried numerous visionary articles about the large quantities of fish that would result from exploiting fully more than five million hectares (12.5 million acres) of huge dam reservoirs of various types. Several such dams have been created in the U.S.S.R. since World War II ended. Some of them have almost been looked upon as high-producing fish ponds. Their depth, however, is the first major obstacle to a complete utilization of these water volumes. To introduce life to all levels of these man-made lakes has proven quite difficult. In addition such estimates generally disregard the fact that the productivity of the dams in most cases is highly limited, due to the cold environments in many northern locations. Only during a few weeks annually do light and temperatures allow a reasonable growth of the primary producers, *e.g.,* algae in the latitudes of Siberia. United States experiences, though on a minor scale, confirm the extent of these hindrances.

Hogs, Ducks, and Fish

The artificial dams built for the conversion of urban waste and sewage into food fish in several Soviet and East German cities constitute a more realistic approach. Even in this case the climate soon raises concrete obstacles in the north. A century before William the Conqueror landed on the English coast (1066), the city of Angkor stood in all its splendor as the capital and center of the Khmer empire in Southeast Asia. The impressive marble palaces, which still stand as ruins in the virgin forest of Cambodia, were surrounded by a system of fish ponds. All waste was utilized and converted into food fish. Costly transportation was superfluous, and the protein needs of the population were met. The calories were largely produced in the surrounding rice paddies. This ideal recycling can still serve as an example for us to follow.

We can foresee the day when the large sewage treatment plants that serve the rapidly growing cities will become huge centers for food production. Sewage constitutes a much too valuable raw material to be discarded, dumped, or burned; still less acceptable is diluting it with water by using lakes and rivers as recipients. Most likely, sewage will in the future be fed into huge algal factories. The algae may be utilized as animal feed, but a simpler way is to produce protein by cultivating yeast and fungi, employing the algae as substrate. Both yeast and algae, however, may serve fish-raising directly, also in combination with duck raising. This is an old Chinese method which is currently being successfully employed in the U.S.S.R. and East Germany. Fish cultivation in combination with hog raising, practiced on some United States farms, is also of Chinese origin. The hog sheds are built so that they hang over the rim of the dam and the droppings fall directly into the dam, fertilizing the water. It is important that not too many hogs are kept for each dam, otherwise the water easily becomes overloaded, causing imbalance disturbances. In Thailand poultry pens are constructed in a similar way, and the nutrient-rich droppings go directly into the cycle and yield new food.

This kind of direct conversion may require considerable sanitary precautions when practiced on a very large scale. It is essential that such future recycling centers of our spaceship Earth do not become focuses for the propagation and spread of epidemics. Much study is needed to avert this calamity.

Conclusion

In conclusion, the aquatic resources of the globe will increasingly be mobilized to provide for the ever expanding human race. The key role played by marine and freshwater fish and shellfish in several important areas of the world as a cheap and superior source of protein will undoubtedly be further exploited. The great postwar mobilization of the oceans, however, has by and large bypassed the hungry world to serve almost exclusively the well fed. A mounting percentage of the increasing harvests of the oceans have moved to bolster the menu of the well fed. Freshwater management and fish cultivation is by and large a substitute operation, used when, almost in despair, the developed countries resort to a last ditch effort, either to salvage these waters from destruction and death or to create, through major investments, substitute waters for exploitation in the form of cultivation ponds and hatcheries. They also may utilize man-created dams, whenever they are shielded from these polluting forces.

Lack of vision and clear awareness of the frightening imbalances created by man characterize most planning in this field. Ambulance services and relief projects are ruling the scene of fish and water management. It is high time we start tackling the crucial recycling needs through a new creative technology coupled with fortuitous action. The backlog is formidable. In all seriousness, our civilization might otherwise join the cavalcade of civilizations which collapsed due to overwhelming waste whether in the shape of salt on the soils or of organics in human settlements. This is indeed our true Achilles heel—our real weak spot.

CHAPTER XII

Tomorrow's Dinner

Algal soup, wood-based steaks, candied insects, grass pudding, and plankton paste are some of the many delicacies that science writers and various categories of specialists propose to put on the future menu of mankind when in ever-increasing millions it flocks around the food kettles. With such exotic items one plans to feed the hungry. We Westerners are hardly ever seriously considered as customers for these foods, unless in emergencies, at any rate not for several generations to come.

What are the realities behind these brain children? Do they actually constitute serious alternatives to such of today's key foods as rice, wheat, potatoes, beans, milk, meat, eggs, and fish? Is the situation so critical that man has to prey upon everything living in order to survive as throughout history many primitive peoples have been forced to do? Indigenous tribes in New Guinea, the Amazonas, and in several regions of tropical Africa are still today eating almost everything living on which they can lay their hands. Bitter experience has taught them what is toxic or they have learned to avoid hazards, *i.e.*, how to remove or eliminate poisonous ingredients. They eat all kinds of seeds, fruits, nuts, and leaves. Locusts are looked upon as godsends. With hearty appetite, termites, ants, and insect larvae are gulped down, not to speak of such more substantial animals as serpents and lizards or the poachers' booty of meat from hippos, elephants, etc.

The Green Leaves

But let us return to the menu of the future as described earlier. Knowing that domesticated animals in certain respects are man's greatest competitors by sapping large acreages of tilled land and pastures, the vegetarians are not the only ones who propound the enormous saving that would accrue to the world household if these competitors of ours were eradicated and all of mankind became 100 percent vegetarians. Literally spoken, the idea is that man, like Nebuchadnezzar's soldiers in the Bible, should start eating the grass of the fields directly, and this for the dubious pleasure of providing space at our eating tables for still more billions.

I have eaten grass pudding, and certainly it is acceptable food—particularly when prepared from young grass. It may then even be quite tasty and flavorsome. The notion behind this is that man cannot afford to give such young grass to his livestock but is forced to eat it himself. It is therefore envisioned that man attack plants and trees, and like locust-swarms or tree-climbing goats, gather everything that is green. Leaves and all should then be brought to huge conversion factories, where through ingenious processes the green cells will be divested of their protein, fats, and other nutritive substances. The resulting pulp or brew can be converted into greenish powder or made into plant milks.

This reveals our dilemma as in a lightning flash. The nutritive riches of the plant kingdom are not accessible for uptake in the human tract without previous processing of a rather profound nature. The plant cell in general is well encased within a wall of cellulose and other substances, which is impenetrable to our gastric juices. The contents of the plant cell are in other words shielded. Early in the history of man primitive methods were discovered and developed for the unlocking of the plant tissue, *e.g.,* through parching, toasting or grinding of the grain seed. The cell walls may also be broken down through various kinds of fermentation. Only in a few such plant products as juicy fruits can man through chewing lay bare the nutritive contents of the cell.

Several thousands of years ago the Chinese saw their salvation in the soybean and devised a series of procedures for making milk and several types of curds from this plant. They were also clever enough to enhance its nutritive value by a kind of cultural enrichment through germination or by boiling, toasting, parching, drying, and fermentation. Thereby the plant cells were opened, or literally, burst open in order to make the nutritive ingredients of the cell content accessible to the gastric juices. Not only did the soybean products become readily digestible but numerous deleterious substances were in addition removed or eliminated.

When the world press recently described to astounded readers how milk is made of various plant products with an ingenious device, the mechanical cow, this was actually not news. It was merely a variant of an invention many thousand years old. The cembra pines of Siberia, mentioned in the chapter "The Forest and the Field in an Ominous Confrontation," produce a couple of million tons of seed annually in the cones. These pine seeds constitute important nutrition to the wild animals of the taiga (the Siberian forest belt), but the seeds are also collected on a massive scale each fall to be used as human food during the winter. The Navajo Indians of the United States Southwest in a similar way collect piñole seed from another needle tree among the conifers. Like the Chinese before them with soybean, certain Siberian people early knew how to produce milk from cembra seeds through various pulping, grinding, and boiling procedures.

A Radical Shift

There exists no doubt that we are moving further along the road to mobilization of the plant kingdom and that we will find ways to utilize its riches more efficiently. But this will change nothing in the great indebtedness to the ruminants in which man stands. As pointed out in the chapter "Food and Microorganisms," the rumen is actually a miracle factory where hundreds of fascinating processes take place which are prerequisites to the transformation of the feed and the making of milk and also for supplementation of the feed. Through the ruminants man has incorporated into his biosphere—*i.e.,* his operational realm—vast areas of the globe from which agricultural techniques had been incapable of extracting food through direct cultivation, and where the prospects of doing so in the immediate future seem scanty. If the humans in a distant future were to be fed exclusively on variations of grass pudding, and this by a direct harvesting of leaves and grass, and thus no longer, as now, via milk, cheese, meat, etc., such a revolutionary change would still not hold the promise of feeding very many more billions. Quite apart from the enormous investments that would be required to build the appropriate conversion factories, in effect gigantic in size, such plants are less likely to function with 100 percent efficiency. To date this has not been feasible in any chemical industry operation. Even if we could achieve the feat of saving three-fourths of the nutritive values in the raw material, only five to eight additional billions would be cared for, *i.e.,* a total of eight to eleven billion. World population will reach such proportions around the middle of the twenty-first century if we do not apply the brakes immediately. If the pastures were harvested annually and in addition several times a year in order to yield young, protein-rich material, the plants would become weakened. There is little likelihood that the pastures of the future would stand such a large-scale attack. In such a case they would furthermore be deprived of all cattle manure, and we would have to rely on commercial fertilizers.

Wild nature, its forests and grasslands, fare badly when the animals become too many. Only a few elephants and hippopotamuses can be fed per square mile. They go forth like huge bulldozers in nature, each animal eating per day half a metric ton of plant matter, and still their manure is returned to the circulation in the soil, the rivers, and the lakes. If the hippos are eradicated, as actually has happened in several regions of tropical Africa, fish production decreases in adjacent waters where he used to relax and defecate. The hippo is in other words a key link in the continuous transfer of organic matter from land to water.

Seaweed

Along the coasts of many continents shallow shelf areas are found where bottom-anchored seaweed grows. These plants have also been eyed as ingredients in the menu of the future and saviors of mankind. The idea has been presented that seaweed should be utilized in the form of flour to be added to bread, or prepared in the Japanese way as dried leaves, or used in special dishes, sometimes fermented. These devices are commonly described as new inventions. As a matter of fact these big plants of the oceans were used as food early in the history of mankind. The Japanese, the Chinese, and the Siamese have even gone one step further and started cultivation of certain species. The average Japanese diet in bulk weight consists of no less than one-tenth of such seaweed products. But if such food is going to be more than a piquant condiment or a source of certain mineral trace elements or key vitamins (such as B_6 and B_{12}) and actually deliver bulk food in the form of carbohydrates, fat, or protein, extensive processing is needed, such as drying, powderizing, fermentation, etc. Seaweed shares with other plants the feature of having cell walls impenetrable to man's digestive juices. There is furthermore no indication that the pastures of the oceans, even with the aid of human magic tricks, will render more food than the land surface does, and under much more complicated circumstances.

Plankton Soup

Knowing that the land surface is limited and that the plant cover cannot endure unlimited stress, caused by intensified exploitation, man has turned his eyes to the sea. Its resources seem limitless. Its vast pastures consist of microscopic plants, called phytoplankton, a drifting flora. These are grazed by such tiny animals as crustaceans and others. This is the zooplankton. In the next link of the lengthy feeding chains of the oceans these swarms of small animal creatures sustain many fish and other animal life. Plankton is thus at the base of the production pyramid in the oceans. At each conversion stage considerable losses are incurred. It has therefore been advocated as a smart move for man to harvest and eat plankton, thus becoming a marine vegetarian.

This idea, which is often seriously launched as a way out in mankind's food predicament, is, however, essentially a fallacy. Phytoplankton in effect holds little promise of becoming a suitable, or much less a cheap, food for mankind. It can hardly even be counted upon as feed on any major scale. Plankton soup, even if we should drink it directly from the sea, is paradoxically enough quite indigestible food to man and not entirely safe. Although tiny, these plants share with other plant cells the hindrance of the cell walls. Man's gastric juices are not equipped to break them down. This has to be done through processing, *e.g.,* fine grinding or enzymatic hydrolysis.

The tiny shrimp and other crustaceans called zooplankton are in contrast good food. Their flesh protein is fully comparable to that of normal-sized shrimp and lobster. In some coastal regions off India and Southeast Asia, particularly Burma, such planktonic shrimp (in the form of mysids) are sufficiently abundant to allow a regular catch, which in turn is converted through fermentation into a kind of shrimp paste, which is preserved effectively with salt.

The oceans do not merely carry lush pastures of flourishing plant plankton. There are in the vast seas, figuratively speaking, also deserts and steppes, when judged from the production of organic plant matter per square mile. In other words plankton appears in a rather patchy abundance, determined by the interplay of a multitude of environmental factors.

Even under ideal conditions one would have to strain a water volume about sixty times as large as an ordinary classroom (for thirty pupils) in order to get a quantity of food, corresponding in terms of nutrition to the caloric content of a pound of beans. Furthermore, one would have to be constantly on guard against plankton species which are poisonous to man, not the least among these the species that abound in blooms.

Plankton has a short life-span. It is quickly eaten by other organisms in the sea or dies. Therefore the living mass of the more edible zooplankton within a given area and at a certain point in time is rather limited. The total production per year exceeds by far the increase in fish, but the standing stock available at each moment of harvest is far less than that of fish. Most fish species have a life-span of several years, but many kinds of plankton are either consumed or finish their life cycle within a few days or weeks. An example may illuminate these intricate relationships. From the North Sea about fifty to sixty metric tons of herring are taken in good years per hundred hours of catching efforts. To obtain the same amount of plankton, one would have to strain approximately sixty million tons of North Sea water! This may not be an impressive part of the North Sea water, but it indicates the immense operation that would be involved in feeding man from such sources, even when they are considered rich.

It would be much cleverer to look for new livestock in the seas, which know how to utilize plankton as well as other aquatic plants efficiently. The green sea turtle played within historical times a key role in the Caribbean and elsewhere in warm regions as food to the Caribbean Indians, almost what the bison was to the prairie Indians. These turtles—in earlier times found elsewhere in warm regions also—are ideal grazers. So is the manatee, the sea cow. These are only two alternatives among several others but with good prospects of success.

The whale has the greatest potential. But man has done his best to eradicate the whale in a globe-spanning endeavor. Yankee whalers were all-dominating in the middle of the nineteenth century and jeopardized the stock in the Atlantic, but still more in the western and North Pacific. More than 700 of the world's 800 whalers were then American. For centuries whales have been chased and captured: by the Basques, the Chinese and Japanese, and most people on the ocean brink. But the peak carnage came in the nineteenth century. The Pennsylvania discovery of mineral oil and the Civil War put an end to this American phase. The Norwegians followed in this tremendous onslaught now directed toward the untapped resources of the North Atlantic. When these herds collapsed, the full force of modern technology was mobilized in the great Antarctic adventure, but it appears in these very days that it is in its final phase. The tragedy seems fulfilled in the imminent vanishing of the blue whale—and many other species that have been viciously hunted may follow them into extinction. The blue whale mother, weighing 75 to 100 tons, converts daily 2 to 2.5 tons of rich crustacean zooplankton, krill, into milk for its suckling baby, growing at 170 to 200 pounds per twenty-four hours. When realizing the magnitude of this remarkable production miracle, we discover the width of man's recklessness and lack of foresight. We may well then pose the probing question: Will man ever be capable of competing with the whales as a krill-catcher and krill-converter?

Whale meat and whale oil—in this century used as raw material for the manufacture of margarine—are first-rate human food. Particularly whale meat is described as a delicacy for our future menu, forgetting that people living in greater parsimony than we have been eating whale meat for centuries. Nature may as it seems hit back and deprive us in a terminal way of this source of meat. Some take consolation in the hope that such other animals as seals or dolphins may move in to indulge in the krill feasts the Antarctic offers. Others revel in depicting the delectable "shrimp" soups technology will offer man, and in abundance, when bypassing a wasteful conversion into meat and fat. Both alternatives are little attractive when one starts formulating the logistics involved in catching 80 to 100 seals in lieu of one single whale or the endless hours of "krilling," with returns far less rewarding than what the whale sieved out when open-mouthedly panting through the plankton soup of the Antarctic—renowned for its ferocious gales and unpleasant temperatures. Man taking the place of the whale in providing for himself is certainly not in an enviable position—it would rather be an act of despair. Undoubtedly mankind would have been far better advised if in time it had diverted its ingenuity and resourcefulness to the domestication of the whales.

On the whole it is remarkable that in spite of modern genetics developed into plant and animal breeding, so few additions have been made to the list of plants and animals that provide food to man. It is questionable if man during the last two thousand years has domesticated one single new animal on land.[1] He has added very few new crop plants.

The Recycling on Earth

There is essentially only one way that holds promise for truly additional gains for mankind, and that is better utilization of our resources together with recycling of the mounting wastes of our spaceship Earth. Two previous chapters, "Food and Microorganisms" and "Better Utilization of World Food Resources," deal with these contributions to the future menu, which will gradually emerge when mankind, due to population pressure, is forced to recycle the sewage and other waste from the human society to greater advantage. The utilization of yeast from breweries or the waste from food processing plants, residues from flour mills, etc., will be other additional sources of food. The nutritive riches of

---

[1] It has just been reported that domestication has been successful for the African eland and the Soviet taiga antelope.

presscakes from oilseed plants, and recovery of protein from whey and skim milk are other key areas for urgent action.

In this context I will not elaborate on the manufacture of wholly synthetic foods. This is reviewed in the chapter "Will Chemistry Offer Mankind the Third Freedom?" The conclusion reached in this respect was that it is highly unlikely that such food will ever amount to more than a modest supplement and consequently will not significantly ease the food worries of mankind, save in a temporary way. It is finally also a poor prospect for the world to depend on microbial farms. It was possibly acceptable to war-harried Nazi Germany to squeeze fat from diatoms and yeasts, grown in hothouses at exorbitant costs and rendering food with considerable nutritional drawbacks, but it cannot be considered a valid solution to a human race, currently adding almost a billion per decade.

No, it is on a much more central place in the machinery of a modern technical society that man will have to concentrate his efforts, namely in converting his wastes into food, thereby accelerating the rate of the recycling process. It is at this very point that modern technology and the civilization it has created exhibit a conspicuous blind spot and both can positively be accused of having gone astray. We devote singular detailed interest to arranging for the recycling processes in space vehicles but close our eyes almost completely to the recycling needs of our own spaceship, Earth. At the best we make an effort to render the stinking city sewage innocuous, but by and large man has failed even in this very limited task. We have neglected the very key need of re-converting all this waste into useful commodities, primarily food and feed.

The growing dimensions of the pollution problem should serve as a serious reminder to everyone of this crisis. Even the most flourishing countries have not kept pace in economic terms with this phase of their alleged progress. The backlog in sewage plants in the United States currently has an investment magnitude of 50 to 70 billion dollars needed to adequately take care of the present sewage and waste from cities and other population centers. Another 10 to 15 billion dollars is required to treat the additional quantities of waste that are expected to arise from sewage systems and industrial plants during the next ten to fifteen years.

As was pointed out earlier, the sewage plants will have to become food industries in the future. That will be part of the price we will be forced to pay for the pleasure of living in an over-populated world, increasingly plagued by congestion and having long ago passed all reasonable boundaries. Those who are horrified at this inevitable development should realize that hundreds of thousands of homes on both sides of the North Atlantic are drinking water from the faucet which only a few days earlier was flushed through the toilet of some neighbor. The waterworks already have to function with raw materials which are nothing but waste water. In the same way the tremendous quantities of city sewage, rich in nutrients, should be looked upon as a raw material and not as a troublesome by-product which we have to get rid of at exorbitant costs; yet, this is presently done so ineffectively that we are jeopardizing public health and completely ignoring all social comfort.

The Tubifex Miracle

Forward-looking engineers and food scientists early saw the necessity for more constructive and long-range solutions and envisioned the transformation of the sewage plants into food-producing entities, which in addition would have the advantage of reclaiming water. No less than one-third of the total United States consumption of water flows into the sewage systems. In Munich, Germany, in Brno (formerly Brünn), Czechoslovakia, in Melbourne, Australia, and many other places the sewage is utilized for large-scale irrigation of agricultural lands. Each one of these cities point with some pride to the thousands of cattle and sheep and the high acre-yields for vegetables which have resulted from this kind of simple direct recycling. Hog-raising based on food waste, prevalent around many cities of Scandinavia and western Europe, is another similar example. This pattern was actually initiated by the old Chinese economic order, where the hog played the key role of a scavenger and converted human and other waste into food.

Fish cultivation is still another method, also employed by the Chinese long ago, to solve this central recycling issue, thereby pointing the way to a balanced, productive society. Alternate recycling solutions along biological lines are presented in the chapter "Lakes and Dams for Fish Cultivation," underlining the cultivation of fish, frequently in combination with other kinds of animal-raising. The method applied in many parts of Southeast Asia is particularly fascinating. Young fish are lowered in cages directly into sewage-carrying rivers. They reach marketable size very quickly. Sanitary risks have in general proved surprisingly small. The key to this short-circuit of the biological recycling chain seems to be that the upper nutrition-rich water layer conjures up a dense bottom forest of oligochaetes larvae of the *Tubifex* genus. This "living" pasture is persistently grazed by the fish as these worms, fixed to the bottom, grow up and penetrate the bottom mesh of the suspended cages.

Yeast Factories

By combining sewage plants with large establishments for algae cultivation considerable quantities of feed could be produced. Such algae can be dried and added to animal feed, but may also be utilized for yeast production. This yeast could in turn be used for direct supplementation of human food. There are yeast strains specialized in producing either fat or protein. These may be selected at will, depending on the most pressing needs. Many yeast factories in different parts of the world are based on such other kinds of waste as that from paper mills (sulfite waste), wood residues, molasses from sugar beets or sugar cane, etc. Yeast produced in such ways is already utilized locally in the United States to enrich a series of food products, *e.g.,* sausages, soups, and stews. In places like Taiwan, the West Indies, and many others, such yeast also serves to supplement the protein of inadequate diets. Yeast itself is not a particularly first-rate food, but as a supplement it holds its position well. A new factory in Taiwan produces about two hundred metric tons daily. But it is quite typical that the lion's share of its production is exported to the United States. There is no reason for limiting this kind of manufacture to yeast fungi. It is well known how to mass-produce several other fungi in nutrient solutions: aside from champignons, also morels, cantarels, and many others. Thus a whole new range of economic crops are gradually gaining a foothold, none as yet banishing hunger, but they might in the future be essential ingredients in man's subsistence.

Algal Cultivation

Cultivation of algae as a basis for the reconversion of sewage into food is a much more realistic proposition than investing in independent cultivation units for algae. The Japanese are most advanced in the field of mass-cultivating unicellular algae, but although they are running a pilot-scale plant of this kind, so far no product has been obtained which is wholly acceptable from a nutritive point of view. The head of the Japanese Public Health Institute informed us about the disappointments in this field at the Tenth Pacific Science Congress in 1961 and there are no new basic developments since then. Rarely ever has so much been written about so little.

As a matter of fact algae do not constitute good human food.

Fig. 46. A designer's vision of a factory installation continuously producing algae

Even if the prerequisites for cultivation are simple, algae remains a questionable and rather expensive product. Furthermore it has poor keeping qualities, even after processing. As an intermediary link in a sewage plant, or under the most favorable circumstances, as feed for domesticated animals, however, algae may defend their place. Even long-distance travelers in spaceships are now, according to latest reports, going to be saved from a dubious algal diet. Instead they will use the algae for the raising of fish or quail, grown as well as processed on board.

In popular terms the developments described here have been presented as man's mobilization of the microorganisms in the form of fungi and bacteria as livestock. But these, our presumptive new helpers, are—as put forth in the chapter "Food and Microorganisms"—by no means magicians creating from nothing. They too must have raw material as feed, and only large modern cities concentrate enough material to be able to profit from their phenomenal capabilities. This is an additional reason for the key position sewage plants will hold in future food production. Furthermore they offer a chance to bypass the crippling and costly seasonality of agriculture, and consequently allow a short-circuiting of the nutritive cycles so that waste is reconverted to food for man within a time lapse shorter than a year.

Insects

In this context there is all reason to underline the fact that ultimately the insects constitute the foremost menace to man and his position as a master of the globe. In the light of this surprising fact one may very well pose the probing question: How is it to be explained that this large animal group, which is so diversified, productive, and fast-growing, only occasionally has been subject to planned breeding and mass production for food purposes? We know that several groups of insects have a high nutritive value and that many peoples throughout the centuries have resorted to insects as food. The Japanese dry and salt cockroaches and grind them to a fine powder, which is sprinkled on rice as a nutritive supplement. The Mexicans dry the eggs of large water beetles and use them as an important ingredient in cookies. These eggs are sold by the pound in the markets. A dish of prepared crickets is a highly estimated meal on several West Indian Islands. Canned chocolate-coated locusts are found on the delicatessen shelves in United States supermarkets. Any number of examples can be given of insects used as food. Their nutritive value is evident from the fact that it is possible to fatten both turkeys and hogs on insects as feed. Two-thirds of all birds on earth are estimated to live from insects. Surveys in the state of Illinois have shown that two-fifths of the feed consumed by the freshwater fish consists of insects. The cocoons of the silk worm are first-rate feed for carp, other pond-fish, and turtles, according to centuries of experience gained in China and Japan.

This does not necessarily imply that we will have to eat maggots, grasshoppers, and other insects dipped in butter or honey, but they could perhaps be converted into cheap fat or protein to be added to bread, soups, etc. Insect breeding establishments might very well become a branch of the huge transforming and converting centers for food which in the future will be part of every major metropolis around the globe.

With a few exceptions, snails have also been overlooked as a food resource, despite the fact that several gastropods are well known as edible. Even quite delicious species are found in this group, such as the French vineyard snail, *escargot*. But snails may also emerge as our helpers in the large visionary sewage farms of future cities.

Dietary Prejudices

In the Western world we are inclined to play up all kinds of taboos, dietary patterns or religious prescriptions, superstitious or not, which supposedly impede or even prevent the consumption of certain foods in various regions. There are innumerable examples of such food prejudices as the aversion of Arabs and Jews to pork, the dislike of the Brahmins for beef, etc. The Americans do not want to eat horsemeat, and Westerners in general refuse to eat dog meat, which the Southeast Asians and some Indians look upon as a delicacy. There is a voluminous literature about banishing hunger from the earth by means of wide-ranging propaganda to change the dietary habits of various peoples. One almost looks forward to a worldwide standardizing of the menu.

Nobody can deny that dietary prejudices constitute an obstacle and whatever can be done to eliminate that type of idiosyncrasy is praiseworthy. But specialists of such various kinds as meat scientists, sanitation experts, anthropologists, sociologists, etc., are gradually becoming convinced that several such dietary rules were by no means arbitrary whims but originated as important protective measures against mass infection by trichinae (pork), tapeworm (beef), etc. Ever so often the prejudices were founded in economic facts, when climate or diseases raised almost insurmountable obstacles to a certain kind of animal husbandry. Experiments that have disregarded such obvious limitations for production ended in many cases in failure or became unnecessarily expensive; compare for instance the so-called Gambia Project described in the chapter "Man's Competitors for Food."

It is highly advisable that we study the basis for the thousands of dietary rules that exist in various cultures. We might then make fewer mistakes in our aid programs for underdeveloped areas and would furthermore learn a great deal about the varied biological environments around the globe in which man must exist. Viewed in a broader context, a dietary standardization on a global scale offers no easy shortcut to improved utilization of resources, nor promise of any substantial increase in total food resources. It should be kept in mind that in most cases where deviations are found from what *we* regard as normal diet, alternatives have usually been found which as a rule are incorporated in a satisfactory way into the plant and animal production prevalent in a region. Naturally, there are exceptions but not of a magnitude which affects these general conclusions.

In particular instances such dietary prejudices naturally become serious obstacles, as when deliveries of food were made in such an emergency situation as the Bengal catastrophe in 1943. Imported wheat was not eaten because the starving people were rice-eaters. This broadens the scope of the whole issue into the question of adapting wheat to fill the needs of hungry rice-eaters. In the Bengal incident the costly flour mills and baking facilities required to convert wheat into edible food were missing. In regions of China and India where wheat has been grown for centuries, the situation is quite different.

This raises a whole series of very fundamental questions, broadening out into many different directions far outside the narrow scope of dietary prejudices or anthropological blockings. Space does not permit the penetration of these complex matters here, but their nature can be elucidated through simple questions such as these: Is it advisable to accustom large groups of people to eating commodities which for obvious climatic reasons normally cannot be grown in the area? Where does one draw the line in terms of millions of such dependents, relying on distant feeding sources? What are the logistic requirements for such large-scale deliveries? To what degree are specialized major investments for such purposes justified on a purely ephemeral basis or merely for relief?

There are many more considerations which have far too little been subject to economic, technical, or social analysis. It is food for serious thought to what an enormous degree world trade, as it has developed in the last fifty years, has made millions crucially dependent on a veritable ferrying of food and feed—an almost continuous inflow of agricultural products. This does not apply only to Japan, England, Holland, and other notorious examples of net importation, but is equally applicable to the importing ports of China and India, most islands of the South Pacific and the Caribbean, etc. Before we support a kind of universal standardization of eating habits and food choices, and induce further reduction of man's alternatives, let us be convinced we can honor our commitments. If not, we may rather be worsening further the precarious living conditions of man, making his daily life still more hazardous, even if the short-range effect might look reassuring.

The current large purchases of wheat by China from the West either prove that the dietary obstacles have been overcome or that the facilities for wheat utilization have been created, at least in the importing cities. Gradually, but fairly rapidly, the city populations of India have also learned to use wheat. But we should not forget that even when these import quantities are considerable, viewed in the context of world trade, they are still small at the receiving end as part of the food balance of these overpopulated countries. At the most such crucial imports only amount to 2 or 3 percent of the annual consumption of these giant countries. A further penetration of these questions would, however, go far beyond the scope of this chapter.

We Westerners frown at locusts, snake meat, and insect larvae, but the day does not seem to be very remote when we, too, due to mounting population pressure, will be forced to consume everything edible in order to sustain life. We will probably also incorporate such foodstuffs into our diet as can be cheaply mass-produced with modern technology and which would mean improved economizing in the use of basic resources. Most likely we have long ago passed the point where continents or considerable portions thereof could be fed through importation. But this raises the question: How far out are we willing to push the boundaries for our present existence? How much more of the biosphere is man going to annex? Would it not be more prudent to try to draw a line of demarcation while there is still time and a buffer margin, although minor, yet is in existence?

Line of Accommodation

The members of the luxury club of the world, comprising four to five hundred million people, are not satisfied with what they themselves produce, but in addition grab food, feed, and fiber literally from the entire world. This is a clear reminder that the menu of tomorrow will change most profoundly in this world of affluence, when in the interest of global welfare we will be forced to accede to other peoples on earth their fair share or at least allow them to keep what they have and produce themselves. It is easy to talk about raising grain, beans, or watercress in every flower pot, to visualize the basements of every home dedicated to cultivating mushrooms and every bathtub as a receptacle for algae growing. It is easy to talk about fencing in ocean bays and the mass cultivating of algae. But are we actually prepared to take such steps? Do we not realize that they merely may become dismal milestones on our way down toward an Asiatic standard, and then, what? In any case it is certainly not *progress* and such measures will be of highly dubious value when nutritional demands and economy enter the picture. Are we willing to accept for our own part algal soup, wooden-based steaks, and plankton paste? Are we willing to sacrifice our own diet of conventional beef steaks, pork chops, milk, cheese, and eggs? Or is all this glib talk about the menu of the future meant, not for ourselves, but only as a program for the hungry? Do we really believe that culture and civilization can flourish on those premises?

Are we, the privileged ones, so completely incapable of grasping the fundamental fact that this spaceship of ours—the Earth—has very obvious and concrete limitations and that its other inhabitants wish to enjoy at least part of our standard of living, enabling them to make their contribution to world culture? Is not the luxury of our traditional diet actually a minimum requirement for a tolerable existence? Is it really possible to exhort the peoples of the world to gigantic efforts in the battle against hunger, undernourishment, poverty, and cultural decline, by promising all these substitute foods, yet only available at the best for a brief lapse of a few decades, each of which is adding close to one billion more people?

Would it not be more realistic to draw a line of accommodation now than to continue the journey down toward a poor man's diet, which seems miserable even when compared with the everyday diet of past generations in the West of clabbered milk, herring, and coarse bread, in hard times mixed with bark? That diet sounds almost like a luxury menu seen in the light of the array of all questionable "delicacies" that will constitute the alleged menu of the future. I belong to those who believe that only through realistic programs of this sort can human culture be expected to survive. It can certainly not do so by having still more billions on a starvation diet. We need all the present resources of the world, all our scientific knowledge and technological know-how to solve our present food problems. It would be an extremely poor solution to offer emergency food only, and that would anyhow not in any way solve our basic dilemma.

CHAPTER XIII

New Heavens
and New Earths [1]

In few areas of modern life has science fiction entered into greater orgies than in depicting the abundant resources of the earth, particularly with regard to food production. The most exaggerated statements seemingly gain credence. Unfortunately, several expert scientists carry considerable responsibility for these projections. From time to time economists, agriculturists, and specialists from many other disciplines put forth all kinds of estimates as to future food production that have little to do with reality.

Two categories of experts are more competent than others to render valid judgments about the feeding potentials of the globe: geographers and soil scientists. For at least two decades, both these groups have persisted in underlining that almost all land suitable for agriculture has been put into use. They have furthermore pointed to the many unmistakable signs that the plowing of new land has already gone too far. As early as 1952, at the International Geographical Congress in Rio de Janeiro, the chairman of the International Union of Geographers summed up the global situation with regard to available soil resources as most critical. One of the resolutions from the meeting stated that knowledge about this fact should be brought to the more general attention of the scientific as well as the political community. Similar conferences later on have further underlined the gravity of the situation.

[1] Isaiah 65:17.

Nevertheless, unlimited project-making continues, which in essence constitutes a swindling of mankind with words and figures. The most common form of this kind of sport is loose talk about how many more millions of acres can be put to agricultural use. Such statements are made without relating these figures either to the total surface of the globe or to already tilled acreages. In most cases the terminology in this field is inexcusably lax or evasive *e.g.,* the use of the term *tillable acreage* without defining what really is meant: whether only the plow has to be put into the soil, or large investments in irrigation systems and other improvements are required. The melting down of the enormous ice caps of the Antarctic regions has been proposed, and the misleading and absurd term "cultivatable land" attached to the gained areas.

THE SUBSISTENCE TRIPOD

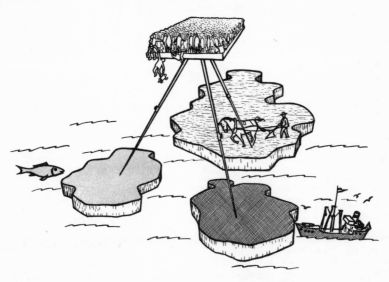

Fig. 47. The subsistence tripod. Agriculture, fisheries, and trade constitute the feeding basis of a country. Net-exporting countries reduce their agricultural land available to the raising of food or feed crops. The picture shows a net-importer. The fish and trade acreages are calculated and termed ghost acreage (see pp. 310–312).

The Truth About Our Earth

What is the real truth about the potential of our earth as regards tillable acreage? Thanks to the dedicated work of geographers and geologists there are no longer *any* white spots of significance on the map of the globe. The structure and composition of the vegetation cover is also well studied. The general quality of the soils is extensively mapped, and an elaborate classification is well under way. The land resources of the globe are consequently well established.

Two-thirds of the earth's surface are taken up by the oceans. Sometimes a slightly higher figure is employed, when the Antarctic continent is not included in the land area. The oceans can then be said to cover 80 percent of the surface. This matter, however, is of secondary importance. As to the land area, it is often said that only one-tenth is under cultivation or tilled. A clear distinction between the two is seldom made, but the statement is frequently worded to imply that man merely utilizes one-tenth of the land surface to feed himself or that only one-tenth of the land surface is used by agriculture. Both these statements are false.

PRESENT UTILIZATION OF LAND AREA
(*in million hectares*)

	TOTAL LAND AREA	TILLED LAND	PASTURES	FOREST	OTHER LAND
Europe	493	151	91	138	113
U.S.S.R.	2,240	229	372	910	729
Asia	2,783	445	452	520	1,366
Africa	3,026	230	696	604	1,496
North and Central America	2,245	260	370	821	794
South America	1,783	76	414	940	353
Oceania	852	37	460	82	273
Total	13,422	1,428	2,855	4,015	5,124
Percent	100	10.6	21.3	29.9	38.2

Source: FAO Yearbook, 1966.

It goes without saying that in the portion of the land surface man utilizes to feed himself one must include pastures and at least a certain portion of the forest acreage. How much, varies from region to region and is difficult to measure in exact terms (*cf.* "The Forest and the Field in an Ominous Confrontation"). Japanese conditions can be referred to as an example. Grass and other plants are regularly collected from half a million hectares (1.25 million acres) of forest land, chiefly openings in the forest called *genya,* and not used as feed but as green fertilizer in the rice paddies or sometimes in fish ponds.

In those parts of the world that are intensely cultivated, the forest has been pushed back, and most of what remains is located in largely inaccessible regions or limited to proportionately small

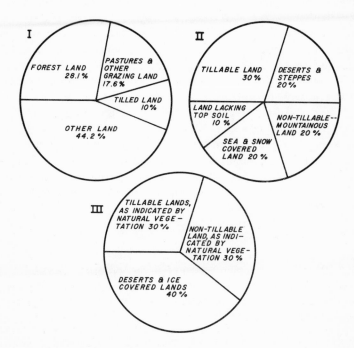

Fig. 48. Classification of globally available land area on the basis of three different principles: I—current use, II—nature of soils, and III—type of vegetation

areas. The present pastures of the world, *i.e.,* those that are actually classified as grazing grounds, amount to 21.2 percent of the land surface. It is therefore a safe estimate that close to one-third of the total land surface is already in use to feed mankind and its livestock. But this figure does not reflect the potential, it only states how large a portion of the globe has already been drawn into the sphere of man's subsistence.

Negative Acreages

How much more can be utilized for agriculture? Is one-third of the land surface a high or a low portion? The experts have given rather clear answers also on this score. The geographers use the expression *negative acreages* to indicate areas that are uncultivable and which are most unlikely ever to be drawn into the sphere of agriculture.

These negative acreages first of all comprise those regions of the land surface that are permanently covered with ice and snow. Besides the Antarctic, there is the huge island of Green'and, almost totally covered with ice, leaving only a few narrow strips along the coast accessible to settlement. There are further vast regions where the snow cover disappears only for such a short period that agriculture, even in theoretical terms, is not feasible. Crops need a minimum period of frost-free days and soils thawed to a minimum depth. In these permafrost regions the soil remains constantly frozen, but in more favored sections is is defrosted in a shallow layer for a few weeks. No less than 47 percent of the land mass of the U.S.S.R. is classified as belonging to this category. Similar areas are found in Canada, Alaska (more than half of the state), and most of the Arctic islands. This empire of snow and ice adds up to one-fifth of the global land surface. Even outside the permafrost territory the summer season might be too brief—too few days between late and early frost—to allow cultivation. Fish might be found in lakes and oceans on those latitudes, but their growth is extremely slow.

Even laymen realize that in addition there are other large areas which cannot be cultivated, among them the mountainous regions of the globe, such as the mighty chains of the Himalayas, the Andes, the Alps, and many others. Many high plateaus in these regions are actually located above the vegetation line. Together this kind of uncultivatable land also amounts to one-fifth of the global land mass.

Finally there are vast expanses of deserts and other arid regions. These latter are defined in the temperate zones as those receiving less than 250 millimeters (ten inches) of precipitation annually, and in the tropics less than 500 millimeters (twenty inches). In both cases little natural vegetation can grow. In some parts irrigation may be brought in, at least in theory by using subterranean or other distant water resources or rivers, but these possibilities are quite limited. Deserts and arid zones together amount to another one-fifth of the land surface, which with presently known techniques, is unusable and cannot be exploited for agriculture at a reasonable cost. Finally, there are several regions that lack adequate humus in the soil and thus do not allow soil cultivation. Such negative acreages together amount to about one-tenth of the land surface (see Figure 48 [II], p. 291).

Adding up all these undisputedly negative acreages, we arrive at a figure of 70 percent of the earth's land area that must be deducted as little fit for cultivation. As stated, man has already taken possession of one-third of the land surface to feed himself and consequently is closely approaching the limit for what can be mobilized totally for this purpose. Inventories also prove very clearly that additional regions, which may offer some potential, amount to only a small percentage of the total land surface and are quite small, in particular when related to a giant world of humans growing, in effect, by an additional United States each third year.

Limitations of Climate

A comparison can be made between the above appraisal of the earth's potential with other methods of classification. After a thorough analysis of vegetation types and climatic conditions, combined with a detailed study of available water—as pointed out in the chapter "Water and Our Daily Bread," this is not identical with the precipitation but with the net balance after evaporation—many scientists have reached the conclusion than 30 percent of the earth's land surface can be cultivated. They classify another 30 percent as "productive," but not suitable for agriculture. In this figure they include the major part of the world's forest lands, poor pastures in Australia, the African bush, mountainous regions, and steep slopes. The remaining 40 percent are covered with deserts of either the arid or the cold kind (the tundra and adjoining areas). According to this classification the wet tropics, including the Amazon region, fall within the first-mentioned category. As will be discussed later, however, it is highly debatable whether these regions actually can be cultivated with currently available techniques. To speculate about what might happen in a distant nebulous future is both futile and of little relevance in the present crisis, when a doubling of food production is the minimum required to provide for those already living on earth.

Whether we resort to one or another classification system, we will still arrive at about the same figure for mankind's potential domain. This means that with the present world population each human should have at his disposal about 1.6 hectares (4 acres) of cultivatable land. Of this, half a hectare (1.2 acres) is presently tilled, 0.8 hectare (2 acres) constitutes pastures, and the remainder, *i.e.,* 0.3 hectare (0.7 acre), is still under forest cover. The distribution of these basic resources is uneven. Some peoples have considerably more, the overwhelming majority of the hungry, far less.

Man-made Deserts and a Shrinking Margin

In order to obtain a correct perspective of the future agricultural potential it is essential to take cognizance of what has occurred in this sphere of human endeavor during the past eight or ten decades. Some data are available which throw light on major changes during the period from 1882 to 1952. Since then development has largely continued along the same lines. Trends have changed little—only the pace of change has accelerated with increased human pressure. These figures may therefore be accepted as quite indicative of what has happened in the entire eighty-five year period since 1882.

During that time span the world's oceans rose somewhat and decimated the land area with about 2.4 percent. The most conspicuous change is that deserts and wasteland increased, from about one-tenth of the total land area in 1882 to nearly one-fourth by 1952, and now still more. As repeatedly stressed in this book, this enlargement is primarily the consequence of man's intervention and little the result of any secular changes in climate. The truth of the matter is that man through his intervention has created more desiccated, denuded, and devastated lands than the amount of fertile land he ever created through new tillage and irrigation. The portion of the land surface used for human settlement has doubled and now amounts to about 15 percent. Pastures increased by 640 million hectares (1.6 billion acres) despite the reverse trend of plowing pastures to increase the production of grain, feed, and leys, etc. The increase of pasture lands has primarily taken place in the well-fed world, which can afford to appropriate even forest regions for this purpose. The net addition in tilled acreage amounts to 210 million hectares (525 million acres) during a period when world population grew by almost two billion people (gain: 0.1 hectare [0.25 acre] per individual!!). The net gain from seventy years of intense effort to broaden the feeding base is consequently not very impressive—one of many signs that the potential margin is rather narrow.

CHANGES IN LAND UTILIZATION 1882–1952
(*In billion hectares*)

	1882	Per-cent	1952	Per-cent	CHANGE 1888–1952	Per-cent
Forest	5.2	45.4	3.3	29.6	− 1.9	− 36.8
Desert and wasteland	1.1	9.4	2.6	23.3	+ 1.5	+ 140.6
Built-on land	0.87	7.7	1.6	14.6	+ 0.73	+ 85.8
Pastures	1.5	13.4	2.2	19.5	+ 0.7	+ 41.9
Tilled land	0.86	7.6	1.1	9.2	+ 0.24	+ 24.5
	9.53	83.5	10.8	96.2	+ 1.27	+ 12.9
Area not especially utilized	1.81	16.5	0.27	3.8	− 1.54	− 79.9
Total	11.34	100	11.07	100	− 0.27	− 2.4

Source: R. R. Doane, 1957. *World Balance Sheet* (Harper, New York).

ACREAGES NOT UTILIZED IN 1882, AS CLASSIFIED 1952
(*In million hectares*)

FOR		TILLABLE ACREAGE NOT UTILIZED	
Pastures	638.8	1882	1,912.3
Built-on land	636.8	1952	426.0
			1,486.3
Tilled land	210.7		
	1,486.3		

Source: R. R. Doane, *loc. cit.*

QUALITY CLASSIFICATION OF TILLED LAND

	1882 Percent	1952 Percent
Good	85.0	41.2
Half of original humus lost	9.9	38.5
Marginal soils	5.1	20.3

Source: R. R. Doane, *loc. cit.*

Against this background it is more easily understood why, since 1882, despite enormous new irrigation systems and other arduous efforts to increase food production through agriculture, and despite better protection by legal means both for forest lands and soil, the frightening end result is that the deserts have grown on an average by 25 million hectares (62.5 million acres) annually, *i.e.*, totally by more than two billion hectares (five billion acres). The boundaries of both the Sahara and the Kalahari deserts are being pushed a couple of miles farther out each year, and this due to man's intervention.

Roads, cities, airports, and industries took during the same time span about 1 billion hectares (2.5 billion acres), *i.e.*, 12.5 million hectares (31.25 million acres) annually. Basically this land is nothing but artificial wasteland. During the same seventy-year period the irrigated acreage of the entire globe was expanded by 128 million hectares (320 million acres), in itself an impressive accomplishment, but nevertheless this gain is of a much smaller magnitude than the devastation. Such achievements lose even more of their luster when viewed in relation to the large-scale tapping of surface and groundwater resources which further accelerates the formation of wastelands.

These are only a few of the many consequences of man's great gamble with the globe. Man thought he had created a safe human existence. We can now read as in an open book about the colossal magnitude of our failure. We must apply the brakes immediately to prevent the damaging effects from becoming still more serious. Man is forced to withdraw within the limitations of nature's huge hydrological cycle and to put an end to the present great water swindle, the prime consequences of which we now experience even in the developed world. The water crisis is no episode. It is the beginning of a drama which will develop into a tragedy unless we interrupt it with epic action.

The Tilled Acreage Since the 1880s

The most telling indication of how far man has pushed the limit of cultivation is the fact that during the seventy years from 1882 to 1952 we brought under the plow soils that were by and large considerably poorer than those broken previously. The remaining soil reserves are in general not what we normally classify as good agricultural land. In 1882, 85 percent of the cultivated acreage was classified as good land for tilling. For 1952 this figure had dropped to 41.2 percent. What we used to call marginal land amounted to 5 percent in 1882, and in 1952, to 20 percent (see table). Soil erosion has taken a large toll, in some instance, resulting in a serious denudation causing abandonment. This explains why the net increase in tilled land did not amount to more than 210 million hectares (525 million acres). In 1882 only 10 percent of the tilled land had lost about half of the original humus; in 1952 close to 40 percent was gone. An ominous wearing down of the earth's soil capital is thus taking place. This is most evident in organic soils, such as muck land, where the persistent breakdown of the organic matter finally results in complete loss of such lands for cultivation. The soil reserve was in 1882 estimated at about 1.9 billion hectares (4.7 billion acres). This reserve has dwindled considerably, and by 1952 amounted to approximately a scant 380 million hectares (950 million acres).

The breaking of new land has, however, encompassed a much larger acreage. Broken down in round figures it amounts to about 640 million hectares (1,600 million acres) pasture, 210 million hectares (525 million acres) tilled land, 10 million hectares (25 million acres) orchards and gardens, but no less than 640 million hectares (1,600 million acres) for populated areas (see table, p. 296).

Adding Up

We thus find that about 40 percent, *i.e.,* two-fifths, of the land surface, either consists of deserts and wasteland or has been taken for rather permanent human habitation. Furthermore we find that 20 percent of the land surface is covered by inaccessible forest almost entirely located in areas and terrain which is difficult to reach for forestry operations as hitherto known. Accessible forest acreage is now given as about 13 percent of the land surface, and it goes without saying that it is within this acreage the productive forests fall. In the chapter "The Forest and the Field in an Ominous Confrontation," it is made clear that this acreage is quite inadequate for the present world population. It is therefore a safe prediction that for a population twice as large as at present, which experts agree we will have prior to the year 2000, the output will not fill minimum vital needs—even with intensified forest management. It is also wholly unrealistic to count on present forest land as a reserve for future agricultural needs.

The Breaking of New Land

How large then is the acreage reserve that may be tilled for food production? Agricultural experts in most parts of the world agree that the degree to which further plowing of pastures is safe is quite limited. Under the pressure of man's staggering needs, the limit has been reached in most regions of the earth. The experience of England during the two world wars is a case in point. On

LAND MASSES
In million hectares

	TOTAL LAND AREA	DESERTS, WASTELAND AND BUILT-ON LAND	%	INACCESSIBLE FOREST	%	POTENTIALLY TILLABLE ACREAGE	%	POTENTIALLY TILLABLE ACREAGE							
								NOT UTILIZED ACREAGE	%	PRESENTLY TILLED ACREAGE	%	PASTURES	%	ACCESSIBLE FOREST	%
Europe	493	117	23.7	5	1.0	371	75.3	7	1.4	153	31.0	78	15.8	133	27.0
U.S.S.R.	2,240	679	30.3	545	24.3	1,016	45.4	—	—	221	9.9	370	16.5	425	19.0
North and Central America	2,426	867	35.7	468	19.3	1,091	44.9	115	4.7	256	10.5	364	15.0	356	14.7
South America	1,776	451	25.4	622	35.0	703	39.6	52	2.9	73	4.1	292	16.4	286	16.1
Asia *	1,739	638	36.7	127	7.3	974	56.0	90	5.2	329	18.9	243	14.0	312	17.5
China	976	612	62.7	49	5.0	315	32.3	—	—	109	11.2	178	18.2	28	2.9
Africa	3,027	1,349	44.5	445	14.5	1,233	40.5	114	3.7	239	7.8	596	19.5	284	9.3
Oceania	854	325	38.1	33	3.8	496	55.8	1	0.1	28	3.8	447	49.5	20	2.4
Total	13,531	5,038	37.8	2,294	16.2	6,199	46.0	379	2.9	1,408	10.5	2,568	19.1	1,844	13.5

It should be noted that neither the U.S.S.R. nor China has any remaining agricultural reserve listed in the table above other than what can be obtained through the plowing of forest or pasture land.

Source: FAO statistics, 1965.

* Exclusive of China.

both occasions the government had to call a halt to the plowing-up campaign long before it had actually reached the intended scope. The topsoil was being lost to the Atlantic at an accelerated pace. There is no doubt that the serious losses through soil eroison, which have been registered in all continents, were caused primarily by two factors: The tilling had been pushed too far; and there was overgrazing due to too many livestock animals per acreage unit. Both phenomena are directly attributed to over-population. Mankind has exceeded reasonable limits. Left to incorporate into the human biosphere is a pitiful 2.8 percent of the land area, *i.e.,* an acreage amounting to 380 million hectares (950 million acres). This is, by all measurements, a frightfully small margin for a world that presently grows by seventy million people a year, with each year requiring 50 million additional hectares (125 million acres) of tilled land in order to meet the minimum food needs of this added population. Consequently the total reserves of the globe are not large enough to cover adequately even the needs of the increment in human numbers for one single decade.

Where Are the Empty Spaces?

How are these remaining cultivable acreages divided among the continents? They are largely to be found in two of them, namely North and Central America and Africa. They each have one-third of the reserve (see table, p. 299). The remaining one-third is shared by South America and Asia. It should be noted that in this classification the Amazon region is not listed as a potentially cultivable area.

We will discuss below some of these so-called lands of the future containing the remaining land potential of the globe, which would allow an additional production of food and feed basically through the breaking of new lands. The lush forests of the tropics seem above all promising, especially those in the wet tropics on both sides of the South Atlantic. The prospects are, however, rather discouraging. In the Congo region the Belgians have for at least thirty years studied the possibilities of replacing traditional shifting cultivation, as practiced by the native population, with intensive cultivation. Unfortunately these studies found that productivity could only be raised nominally, *i.e.,* far too little to create anything close to the high-yielding agriculture of temperate zones. When the forest cover was removed, soil temperatures rose drastically. The humus was rapidly degraded, and the plants suffered. The conclusion was reached that agriculture could only be successful if long, narrow, tilled corridors were created in the rain forests and for a strictly limited time period before returning the soil to the grip and protection of the forest canopies (*cf.* p. 11).

The Humid Tropics

Major portions of the Amazon and the Congo basins belong to the humid tropics, characterized by regular afternoon rains. To this climate zone belong Ceylon, parts of Indonesia, New Guinea, tropical West Africa, Brazil, and the Caribbean. Their potential in tilled land has been estimated as 400 million hectares (1 billion acres). Yet this climatic region, with around 52 million people, embraces only 14 million hectares (35 million acres) under tillage.

There are very concrete reasons why this alleged soil reserve is seemingly so poorly utilized. Arduous efforts to expand cultivation have persistently resulted in failure and loss of topsoil (*cf.* p. 11). Other limitations are that outside of trees only six crops—dominated by rice, sugar cane, and some tubers—are adaptable to this area, but they consistently yield less than in the arid tropics. This is due to the reduced influx of sun energy, caused by the extended cloudiness, which thus affects crop productivity. Insects, fungi, and weeds all abound; yet the removal of weeds only exposes the soil to rain erosion. The net retention of photosynthetate is diminished through intense respiration during the warm nights. The green paradise of the tropics is consequently treacherous. Hawaiian efforts to diversify cropping has failed, due to the adverse conditions.

Tropical Africa

The soils of tropical Africa are for the most part deficient, above all in mineral nutrients. This is a major factor in the slow development of this continent. In addition, in large regions debilitating diseases of both man and animal are endemic. Despite many efforts to fight malaria, the population is by and large saturated with this disease. It will probably take centuries of progressive

and well-planned efforts to make African agriculture produce reasonably well. But this would certainly not provide food in adequate quantities to feed the many millions which will be flocking
to the cities in the next hundred years. To begin with, it would be
quite an achievement for the farmer to feed himself and his
family, *i.e.,* reach true subsistence. As pointed out earlier, the crop
yields of the colonizers are highly misleading and give a poor indication of what is feasible with African soils. The white-owned
farms without exception encompass all good soil there is, leaving
inferior soils to feed the colored peoples. The white farms are
above the average as regards size of the units, quality of the soil,
availability of water, etc.

The conclusion is self-evident: The talk about Africa as a continent with vast open expanses only waiting the wand of human
initiative and enterprise, ready to yield food for new billions, is an
illusion. This illusion was probably born when the Europeans
started their exodus to all corners of the globe and became large-
scale exploiters, not only of Africa, but of the enormous grasslands in Australia, Argentina, and North America, and ruthlessly
cut down the forest in New Zealand, the Malay Peninsula, southwest Australia, and North America. Viewed in historical perspective, it is a tragic fact that, by and large, it was only a minority of
the world's peoples who profited from this worldwide accomplishment, which in certain respects was also impressive.

Land Reforms

Demands for land reform are heard with greater insistence with
each passing year. To tens of millions in Latin America, tropical
Africa, and the Middle East, "new land" is equivalent to land reform. They look askance at the huge estates and the few who live
there in relative luxury while the majority of the people go hungry.
From country to country figures may be quoted that prove a few
landowners possess more than one-third, one-half, even three-
fourths of the agricultural land of their nations. From a psycho-
logical viewpoint, it is highly understandable that this breeds
social and political tensions. It is obvious that more people could
be fed if the pastures of these estates were tilled and used for the
raising of crops like potatoes, beans, or grains. When the Peruvian

sugar plantations obtain bumper crops by growing beans on the sugar acreage for two consecutive years—in effect world records —not to feed the hungry of the land but to plow these beans down into the soil to feed the soil microbes—the economical system is in direct collision with humane and social demands.

In some countries of Latin America land reforms undoubtedly would constitute prudent and farsighted progress. The food needs of more people would in this way be met. But unfortunately, in most cases the problem is not that simple, due to the fact that the small-scale farmers are too poor to procure enough capital for such improvements as irrigation or machinery and the creation of storage facilities serving to tide them over bad crop years. Making of small farm units by the splitting of bigger ones is not necessarily conducive to increased production. And even if the big estates were divided up into small agricultural units, there is in most countries not enough land to go around in order to provide for the many landless. The queue of landless awaiting land in Mexico exceeds one million people. All this is a consequence of there being too many people. Most proposals for land reform are unrealistic, not recognizing the scourge of overpopulation. Despite actual reforms and real success in land redistribution, the rural areas of East Pakistan have a landless proletariat of no less than one-fifth of the population.

But putting this aspect aside and looking upon the world at large, one discovers that most nations have the farmland parceled out into plots of from less than one up to four acres. The alleged "farms" do not justify this designation. Other terms have been used: microfundi, postage-stamp cultivation, and miniature plots. In Japan, 70 percent of the farms are less than one hectare (2½ acres) in size. The average Indian farmer has less than three hectares (7.5 acres) at his disposal. Many more such examples could be given as typical for the majority of the world's population. Most agricultural economists agree that such units are too small and recommend industrialization as well as consolidation of farmland holdings as a cure. In most regions overpopulation is the direct obstacle that prevents wiser management; the totally available acreage is inadequate. Man is hitting the ceiling. There are too many people, and even the most extreme industrialization would not allow the creation of farms of reasonable size. Man is not willing to face reality and recognize the very obvious limitations that exist in our spaceship Earth. The remaining margin for human expansion is exceedingly narrow.

Employed in the Soil

Lengthy and tedious remarks are frequently encountered, lamenting the fact that more than half of mankind is still toiling in the soil. Attention is directed to the fact that countries like the United States, England, Sweden, etc., only have a modest 5 to 20 percent of the population employed in agriculture, and yet these nations enjoy a high nutritional standard. These figures are grossly misleading, since a great many more people belonging to the labor force in those countries are tied to food production. The number of farmers is no longer an adequate measure of how many are involved in providing food. Many of those working for fertilizer factories, oil refineries, tractor manufacturers, highway constructors, chemical industries, freezing and canning plants, and numerous others, more or less intimately take part in the big task of producing food and feed, in charge of chores which as late as 1900 were part of the farm activities in self-sustaining units. The farmer used to process his milk and take it to adjacent cities for sale or delivery. He slaughtered on the farm but also packed and cured his meat. He collected and marketed his eggs. He further produced his own fuel and most of his feed, collected manure, and provided most of his fertilizers.

Can Forest Land and Pastures Be Further Reduced?

Many who write about the new lands of the future do not limit themselves to the 380 million hectares (950 million acres) mentioned earlier as the present global reserve of potential agricultural land. They take it for granted that man will continue to incorporate more forest land into farm cultivation and put more pastures under the plow. As already pointed out, we have probably reached the limit in both these respects. Nevertheless, we will take a brief look at how the tilling of new lands would be realized according to these recommendations.

It is estimated that the tropics—mostly through the felling of forests and tilling of grasslands—could be forced to submit another billion acres and the temperate regions maybe half a billion acres, *i.e.*, together 1.5 billion acres, about twice as much as calculated above. In addition to opening up the Congo and Amazon regions, these plans envision the colonization of the inlands of South America as well as those of New Guinea. We have touched upon the difficulties in the Congo and the Amazon; they are equally great if not greater in New Guinea. This country is highly mountainous with little land in plain fields. The same is true of South America; all major flatlands, with the exception of the northern *llanos,* are already in agricultural production. See further my book *The Hungry Planet,* p. 290.

The border areas between Brazil and Bolivia and the adjoining Bolivian lowlands constitute another such potentially agricultural region, which is already being developed to a considerable extent. On the Brazilian side of the border, efforts are concentrated on animal husbandry. Optimistic estimates indicate that at the most ten million hectares (twenty-five million acres) might be opened up in the Pantanal, and this to serve a country currently growing by more than three million per year. This new land is not much. Mexico has broken that much new land since the Second World War and largely in this way been able to keep pace agriculturally with its population growth—as pointed out in the chapter "Could the Yield Spiral Be Pushed Further Upward?" These agricultural achievements are respectable as such, but they lose their long-term significance when put into the population equation of the respective countries. Mexico grows by more than one million people a year, and ten million hectares (twenty-five million acres) would consequently suffice only for a decade or less (see Figures 52 and 53).

It is in this context that the correctness of the basic assertion of Malthus becomes most evident in its simple logic. The sustained growth of the population in geometrical progression inexorably takes place at another pace, and above all with a much greater acceleration than the plowing up of new lands and other cultivation measures, which can only take place in a simple additive way. One has to add one hectare to another. Even impressive accomplishments dwindle in relative significance when the population growth is taken into account.

Even if it were true that 720 million additional hectares (1,800 million acres) could be developed, most geographers would probably agree that we would then have taken the irrevocably last reserves of the earth. There is no evidence that these new areas would become grain larders for the world at large. If the Amazon Basin sometime in a distant future might be cultivated, it is most likely that the people who move in there will first cover their own needs. Next in line will come the continent's own inhabitants, increasing before the year 2000 by more than three hundred million at the present rate of growth. Presently the increase is more than ten million annually. This growth will, however, accelerate during the next forty to fifty years, which would, at the least, be the period of time required for such a large-scale development.

Something similar applies to Siberia, where the Soviet Union has broken new lands in the southern parts of west Siberia and in Kazakstan, the largest single event and biggest new settlement in postwar agriculture. These measures were undoubtedly well motivated in the strivings to produce more food for the Soviet people. But experience bears witness to what geographers and soil experts have always stressed, the hazards involved in the cultivation of these poor soils, which in addition are jeopardized by recurrent droughts.

Man finds himself at the limit for his feeding potential on earth, and it can be safely stated that practically all good soil has been taken. The new lands that have been developed during the past hundred years have all been of poor quality compared to the average of those already under cultivation. Whether we figure on another 720 million hectares (1,800 million acres) or merely half that amount, it is not enough for more than fifteen years' growth of the present world population. In another decade the annual increment will amount to eighty million people. Additional food must therefore primarily come from already cultivated acreages, but increases in yields do not take place at this rate.

The Feeding Base per Individual Is Rapidly Shrinking

As pointed out in the chapter "Could the Yield Spiral Be Pushed Further Upward?" a great deal more can and may be done toward obtaining larger production from the tilled lands of the world, but man is confronted with very real and severe limitations in future operations. Viewing the question realistically, and taking England as an example, we can establish that since 1801 the average agricultural acreage per inhabitant in this island country has shrunk to one-tenth of what it then was. The yields have *not* increased correspondingly. More than half of what the nation now is eating comes from acreages in other countries. Similar figures, showing how the agricultural acreage per individual has diminished, may be given for a great number of countries. Naturally such a process cannot go on indefinitely. The feeding acreage per person is presently diminishing so fast in the world that despite vigorous countermeasures man has not been able to produce additional yields at the same pace. We are therefore losing the race between the baby crop and the grain crop.

The Uneven Distribution

Three other factors are overlooked in the popular discussion of these matters, not the least in the United States. First of all the basic fact is entirely overlooked that the developed world on the whole possesses much larger agricultural acreages per individual than most developing countries do. The average American has at his disposal ten to twenty times more land than each Mexican, Egyptian, Brazilian, or Ceylonese. It is no mere coincidence that the two powers which compete for world supremacy are the only ones which possess unique assets in terms of agricultural lands. For several west European countries the corresponding figures approach those of the developing countries. Holland and Belgium have for instance less acreage per person than India and China. But this is only superficially correct and gives no fair basis for comparison. The west European climate in regard to amount and distribution of precipitation, seasons, daylengths, etc., is much more suited for plant production than the climate in the larger portions of India and China. Besides it is a grave misconception to believe, as frequently is pretended, that the Dutch and the Belgians feed themselves on their own acreage. Neither of these two countries manages on its own soil, both are net-importing nations and on a big scale, and this despite their much advertised food export. They import large quantities of bread grain and other foods, but primarily such animal feed as feed grain, oilseed cakes, and meal, etc.

NUMBER OF ACRES PER PERSON (1966)

	TOTAL LAND AREA	TILLED LAND	PAS-TURES	FOREST	OTHER LAND	POPULA-TION IN MILLIONS
Europe	2.75	0.84	0.51	0.77	0.63	450
U.S.S.R.	23.72	2.42	3.95	9.65	7.70	236
Asia	3.76	0.60	0.61	0.70	1.85	1,848
Africa	23.76	1.82	5.38	4.76	11.80	318
North America	22.63	2.60	3.18	8.55	8.30	218
Latin America	20.66	1.09	5.10	10.18	4.29	251
Oceania	118.34	5.14	64.00	11.40	37.80	18
World Average	9.86	1.05	2.10	2.95	3.76	3,400
China	3.09	0.35	0.56	0.24	1.94	790
India	1.59	0.80	0.07	0.26	0.46	510
U.S.	11.72	2.32	3.21	3.78	2.41	200
Pakistan	0.62	0.54	—	0.08	—	120
Indonesia	2.64	0.39	—	2.02	0.23	112
Japan	0.48	0.15	0.02	0.017	0.29	100
Brazil	24.30	0.85	3.09	14.70	5.66	88

Calculated by author on basis of FAO Agricultural Yearbook data.

The Earmarked Soils

These major contributions to the feeding of the well-fed have their counterpart in corresponding reductions in the feeding basis of countries sustaining such exportation. Mathematically each Peruvian has 0.55 acres to feed himself, but the large exportation of cotton, sugar, etc., cuts this small allotment in half. This is one aspect of the inflamed cash crop issue. Besides the dwindling net returns stands a shrinking feeding basis with encroaching malnutrition, as far too many are not only forced to survive on the yield from inadequate acreages but in addition must eke out an existence from inferior soil, lacking fertilizers and irrigation, which are largely the privileges of the cash-crop lands.

The Farm Concept—a Misnomer

Most "farmers" of the hungry world are tied to units of a few acres (*cf.* p. 303). These miniplots are in addition further fragmented holdings due to inheritance rulings. The Indian "farm" is on the average 7.53 acres but split in five holdings; in the heavily populated state of Kerala it is less than two acres. Mankind is in a harsh manner hitting the ceiling, and the blow is felt most unmercifully among those who are already suffering the most. Most "farmers" of the teaming island of Java (Indonesia) till for the entire family less than one acre (74 percent of the farms are smaller than one acre). In East Pakistan most farms are equally small; with some justification such tiny plots have been given the designation postage-stamp cultivation. In drought-ridden West Pakistan the individual plots are less than ten acres. Yet we pro-

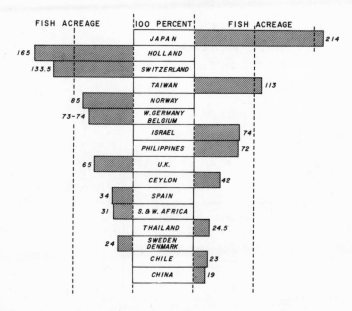

FISH ACREAGE
PERCENTAGE OF TILLED LAND

Fig. 49. The tilled land (in percentage of presently tilled land in each country) calculated as needed to provide an amount of animal protein comparable to what fisheries currently are moving into domestic consumption in each listed country both in the form of human food and animal feed. The vicarious protein would in most instances come from dairy products, with skim milk and whey as feedingstuff.

gram and discuss as though it were a question of viable farm units. These small land areas not only jeopardize the indispensable switch from subsistence to market economy but make the beneficial effects that allegedly were to accrue from large-scale industrialization rather questionable.

Ghost Acreages

In my book *The Hungry Planet* (1965 and 1967) it is pointed out that a series of countries have what I term *ghost acreages, i.e.,* acreages which are not directly visible; they are represented by their fisheries and net import of food, feed, and fish. If these ghost acreages are brought into the picture, the differences between the food-producing achievements of the various nations on earth become more equalized. Thus Belgium's ghost acreage is 3.4 times

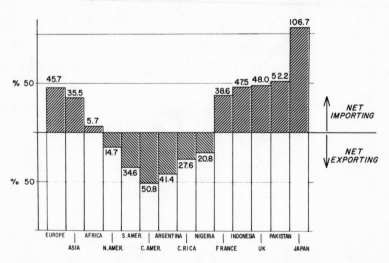

Fig. 50. The tilled land (in percentage of presently tilled land in each country) calculated as needed to produce quantities of foods and feeds equivalent to present importation. Exported quantities are subtracted. The figures are consequently net values.

as large as what could be termed its visible acreage, *i.e.*, tilled land and pastures within its own borders (see table below).

Holland is often put forth as an example to be followed by the entire world. Several economic handbooks and publications repeat this statement despite the fact that it is wholly unrealistic, almost absurd. If the world as a whole did follow the Dutch example (I am not here discussing whether this were feasible), we would at any rate need an additional satellite one and a half times the present agricultural acreage of earth. From this extra satellite we would have to bring in food and feed. In addition, a world fishery, many times the present one in magnitude, would be required to supplement the world food budget to the degree fish now is doing this as feed and food on the Dutch scene. This would

GHOST ACREAGE OF SELECTED COUNTRIES (1963–1965)
Ares (1/100 hectare) per capita

	TILLED LAND	GHOST ACREAGE		TOTAL
		Fish acreage	*Trade acreage*	
China	14.3	3.9	− 0.5	17.7
India	33.5	1.0	5.0	39.5
Pakistan	23.0	1.3	12.0	36.3
Indonesia	16.8	3.6	8.0	28.4
Japan	5.9	12.0	7.3	25.2
Brazil	36.8	3.0	1.0	40.8
Egypt	9.2	1.5	0.7	11.4
Nigeria	37.4	3.8	− 7.8	33.4
Peru	22.2	15.1	− 8.5	28.8
U.K.	13.7	8.9	16.6	39.2
Italy	29.6	5.7	12.2	47.5
France	42.7	5.1	16.5	64.3
Poland	49.9	7.5	10.0	67.4
Scandinavia	47.0	12.9	13.4	73.3
Holland	7.9	13.0	12.0	32.9
Belgium	9.9	7.9	25.8	43.6
Ceylon	16.7	7.7	4.0	28.4
Taiwan	7.2	6.9	4.5	18.6
Israel	16.1	11.7	17.5	45.3
El Salvador	22.2	1.2	7.2	30.6
Costa Rica	43.5	1.8	− 12.0	33.3
Jamaica	12.9	3.9	5.0	21.8

surpass what any estimate considers a possible outtake from the oceans and far exceed anything advisable for minimum sustainable yield.

The Land Robbery

In industrialized countries a large-scale land-gobbling is taking place—seemingly unavoidable due to the growth of the cities, particularly in the suburbs. Besides, land is taken for airfields, industrial sites, sports fields, and large highway nets. Even worse is the fact that this land-swallowing operation involves a great deal of first-rate agricultural land. Its location close to population centers often brings about better care of the soil and more intense fertilizing, not to mention the basic relationship that human settlement often started and flourished where soils were good. Through this process the United States is deprived of more than two million hectares (five million acres) annually. A prosperous state like Michigan loses a quarter of a million hectares (625,000 acres) per year. At the present rate of disappearance several of the Swiss cantons will have lost all tilled land before the end of the century. Denmark now sees the end to the breaking of new land on the poor marshlands of Jutland in compensation for the good, fertile soils lost to urbanization, etc., on the islands of Fyn and Sjaelland.

When pondering these enormous losses of good agricultural lands, an American story frequently comes to my mind about a man who fell from the thirty-second floor of a skyscraper and when passing the thirteenth floor optimistically exclaimed, "Everything is all right so far." As a human race we react in a similar thoughtless manner when confronted with our large-scale robbery of agricultural lands. In the era of human masses the skyscraper is actually the best friend of the farmer—constituting one of the few safeguards against the border-jumping now taking place on a wide front, not the least in the rich world, into the narrow margin of land still left to a burgeoning world.

Pie in the Sky

An economic study recently published in a leading economic journal maintained that the world could easily bring another five billion hectares (12.5 billion acres) into cultivation and this without further capital investments in irrigation and other improvements. Knowing that the entire land surface of the globe amounts to 13.5 billion hectares (thirty-three billion acres) and that already practically all land which can reasonably be developed is incorporated within man's subsistence sphere, such speculations seem totally unrealistic. Even if man placed the world's entire forest land under the plow, this would still not produce the promised acreage. Time and time again, one notes with amazement and bewilderment the fact that such fanciful statements are accepted for print by respectable journals and, what is still worse, given credence even by some experts who should be aware of the facts. Even the layman realizes how shallow, dubious and even nonsensical most of these lofty promises and oversimplified assertions are. Mostly they lack any scientific justification. This modern form of science fiction, more than anything else, gives reason for pessimism on behalf of mankind. Pie in the sky and semantic exercises are a poor substitute for the real pie desperately needed by the hungry billions.

Faith vs. Knowledge

The fact that discussion concerning world feeding still remains to a considerable extent in the sphere of unfounded speculations is in my view a serious cause for concern. Glib talk is floating around about New Heavens and New Earths, completely removed from any reality, no better than the utopias of bygone days. Even facts that are irrefutably and universally recognized are deleted from consideration—a form of deception worse than untruth. It is an old adage that man believes what he wants to believe, and pays less attention to what he knows. The universe seems enormous in this era of space hysteria. Even in that field almost anything gains credence. A heedless escapism prevails, not the least among the scientists and technologists. We talk ourselves out of reality. According to all definitions this is the most typical characteristic of insanity.

If the world cannot feed its population, one reasons, there is always the possibility of sending the excess millions to other planets such as Mars, Venus, and others, of which, on top of everything, some are believed to be inhabited already. No one bothers about the logistics of such operations. Who is going to decide which fifty or even hundred million people should be dispatched annually on these frightening excursions. The faith in the wonders of technology is so unlimited that few people seem to doubt that man in the future will be able to launch spaceships on an around-the-clock basis from all kinds of stratospheric ports with hundreds of humans on board. Evidently, it will have to be thousands of people, 6,000 to 7,000 each hour if the population increase is to be kept under control. No taxes on earth could finance such a project, far exceeding the gross national product of the United States. It would be an expenditure of billions of dollars, even more grotesque than those now going on for armaments and space adventures. One does not even want to admit that man has already outgrown the universe. Even a well-planned and organized exodus to other planets, either those mentioned above or some other distant celestial body, holds out little promise for relief.

Ostrich Policy

It is about time that we return to a factual discussion and put an end to the fables about new planets (heavens) and new earths and concentrate instead on how to save our own spaceship and provide a decent existence for those who already are on board. The measures taken during the last hundred years to this end have been wholly inadequate and have failed badly despite a speeded-up effort during the postwar period both by governments and private and international organizations. We stick our heads into the sand and do not want to face the terrible reality of the population explosion. We do not want to see that birth control is an indispensable corollary to death control, which anyhow is only in its initial stage. It is therefore safe to predict with rather great accuracy and certainty that even if we manage to implement an international convention for birth control, and do so effectively, man will still—already in this very century—be faced with the tremendous task of providing for twice as many humans as are now living on earth, at least one half of which suffer from lack of most necessities of life, above all food and water. Nevertheless a European nutritionist recently concluded that a major part of the world's population nowadays lives in abundance. He also opined that man's diet had become rich in fat and thereby also in number of calories, although the caloric requirements in effect had been reduced, due to widespread mechanization. The conclusion was further drawn that in normal times the supply of food could be guaranteed through importation from other countries when domestic yields were inadequate; man no longer seriously ran the risk of becoming hungry; on the contrary, there was a much greater likelihood of being overfed. It is indeed not only the general public that needs to be informed on the true conditions of man. A great many experts in various fields, and evidently also nutritionists, need to take cognizance of elementary facts about the world and its straitjacket.

CHAPTER XIV

Food—the Great
Challenge of
This Crucial Century [1]

American and Soviet scientists asked by the French weekly *l'Express* in 1962 about mankind's future and how it will shape up in the year 2000 concluded that voyages to the moon and also inhabited artificial satellites will then be commonplace. These experts were selected from among Nobel Prize winners, members of scientific academies, and other notables whose qualifications were beyond dispute. Among their predictions were the following:

By the year 2000 all food will be completely synthetic. Agriculture and fisheries will have become superfluous. The world's population will by then have increased fourfold but will have stabilized. Sea water and ordinary rocks will yield all the necessary metals. Disease, as well as famine, will have been eliminated; and universal hygienic inspection and control will have been introduced. The problems of energy production will by then be completely resolved.

Reading about those hilarious excursions into our future dreamlands, one gets seriously concerned about our academic education, but still more, profoundly worried about this almost dimensionless

[1] Also published in *The Centennial Review* (MSU), Vol. XI, No. 3 (1967), pp. 287–311.

flight from reality. In pessimistic moments I sometimes wonder if these spokesmen for the academic community already have taken residence in their own Utopias of words and are beyond reach of reason.

The leading British science journal, the *New Scientist,* invited a similar galaxy of scientists, technologists, and writers to outline the World of 1984 in contrast to the original Orwellian design. These prognoses have been made available in paperbacks. Only four out of more than one hundred answers considered food worth mentioning as an issue in our future. Only one respondent foresaw difficulties in this respect. Yet, looking twenty years ahead, we see two issues dwarf all others in significance regarding man's future: hunger among the augmented billions of the globe, and the risk of nuclear war. The atomic issue was ignored completely. Three out of more than one hundred questioned asserted flatly that no major war will take place during this period, yet they were all asked to forecast conditions in 1984 "on the basis of known possibilities and trends." Those few that touched upon world food production were equally sanguine, reiterating the double-barreled evasive phrase, "We could feed them, *if* we tried." One reply went one step further and repeated the often heard assertion "The technical problems are not hard to solve."

The fact is that the world in all likelihood, and this on the basis of most available evidence, is on the verge of the biggest famine in history—not, to be sure, the world *we* live in, but the poor world, the countries of Asia, Africa, and Latin America. Such a famine will have massive proportions and affect hundreds of millions, possibly even billions. By 1984 it will dwarf and overshadow most of the issues and anxieties that now attract attention, such as nuclear weapons, communism, the space race, unemployment, racial tensions, Vietnam, the Middle East, the Congo, the Dominican Republic, Cyprus, etc. These current issues will fade into the background as the enormous task of feeding mankind impresses itself on the Western world.

The Scientist's Role

The main function of the scientist in a modern society—besides accumulating, discovering, and disseminating facts and knowledge

—is to be a lookout on mankind's vessel, constantly interpreting the radar signals picked up and warning of dangers lurking ahead. The mapping of the future course to pursue is a joint undertaking in which the politicians have prime responsibility. The most disquieting aspect of this particular food issue is the fact that with few exceptions the scientific and technical community has been signaling green light to mankind, when red signals are far more appropriate. With semantic exercises and iffy proposals mankind has been made to believe we could take care of almost any number of people, at any rate for the foreseeable future. An analysis of statements and pronouncements made by leading Western scientists of almost all disciplines reveals a shocking disregard for the abject conditions prevailing for almost four-fifths of the human race and a corresponding lack of awareness of the plight of man. Whatever happens, whatever urgent measures we may take, food is going to be the overriding issue of this crucial century. Let us briefly review some relevant facts pertaining to this calamity.

The Population Upsurge

Human numbers are rapidly reaching unmanageable proportions. Our resources are in most respects, possibly with the temporary exception of energy, grossly inadequate. The gap between the rich and the poor nations is rapidly widening and threatening within this very century to engulf the few remaining oases. At a breathtaking speed, mankind in this twentieth century doubled in numbers by 1960, thereby passing the three billion mark. There is every sign that another three billion will be added within little more than thirty years, and yet this figure is predicated on a gradual universal practice of birth control within this brief period. If no efficient control is applied, which is the more likely alternative, this crucial century will see the world population zoom above eight billion, barring a major catastrophe.

Has any world politician faced up to the ominous fact that in the year 2000 we will have at least four billion Asians, half a billion Africans, and 600 million Latin Americans? Has any American politician formulated a workable constructive program to cope with a teeming Latin-American world, right at our doorstep, three times as big as the present? The policies of the past have been wholly inadequate. The failure is made glaringly evident by the fact that 100 million Latin Americans, half the present number, are lacking almost everything—food, homes, water, and soil. President John F. Kennedy sounded his solemn warning when, meeting with the Central American presidents in 1963, he said: "If we do not stem this human tide now, we will all be inundated in an immense ocean of poverty."

Population Control

The first glimmer of light is the rapid global recognition of the imperative need for birth control. Nehru led the parade of world leaders with his historic broadcast of 1953, later followed with similar initiatives by Ceylon's prime minister, Indonesia's Sukarno, China's Mao, Egypt's Nasser, and Tunisia's Bourguiba. The West, very tardy in responding, finally did. It is almost unbelievable that this country now has an Assistant Secretary of Health exclusively devoted to birth control matters, both on the national as well as global scene. Despite courageous efforts by devoted groups this matter has not yet received the prime priority it deserves and desperately demands. If pestilence is raging, vaccination and other epidemic counteractions are immediate executive duties. So far there is little evidence of similar urgent countermeasures in the area of birth control. Timid group action and inadequate administrative handling once again reveal a striking discrepancy between actual needs and measures as well as between oratory and action, even in cases where there is unanimity about purpose.

Let us make it unequivocally clear that population control not only is imperative but indeed indispensable and inevitable; but more than this, it is a prerequisite to averting catastrophe as well as to preparation for subsequent progress. The present almost dazed public discussion, which has suddenly been awakened to the realities and the gravity of the situation, seems to suggest that ours constitutes the first human generation faced with the need of population control; yet it is historically well documented that almost every advanced civilization in the past has resorted to rigorous family limitations. Both China and Egypt were well acquainted with such procedures, millennia prior to the Roman Empire, and so right through the centuries up to our days.

The Unthinkable

Both as a human family and as agriculturists or food scientists we have lost the race between the baby crop and the grain crop, and this despite many miraculous accomplishments, valuable measures, and ingenious devices. Man's proliferation has hollowed most of our gains—even the most glorious ones—but in addition mankind is "hitting the ceiling." Until quite recently we thought, in contrast to Charlie Chaplin in the movie *Modern Times,* we were going to make it, that is manage to run up the down escalator. We were, in addition, going to perform this feat with an escalator which constantly was accelerating its downward velocity. In this respect there is a notable switch in public opinion, which is gradually accepting population control as indispensable to our future as well as to that of the world. There are several indications in books, articles, and conferences testifying to a beginning realization that it is "later than we think."

It is nevertheless almost macabre to witness the present auction in human numbers. The bidders are specialists of various categories. They delve into the futile game of calculating how many the world could nourish: 15 billion, 25 billion, 40 billion. The bids go still higher: 100 billion, 270 billion, 900 billion. Even among humanists, few raise their voices in defense of human dignity and values, although it should be self-evident that such numbers would by their very size annihilate anything worthy of being called civilization. And if there were a trace of realism in these armchair exercises, it is a superscandal that the world looks in the direction it does. It has failed to provide satisfactorily for more than half of its present population of 3.5 billion. A doubling of world food production is called for to give everyone now living his minimum needs.

The Great Western Trek

This increase in human numbers is indeed of grave concern to the modern world, particularly as it affects demands for space, water, and food. We are presently adding seventy million to the world population each year. Do we recognize the true magnitude of this added board-and-lodging burden? Do we realize that the greatest exodus in human history, the big European trek to all continents, comprised in all seventy million people, and yet this one event shaped human history for almost 400 years? It brought about the Europeanization of the world and is also the great epic of the North American continent. Never did man collect a greater booty than the vast forest lands of the Northeast and the rich soils of the prairies. Hardly any other people has been more fortunate in the great lottery of mankind. This accident of history constitutes the foundation for our firm conviction in universal abundance and in the supremacy of technology.

The Finale

The Second World War brought an end to this era in human history. But as late as 1939 shipload after shipload of peanuts left starving India to fatten the cows of the distant empire rulers of the British Isles. More than 1.5 billion people in Asia and Africa have since then attained independence. World food markets have adjusted to this new scene; annually more than 25 million tons of grain are now moving from the rich world to feed the hungry, as against the latter part of the thirties when eleven million tons of grain were dispatched from the hungry to provide for the well-fed. This adjustment is only partial, since most of the grain going to the hungry has moved outside of regular trade channels and within the framework of special programs like Public Law 480, Food for Peace, World Food Development Program, and now Food for Freedom.

The monopoly of the European race, however, is sustained. Public attention is focused on grain, but when we direct the searchlight to other commodities and the key nutrient of protein, the scene changes radically: The 2.5 million tons of grain protein delivered annually by the rich and well-fed are counterbalanced by a flow to the Western world of no less than 3.5 million tons of other proteins of superior rating in the form of soybeans, oilseed cakes, and fish meal. We in the Western world are actually making what amounts to an almost treacherous exchange.

Tragic Paradoxes

At a time when nutritional science has provided us with the means of creating the most perfect diet ever offered man, the necessary ingredients are becoming scarce, and the nutritional basis in terms of food is lagging more disastrously than ever before.

At a time when microbiology can report almost complete control of man's microbial foes and is marshaled as never before to support human life, these very successes sound doom to man by the mighty human tidal wave they have inadvertently nursed.

At a time when agriculture and farming have almost attained mastery in the raising of crops and animals, in turn rendering healthy and wholesome products, food inadequacy prevails and encompasses mounting numbers of humans, already to be counted in the hundreds of millions.

At a time when food science offers mankind the best tools and methods ever placed at its disposal, food is becoming less and less available to growing millions.

At a time when medicine, in both its human and veterinary branches, has acquired the finest and most potent arsenal of weapons in its fight against disease and poor health, their effectiveness is blunted and enfeebled by expanding malnutrition, and dwarfed in efficiency by an oversized task.

At a time when educational facilities in the form of paperbacks, schools, and teaching devices surpass anything available to earlier human generations, more millions than ever before are deprived of education.

We could pursue these paradoxes into almost any discipline. The examples here are selected to bring home two major points: our grave error in confusing means with ends, and our evident inclination to think in domestic or regional terms rather than to recognize the global and universal scope of the problem.

The drama of our days is the persistently widening gap between the hungry, poor nations, now comprising 2,400,000,000 people, and the adequately fed, rich countries, with around 1,100,-000,000. But there are only 300 to 350 million enjoying the kind of daily diet which is ours in the United States. Despite extraordinary efforts and impressive accomplishments in the realms of both agriculture and technology—in several cases unique in world history (as, for example, in large-scale irrigation)—mankind is losing the race between food production and population growth and is thus undermining both health and prosperity. Let us also put to rest the glib notion that feeding the world is merely a question of distribution.

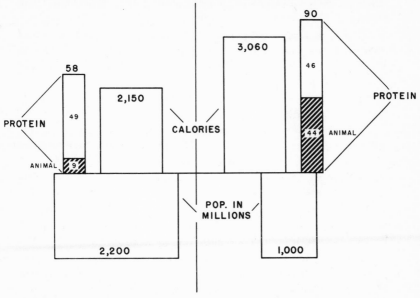

Fig. 51. The hunger gap, 1960–61. The poor malnourished world in the left half of the diagram and the satisfied world in the right half are described in terms of numbers of people and intake of calories and protein (split into plant and animal protein). An ominous feature is the persistent widening of the gap. The well-to-do nations have improved their standard with nine grams (one-third ounce) animal protein per person and day since 1939, *i.e.,* equivalent to the total intake per individual in the hungry world, which in turn has decreased approximately twelve grams per day.

Neither charity deliveries—in many instances, as in the case of India, unprecedented as to magnitude in the annals of world shipping and food trade—nor the global exchange of food and feed on the world market have managed even approximately to equalize the present wide nutritional discrepancies. Most dealings in agricultural products are in effect between the rich nations. The total net deliveries of the United States to the world household do not suffice even to provide England with her present transoceanic purchases of food and feed. Equal distribution of all available food would only make hunger universal and shared by everyone.

This is the most ominous feature of our day. Mankind is on a collision course with its own destiny. If we cannot bridge this quickly widening and steepening hunger gap, we face a cataclysm that may not be the end of the human race, but will gravely jeopardize all we associate with humanity. As a consequence, Western civilization may well join the ominous march of vanished cultures into oblivion.

Nutritive Absurdities

Our image of reality is distorted to the point that we in all seriousness describe not only the United States but also western Europe as plagued by surpluses. Western Europe is, and since 1500 has been, one of the most demanding partners of the world household, nearly parasitic. Few seem to realize such facts as this: Denmark is currently (in the sixties) importing in the form of feed grains, oilseed cakes, soybeans, milk powders, and fish meal an amount of protein exceeding the milk production of South America, or no less than 240 pounds per capita annually, *i.e.,* almost nine times more than each Dane is eating as plant protein. The famed Danish export of bacon and eggs is consequently more the result of African oil palms and United States soybeans, feed grains, and dairies than of its homeland soils.

To take another similar example: Why should the United States have priority to the tuna of the ocean by combing the entire western Pacific down to Chile? When these resources turned out to be inadequate, we moved into the chain of Pacific Isles (based in the Samoa Islands) and from there into the Atlantic with a new big base in Puerto Rico. There we were aided in our hunt for tuna to feed our nation by Japanese, Korean, French, Spanish, and Taiwanese deliveries.

Such nutritive absurdities cannot be sustained for long. If the degree of profitability is to dictate what is done, mankind is bound to go astray and is doomed. The world has no true margin left in the realm of food. The human race has become too big. The era of exploiters is irrevocably coming to an end. Our action programs as formulated in technical aid have been Westerly oriented. It is high time we start looking at the world not from our vantage point but from that of others and arrive at a program serving the *whole* of mankind, not merely a few hundred million. The United Nations and its specialized agencies should take the lead in this urgent task and return to its chief goal of internationalizing the world after almost a decade of nationalistic fumblings.

New Patterns

At the end of the nineteenth century, when it became evident to most thinking people that the prevailing economic system was creating serious evils, resulting in the rich getting richer and the poor still more impoverished, there emerged from classical economics an entirely new school of thought, characterized by social conscience. Now, eighty years later, we discern how the prevailing economic systems, whether private capitalism as in the United States, state capitalism as in the U.S.S.R., or national communism as in China, all dismally fail in an international context.

The conventional world trade pattern is evidently not the result of any natural law over which man and governments have no control. Now, as well as eighty years ago, a new deal is needed, this time on the international level, which takes on the crucial task of remodeling world economy with particular emphasis on food. This task may be formulated in another way: The world now faces the alternative of either a global class struggle between nations or the farsighted creation of a mechanism for universal solidarity.

The Privileged West

A completely new technology is needed which respects the basic laws of ecology and tackles the fundamental grave contradiction of pursuing an economic and technological advancement, aiming at making man superfluous, in a world that has only one true surplus, man himself. This new technology has further to make a complete accounting for total costs including basic resources. It can be safely asserted that our particular form of civilization with regard to the use of energy, water, forests, and soils cannot be copied on a global scale.

We should never lose sight of the historical fact that in the Western world the Golden Age lies behind us and in effect never was anything more than the privilege of a minority. Due to its power position the West tapped an unreasonable part of the resources of the globe. Currently, about 450 million enjoy affluence and abundance. Five to six times that number live in parsimony, scarcity, or serious shortage. This is basically the reason why our high-handed projections into the future may not materialize at all, even when seemingly well founded.

A new global trade pattern is urgently needed. We in the Western world not only have greater soil and water resources, but we are intruding on the meager subsistence basis of this other world. Hundreds of millions in the tropics are forced to shrink their food production to raise peanuts, cotton, bananas, coffee, tea, cacao, etc., for export, in order to accrue foreign currency. This is particularly explosive, as such cash crops are now enjoying high priority with regard to credit, fertilizers, irrigation, etc. Yet their hard-won currency is dwindling in relative value. Since 1952 the deliveries of agricultural products from the poor to world markets have increased by one-third in tonnage, but in value only 4 percent.

By changing over from food production for domestic consumption to food production for export crops, cultivation could in most instances provide a subsistence wage. Increasing numbers of the rising populations in underdeveloped countries therefore took to the cultivation of such crops. It is highly debatable if this pattern can be sustained in a world desperately short of food, water, and land.

Most Western commentators looked upon the UNCTAD Conference (UN Conference on Trade and Development) in Geneva in the fall of 1965 as a set of Platonic declamations or oratory exercises by the have-nots, but we should remember they were deadly serious. Cash crops as earners of coveted currency have a vanishing role, as a growing percentage of this money has to be devoted to the buying of food. Before long food protein will presumably have to be installed as the new gold standard of world trade.

The Magnitude

Our main dilemma is that we never seem to have realized the true magnitude of the needs and tasks facing the world. Our programming and thinking are almost completely geared toward a world of entirely different and much smaller dimensions, both in time and size. We have figuratively been looking through the wrong end of the binoculars, where everything appears small and distant, when in effect the needs are gigantic and right at our doorstep. This major fallacy is evident in the operations of the World Bank, our technical aid programs, and most of our other programming. Even the largest enterprises fall desperately short of man's requirements.

The World Development program, with some 300 million dollars, can be contrasted with the food bill for our own nation which exceeds eighty billion dollars. The huge irrigation dams of India, planned for three, five, or seven million acres are yet wholly inadequate in terms of feeding the teeming millions of India, presently growing at a rate of twelve million per year. We squabble about whether Australia in the future can feed fifty million or 250 million people. Basically it is irrelevant whether it can harbor one and a half or eight years' growth in its Pacific context.

Hitting the Ceiling

There are innumerable things we can do. We can repeat our mistakes as long as possible and in the short run provide for more millions. By and large we *prefer* to look to such immediate returns in most of our actions. The pressing needs and humanitarian imperatives are in several instances so overwhelming that we have no longer a reasonable margin of choice. As a human race, however, we must start to think in strategic terms. We must learn to weigh short-range benefits against long-range goals.

Sooner or later we must come to a recognition of the self-evident fact that our spaceship is limited, and accommodate ourselves to this obvious condition. Do we ever give this irrevocable fact serious attention in our planning? Do we recognize that a single generation has taken for itself the benefits of farm mechanization? By this one-time trick we have freed the farm soils from producing energy. Some 250 million people in our luxury world are today provided with food thanks to the replacing of the horse with the tractor; the next generation has no such trick up its sleeve.

How far are we prepared to go in jeopardizing the millions by placing them in direct dependence on the chemical industry and thereby greatly increasing their vulnerability? At least 500 million people today depend on fertilizer plants for their survival. If all were to be adequately fed, this figure would in effect exceed one billion. Looking ahead at the prospects of this crucial century, we see that it is highly unlikely that present soils can be made to yield more than twice as much food as they now do. In excess of 120 billion dollars will be needed in investment for this purpose alone. On the basis of these considerations one can seriously question whether future chemistry is not already committed to a seriously oversized burden, yet we encounter glib talk about moving the entire feeding burden to chemical plants, in effect reducing agriculture and fisheries to hobbies. The truth is that the fertilizer industry is already facing the tortuous and herculean task of providing for at least 1.5 billion additional humans within thirty years. Railroads, road trucks, airlines, and the merchant navy of the world will encounter an additional transportation load far exceeding the weight of the human population as such.

The Debit Entries

As a kind of self-persuasion, mankind has chosen to dwell on the credit side of the ledger, paying only casual attention to debit entries. This explains why our image of reality is blurred and our concept of costs so vague. We have in many key areas confused productivity with capital resources. This is particularly obvious in the realm of soils, forests, and water. The son living on his rich father's bank account never was considered smart or successful. But our judgment seems to be reversed about our collective behavior. Even when we are dipping into Pleistocene water, as in California and Texas, we still regard this as clever.

It is inconceivable that the rich, well-fed Western world should remain gluttonous in the markets of the pauperized other world. In this way it is drastically reducing the net value of North American contributions. Is it reasonable that tropical Africa, so critically short of both fat and protein, is parting with a quantity of protein in the form of peanuts, consisting of one-third of its production, to feed the dairy cattle and poultry of western Europe and to bolster the fat intake of the Europeans?

Feeding the Well-Fed

Few seem to realize that European dairy production is depending for its high productivity upon the influx of high-protein-concentrate feeds from the hungry world of tropical Africa and Latin America. It is almost ironical that at the same time this is accompanied by a corresponding flow of fat, constituting the raw material basis of the European margarine industry, the chief competitor to butterfat. The Nigerian sales of peanuts on the world market deprives this country of an amount of protein which is approximately half of what it needs to fill the present protein gap. The United States dairy production is chiefly based on soybeans, but little thought is given to the fact that in this way the world's protein market is indirectly deprived of more invaluable protein for human food than what the Asian people totally are consuming. These matters will be key concerns to any future world allocation and redistribution of world food resources.

Our "Superiority"

We proudly point to our technical superiority, our famed ingenuity, and our legendary thriftiness as contrasted with the technical backwardness, notorious listlessness, and wavering creativity of the poor countries. There is some truth to all this, but we should not forget the ingenuity required to survive and economize in their parsimonious existence. A leading United States economist, Thomas Schultze, in his recent study, *Traditional Agriculture,* reached the conclusion that within the framework of the resources available to them, many Indian farmers are quite outstanding in terms of efficiency and employment of their inputs and resources.

More Food

Seventy million more mouths to feed—the present annual growth—mean that thirty to forty million new acres are needed each year simply to keep the world's people at their current malnourished level. To improve nutrition throughout the world, a doubling of world food production is required by 1980 and a quadrupling by the year 2000. It is both feasib'e and imperative to produce more food, but it is not self-evident that this is feasible where it is needed most. We have taken it for granted it could be done and that we know the techniques.

The impression is frequently conveyed that past and present efforts to produce more food have been negligible, while future

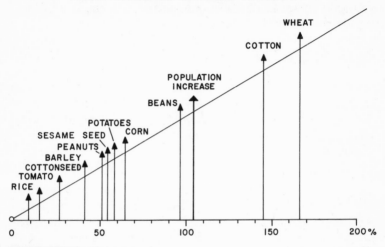

MEXICO
YIELD INCREASE 1934/38-1963/64

Figs. 52 and 53. The increase in the agricultural production of Mexico 1934/38–1963/64 (Fig. 52) has in terms of yields (pounds/acre) kept pace with the population growth only in wheat and cotton (not seed). Larger crop production (Fig. 53, p. 331) has been attained primarily through breaking new soil and thus expanding acreage, not through more intense cultivation. The soil resources of Mexico are now at an end, and this at a time when population is zooming ahead by 3.2 percent a year, meaning a doubling within twenty-two years.

undertakings in this respect are sure to meet with great success. On the contrary, in many places in Asia and Central America an astonishingly efficient use is being made of available land. In Taiwan and Guatemala the mountainsides have been painstakingly terraced high up in a series of gradations. Thousands of acres of tidelands have been reclaimed in Asia. The degree of double-cropping whenever feasible has mounted and at a rather rapid rate, as in Burma, Malaysia, Thailand, Taiwan, China, and Japan.

The hungry people live in the tropics and are governed by a rice market economy and small feeding plots. The feasibility of

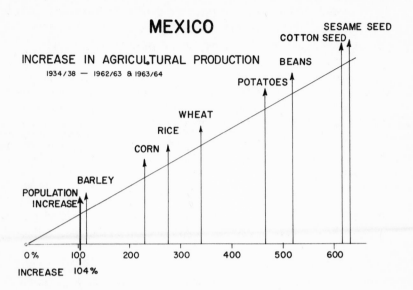

large-scale production is questionable in terms of available land. Yet we expect these people to double and quadruple their production over a short time span, something we in the Western world never have been able to do, even with our enriched soil and ample land. One can in all seriousness raise the quite opposite issue: Are there not good reasons for *not* trying to farm some areas? Several Latin American experts anticipate that thirty or forty million people will have to be removed from their impoverished impossible lands, which never should have been broken into cultivation.

The agricultural history of this century is replete with serious incidents where the excessive zeal of colonizers or the technical aid programs have caused disasters and detrimental rebuffs. Mention may be made of the Dutch deep-plowing of the rice paddies in Java, the corresponding operations by the British in Burma, and excessive fertilizing, which destroyed crops by accelerating water depletion and reducing drought or frost resistance.

The most spectacular failure is the Tanganyika Groundnut scheme. Many thousand acres were turned into dust bowls, the end result of an ambitious, 2.64-million-acre project, costing in excess of 100 million dollars. This failure cannot be blamed on the backward indigenous population, nor on the British Socialist government. It was Western technology and agricultural techniques that failed in this fateful encounter with African realities.

How many Mekong projects—around ten billion dollars for two million acres—would available development funds support? How many are, in geographical terms, really promising? In too many cases they are a big gamble with high stakes, as we do not know how the involved soils will stand up to irrigation and its long-range consequences. What is the life-span of the dams? How many Mekong projects would be required to keep up with the current population growth?

Presently, it costs on an average about fifty dollars to bring an acre of new land into high productivity, which means that 3.50 billion dollars—2.6 billion of this in underdeveloped countries— are needed per year, merely to keep up with present population growth.

In theory it is possible to produce, by means of rational exploitation of natural resources, enough food to nourish five billion human beings. But this can be accomplished only at the price of forced labor, a new kind of slavery, and tremendous investments —presumably pricing still more food than presently out of the markets of the poor.

Resources and Technology

Although industrialization unquestionably would help to solve part of the economic woes of some poor countries, it is highly unlikely that it could come fast enough to overtake an unregulated population expansion. Very few countries have the investment capital required to employ gainfully the swelling numbers entering the labor forces. Even with a very low investment figure of 2,000 dollars per person, few budgets of Latin American countries could afford to accommodate these entrants and are presently very far from doing so.

The most serious fallacy of all is to believe that the world's resources are abundant and are limited only by man's ingenuity. It is commonly thought that man is capable of substituting technology for resources. This is feasible only to a very limited degree.

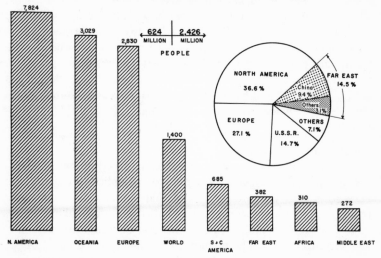

Fig. 54. The global energy balance, 1960–62. The developed world uses more than four-fifths of all energy.

Furthermore, the basic distinctions between renewable and non-renewable resources are woefully neglected. The world's nonrenewable resources have lasted as long as they have principally because so few of the world's people have been using them. The United States, with 6 percent of the world's population, is consuming more than one-third of the world's production of raw materials. Quite aside from the moral aspect of our right to this kind and degree of voracity, there is a much more far-reaching question. Will not the 2.5 billion poor people, multiplying within thirty years to more than four billion, demand their share?

It is sobering to keep in mind that in this very century, when the United States population doubled from 1900 to 1950, the "rising expectations" of the American people resulted in an eight-fold increase in the use of minerals and a thirteenfold increase in the use of fuels. The total remaining resources of the globe are grossly inadequate to allow a similar extravagance among the have-nots; the meeting of even legitimate and reasonable demands will mean an unprecedented and devastating drain. In this light we have to examine our own blueprints for this other world. The average investment in machinery and equipment required on the farm in present-day United States agriculture exceeds 30,000 dollars per farm worker. This is in effect two to three times above that required for an average industrial worker. Even when recognizing chances for somewhat lower costs (in absolute figures) in poverty-ridden countries, it is still this disproportion that raises doubts whether this kind of capital-devouring agricultural operation is on the whole feasible in this hungry, poor world.

The Nutrition Syndrome

The medical expert talks wisely about the syndrome of a disturbance or disease, meaning thereby a multiplicity of symptoms. He also is clearly aware of the fact that curing is not merely the removal of symptoms. This is the kind of mature thinking we require for world feeding in the application of technical, economic, and social remedies. The malnourished child may be cured of the symptoms of disease, whether this be kwashiorkor, marasmus, or some other deficiency, but will soon relapse when he returns to the hunger environment of his home, village, or country. Prevention in this case becomes the only truly effective remedy. There is a growing realization and recognition in most medical circles that lack of food is the primary culprit opening the door to a wide gamut of infections and other diseases. Large numbers in tropical African and Brazilian rural areas are very sick due to this undermining convergence of food scarcity and multiple disease attacks. It is very urgent that the artificial split between the Food and Agriculture Organization (FAO) and the World Health Organization (WHO) be bridged and a joint attack be made. The strategy of a two-pronged attack invites defeat from the start.

From Hunger to Starvation Crisis

We are currently moving from the chronic hunger crisis of the postwar years into an acute starvation crisis, which in all likelihood will be permanent if drastic long-range countermeasures are not implemented. Despite our wheat deliveries to India in 1967, exceeding one-fourth of the United States crop, the situation was grave. Our mass media only casually reported on the African tragedy—the eastern part of its tropics experienced in 1966–1967 a sixth consecutive year of drought. Cattle died by the thousands every week, and many thousand had to be moved to water. Men, women, and children were in despair. Food had to be airlifted to Bechuanaland. These happenings were described as "scourges" or "temporary setbacks," but we forget that in all instances recurrent drought is part of the regular climatic pattern of these regions. Drought is in effect a normal, almost intrinsic feature on the Indian, South American (northeast Brazil in particular), and east African scene. Even rain-rich Uruguay experiences years almost devoid of rain.

Despite the extensive irrigation of India, some 80 to 85 percent of the tilled land is exposed to the vagaries of the monsoons which through the centuries have shown a great degree of fluctuation in regularity. This also indirectly affects irrigation efficiency. Even at a future time when most of the average runoff may have been fully harnessed for irrigation, India will retain this kind of vulnerability; two-thirds of the tilled land will remain in the throes of the monsoon. Eastern tropical Africa is in a far more critical dilemma. During most of this century, water use has been such as to create a negative water balance. The hydrological cycle has rarely ever been able to compensate the losses.

The Rhetoric

When the UN charter was signed, President Roosevelt remarked: "Our earth is only a little star twinkling in the universe —yet we can make of this—if we care to—a planet undisturbed by wars, unperturbed by want or fear. We can eliminate all segregation due to race, skin color, or theories." This line of thought has been repeated in Western orations, and particularly in the pronouncements by United States leaders, from the Four Freedoms launched by Franklin Roosevelt via Harry Truman's Point-Four program to the speech given by Dwight Eisenhower to the multitudes at New Delhi in 1959. He then said: "We have today the scientific capacity to abolish from the world at least this one evil. We can eliminate hunger—this pursuit will ennoble the human spirit."

We talk, discuss, and plan in a world of dimensions utterly removed from reality. During a recent visit to Guatemala I examined a four-year program led by four prominent agriculturists to diversify the coffee acreage. Their main project of creating feeding lots for dairy cattle would, if implemented, provide milk for one-seventh of one single year's growth of the present population. In a number of countries national prestige has given priorities to atomic reactors, dams, and steel plants, when the true needs have been food processing plants, storage, and village industries.

There is a vast discrepancy between our rhetoric, our programming, and the actual needs. We talk about the United States feeding the world, when at the best we can provide relief, crumbs. Ambulance service is laudable and most creditable but serves a very limited function. In the newly instigated Food-for-Freedom program, the notion of committing United States agriculture to a real feeding role in the world is involved for the first time, but this is only a minute start.

Failures

We have seen in our generation more than the colossal failure of Western education, in which the West has proclaimed an abundance merely waiting for man's ingenuity and resourcefulness to provide for all. We have also witnessed a serious emasculation of all religion; the basic belief in the universal brotherhood of man has become empty phraseology. We have further evidenced the failure of technology to assert its human aims. In a world where less than 500 million have satisfactory water facilities, where 2,000 million lack homes, sanitation, clothing, and beds, we are engaging in an armaments race and the maintenance of a terror balance costing more than the total gross national product of all the developing countries. And, as the climax of absurdity, we are deserting the globe for celestial adventures of highly questionable value to man's future.

The aims of technology, which were clear enough a century and a half ago, have gradually disappeared from view. Humanity seems to have forgotten the wherefore of all its travail, as though its goals had been translated into an abstraction or had become implicit, or as though its ends rested in an unforeseeable future of undetermined date. Everything today seems to happen as though the ends had disappeared, as an outflow of the magnitude of the very means at our disposal.

Futile armchair exercises, guessing or calculating future human numbers, or *mañana* promises are of little help in the greatest crisis ever to hit the human race. We can ill afford our present childish armaments and space race. We need to mature and show some degree of responsibility to our own future as well as to that of all humankind. The world has become one whether we like it or not. Four hundred years of Western leadership carry many glories but much disgrace; the spearhead of progress no longer rests in our hands and is now pointed against us. If we do not take our place among the forces that mold destiny, our civilization may well vanish. To achieve this end, the priority lists of mankind need a drastic and urgent revision. The educational failure to acquaint ourselves with reality, and the bankruptcy of religion both point to the need of a revival and renewal in the form of a new religion and a new education.

Despite the purported end of ideologies, we cling to their stale concepts and slogans. The misery and poverty of the world are basically not the result of the doings of communism. The rhetoric shrouds reality in embellishing veils. Had communism never existed, we would yet be faced with the deprivation of billions. If communism vanished overnight, we would still be struggling desperately with the tremendous hunger gap and its ramifications.

The White Man's Burden

We in the Western world have frequently quoted Kipling in describing, almost condescendingly, our role in the world as the white man's burden. Judged in global terms and in historical perspective, the white man himself has truly been the major burden. Still today, after the alleged death of colonialism, we remain in terms of food and other agricultural products the true parasites of the world household. The riches of the soils, the seas, and the forests are by and large flowing into the Western world. Although constituting only one-third of the world's population, we consume two-thirds of the world's agricultural output and more than two-thirds of the aquatic harvest.

Whatever happens, we should realize that this minority will not be allowed to continue to dispose of twice its share. We cannot remain seated in the front row and witness this tremendous human drama, the greatest tragedy ever. We must regain control of our destiny. We unquestionably have the means to avert a future catastrophe, but none of our present palliatives has so far been adequate.

The Brain Drain

In one more basic respect the Western world is baffling the expectations of the emerging countries. They not only are subject to large-scale plunder of invaluable protein, deprived of essential food-producing lands through cash crops, and tapped of essential raw materials; they are also drained of their brainpower—medical experts, scientists, engineers, etc., trained in their homelands or in Western universities. India is losing in medical professionals alone what corresponds to the annual turnout of no less than three large medical schools. Chile has given the United States more than 5,000 academically and technically trained people. In growing numbers they flock into the underdeveloped sections of our own economy and learning. This is a key issue, never tackled by any international body. In a world desperately short of doctors, public health workers, engineers, and nutritionists, this phenomenon is absurd. Thousands of teeming villages around the world have no physician within a range of 100 miles. Experts by the millions are needed to save the future billions. Our country is jeopardizing the health services of several Asiatic countries by a flow of doctors, nurses, and nutritionists to United States jobs, besides absorbing a large excess number from Europe, who could serve these needy people.

A crash program is overdue for the rapid training on a massive scale of the experts the world desperately needs. Our conventional categories poorly fit such requirements. The hungry, poor world cannot afford home economists, water experts, nutritionists, public health workers, food scientists, etc. Water, nutrition, and health are so intimately related to medicine that these fields need to be coordinated into one single discipline, which concentrates attention on immediate needs. Food is closely interrelated with *all* these fields.

The Sobering Sixties

The conspicuous contrast between rhetoric and reality has become almost offensive. Today we find a world where the surpluses, once given the absurd designation "eternal," are almost at an end. Chinese and Soviet purchases have taxed the grain stocks of Australia and Canada to the limit. India and to so some degree tropical Africa and the Middle East are quickly emptying the grain bins of the United States, and we are close to a danger point.

John F. Kennedy went in person to the UN in 1961 to proclaim the sixties as the United Nations Decade of Development— "to enable all nations, however diverse in their systems and beliefs, to become in fact as well as in law, free and equal nations." The results so far are deeply discouraging. Harsh realities have not only created stagnation but in the needy world severe retrogression. There are, however, some glimmering rays of hope in the rapidly growing recognition of the indispensability of population control. There are, furthermore, many signs of a more realistic appraisal of regional resources, as well as of the shortcomings in our technology and methods and their limited universal applicability. Most essential is the growing awareness of the urgency of these matters. The notion is also gaining ground that our own spaceship Earth needs an overhaul, is clearly defined as to its size, and cannot take on any number of additional dwellers. Many compartments are already seriously overfilled.

The business community, largely supported by science and technology, gave to the sixties the designation "Soaring." It is to be hoped that future history will rather describe this decade as the "Sobering Sixties" which put an end to the rhetoric and laid a more solid foundation for man's future. Thus once again we would assert the viability of man's mind by mobilizing science and technology for great new endeavors to the benefit of *all* mankind, in support of the only war mankind can still wage, that of human survival. Our future is at stake in this very century, and food is the key issue.

A Swedish author and thinker, Verner von Heidenstam, speaking to the faculty and students at Upsala University once asserted that "the most dangerous thing that can happen in the life of an individual as well as in that of a nation is to become farsighted too late." This is equally true when it comes to the world community. But in such an undertaking we are operating against formidable odds. Shelley once said: "Man is a peculiar creature—he lacks the capability of imagining that which he knows." This *is* our dilemma. Even when we read our future almost as an open book, we refuse to accept reality. Winston Churchill said in his last great speech in the House of Commons: "Mankind is facing the ominous choice between Supreme Disaster or Immeasurable Reward." Our tragedy is that in the Western world we believe we have made the choice in favor of Immeasurable Reward along the lines the opening quotation of this chapter indicated, but I can assure you that our present course follows the tragic alternative. As a human race we are heading for Supreme Disaster, and the great challenge to our generation is to avert this calamity. It has to be done in this crucial century, or mankind many well deprive itself of both its future and its history.

Chapter References

CHAPTER I:
The Forest and the Field
in an Ominous Confrontation

BAKER, R. S. B. *Green Glory—The Forests of the World.* New York, A. A. Wyn, Inc., 1949, 253 pp.
——. *Dance of the Trees.* Belmont, Mass., Wellington Books, 1956, 192 pp.
CUREVEN, E. C., and SLATT, G. *Plough and Pasture—The Early History of Farming.* New York, Crowell-Collier and Macmillan, Inc., 1961, 250 pp. (First edition, 1953).
FORDE, C. D. *Habitat, Economy and Society.* New York, E. P. Dutton & Co., Inc., 1963, 500 pp.
GUEST, S. H. (ed.). *A World Geography of Forest Resources.* New York, The Ronald Press Company, 1956, 736 pp.
HINDUS, M. *House Without a Roof.* New York, Doubleday & Company, Inc., 1961, 562 pp.
HOLBROOK, S. H. *Burning an Empire—The Story of American Forest Fires.* New York, The Macmillan Company, 1945, 229 pp.
OVINGTON, J. D. *Woodlands.* London, The English Universities Press Ltd., 1965, 154 pp.
PALMGREN, E. *Entwaldung, Versteppung und Wüstenbildung in Südeuropa.* Berlin-Grünewald, Haller, 1953, 72 pp.

PHILLIPS, J. *The Development of Agriculture and Forestry in the Tropics*. New York, Frederick A. Praeger, Inc., 1961, 206 pp.

VIDAL, J. J. *El Arból en el Campo*. Buenos Aires, El Ateneo, 1947, 322 pp.

WAGNER, P. *The Human Use of the Earth*. New York, The Free Press, 1960, 270 pp.

Magazines
American Forests
Forestry (U.K.)
Forstwissenschaftliches Zentralblatt
Journal of Forestry (U.S.)
Lesnoye Khozyaistvo Proejvodslvennuyi i Naucknoechnichiski Zhurnal (U.S.S.R.)
Montes
Revue Forestière Française
Unasylva (FAO)

CHAPTER II:
Will Chemistry Offer Mankind
the Third Freedom?

BARM, E. L., HEADY, E. O., PESCK, J. A., and HILDRETH, C. G. (eds.). *Economic and Technical Analysis of Fertilizer Innovations and Resource Use*. Ames, Iowa, Iowa State College Press, 1957, 394 pp.

CUTHBERTSON, D. P. *Progress in Nutrition and Allied Sciences*. London, Oliver & Boyd Ltd., 1963, 452 pp.

NATIONAL ACADEMY OF SCIENCES—NATIONAL RESEARCH COUNCIL. *Progress in Meeting Protein Needs of Infants and Preschool Children*. Washington, D.C., NAS-NRC Publications, No. 843, 1961, 569 pp.

PEI-SUNG, T. *Green Thraldom*. London, George Allen & Unwin Ltd., 1949, 127 pp.

WHITTEN, J. L. *That We May Live*. Princeton, N.J., D. Van Nostrand Company, Inc., 1966, 251 pp.

Magazines
Chemische Industrie International
Chemische Weekblad
Chemistry and Industry
Chimica e Industria

Industrie Chimique
Química
Uspekhi Khimii (U.S.S.R.)
Zhurnal Prikladnoi Khimii (U.S.S.R.)

CHAPTER III:
Could the Yield Spiral
Be Pushed Further Upward?

FUSSELL, G. E. *Farming Technique from Prehistoric to Modern Times.* London, Pergamon Press Ltd., 1965, 269 pp.

LABORIT, H. *Du Soleil à l'homme.* Paris, Masson et Cie, 1963, 157 pp.

LE CREN, E. D., and HOLDGATE, M. W. (eds.). *The Exploitation of Natural Animal Populations.* New York, John Wiley & Sons, Inc., 1962, 383 pp.

LIETH, H. *Die Stoffproduktion der Pflanzendecke.* Stuttgart, G. Fischer, 1961, 156 pp.

MAYNARD, L. A., and LOOSLI, J. K. *Animal Nutrition.* 4th ed. New York-London, McGraw-Hill, Inc., 1956, 484 pp.

MITCHELL, H. H. *Comparative Nutrition of Man and Domestic Animals.* Vol. I. New York, Academic Press, Inc., 1962, 701 pp.

MOSEMAN, A. H. *Agricultural Sciences for the Developing Nations.* Washington D. C., Association for the Advancement of Science, 1964, 218 pp.

NAGAI, I. *Japonica Rice—Its Breeding and Culture.* Tokyo, Yokendo, 1959, 844 pp.

PAWLEY, W. H. *Possibilities of Increasing World Food Production.* Rome, FAO, 1963, 231 pp.

PHILLIPS, J. *The Development of Agriculture and Forestry in the Tropics.* New York, Frederick A. Praeger, Inc., 1962, 205 pp.

ROSSEAU, M. *L'Animal civilisateur de l'homme.* Paris, Masson et Cie, 1962, 166 pp.

SOUTHWORTH, H. M., and JOHNSTON, B. F. (eds.). *Agricultural Development and Economic Growth.* Ithaca, N.Y., Cornell University Press, 1967, 608 pp.

STAKMAN, E. C., BRADFIELD, R., and MANGELSDORF, P. C. *Campaigns Against Hunger,* Cambridge, Massachusetts, The Belknap Press of Harvard University Press, 1967, 328 pp.

WILLIAMSON, G., and PAYNE, W. J. A. *An Introduction to Animal Husbandry in the Tropics.* New York, John Wiley & Sons, Inc., 1959, 435 pp.

Magazines
Agronomy Journal
Australian Journal of Agricultural Research
Crops and Soils
Deutsche Landwirtschaft
East African Agricultural Journal
Indian Farming
Journal of Animal Science
Pochvodenie (U.S.S.R.)
Soil Science
The Journal of World Phosphorus and Potassium

CHAPTER IV:
Food and Microorganisms

DUDDINGTON, C. L. *Micro-organisms as Allies—The Industrial Use of Fungi and Bacteria*. London, Faber & Faber, Ltd., 1961, 256 pp.

GILMOUR, C. M., and ALLEN, O. N. (eds.). *Microbiology and Soil Fertility*. Corvallis, Oregon State University Press, 1965, 164 pp.

GRAY, W. P. *The Relation of Fungi to Human Affairs*. New York, Holt, Rinehart and Winston, Inc., 1959, 510 pp.

HOCKENHULL, D. J. D. *Progress in Industrial Microbiology*. Vol. I–IX. Heywood, 1959-1967.

KAVALER, L. *Mushrooms, Moulds and Miracles*. London, George G. Harrap & Co., Ltd., 1967, 240 pp.

KLUYVER, A. J., and VAN NIEL, C. B. *The Microbes' Contribution to Biology*. Cambridge, Mass., Harvard University Press, 1956, 182 pp.

PRESCOTT, S. C., and DUNN, C. G. *Industrial Microbiology*, 3rd ed., New York, McGraw-Hill, Inc., 1959, 340 pp.

ROSE, A. H. *Industrial Microbiology*. Washington, D.C., Butterworth, 1961, 286 pp.

UMBREIT, W. W. (ed.). *Advances in Applied Microbiology*. Vol. I–IX, New York, Academic Press, Inc., 1959-1967.

WYLIE, J. C. *Fertility from Town Wastes*. London, Faber and Faber, Ltd., 1955, 224 pp.

Magazines
Anton van Leuwenhoek, Journal of Microbiology and Serology
Applied Microbiology (U.S.)
Archiv für Microbiologie
Canadian Journal of Microbiology

Japanese Journal of Microbiology
Journal of Applied Bacteriology (U.K.)
Journal of Microbiology, Epidemiology and Immunobiology
Mikrobiologiya (U.S.S.R.)

CHAPTER V:
Man's Competitors for Food

CAREFOOT, G. L., and SPROTT, E. R. *Famine on the Wind: Plant Diseases and Human History.* London, Angus & Robertson, 1969, 222 pp.

CRAMER, H. H. *Plant Protection and World Crop Production.* Leverkusen, Farbenfabriken Bayer, 1967, 524 pp.

DARLING, F. F. *Wildlife in an African Territory.* New York, Oxford University Press, 1960, 160 pp.

FABRE-LUCE, A. *Men or Insects? A Study of Population Problems.* London, Hutchinson & Co., Ltd., 1962, 160 pp.

GLASGOW, P. *Distribution and Abundance of Tsetse.* New York, Pergamon Press, Inc., 1963, 256 pp.

GUNTHER, F. A., and JEPPSON, L. R. *Modern Insecticides and World Food Production.* London, Chapman & Hall, Ltd., 1960, 284 pp.

KEVAN, D. K. M. *Soil Animals.* New York, Philosophical Library, Inc., 1962, 237 pp.

MCMILLEN, W. *Bugs or People?* New York, Appleton Century, 1965, 228 pp.

METCALF, C. L., and FLINT, W. P. *Destructive and Useful Insects, Their Habitats and Control.* 4th ed. New York-London, McGraw-Hill, Inc., 1962, 1088 pp.

ODUM, E. P., and ODUM, H. T. *Fundamentals of Ecology.* Philadelphia and London, W. B. Saunders Company, 2nd ed., 1959, 280 pp.

PFADT, R. E. *Fundamentals of Applied Entomology.* New York, The Macmillan Company, 1962, 668 pp.

RIVNAY, E. *Field Crop Pests in the Near East.* The Hague, Junk, 1962, 450 pp.

ROSE, G. J. *Crop Protection.* 2nd rev. ed. New York, Chemical Publication Company, Inc., 1963 (first edition, 1955).

THORNE, G. *Principles of Nematology.* New York, McGraw-Hill, Inc., 1961, 553 pp.

USDA. *The Yearbook of Agriculture 1952—Insects.* Washington, D.C., USDA, 1952, 780 pp.

USDA. *The Yearbook of Agriculture 1956—Animal Diseases.* Washington, D.C., USDA, 1956, 591 pp.

WEST, L. S. *The Housefly*. Ithaca, N.Y., Comstock Publishing Associates, 1951, 520 pp.

WHO/FAO. *Advances in the Control of Zoonoses*. Geneva, WHO and FAO, 1963, 276 pp.

Magazines
Angewandte Parasitologie
Boletim Fitosanitario
Canadian Insect Pest Review
Helminthological Abstracts
Journal of Economic Entomology
Pest Technology
Pest Control
Weed Research (U.K.)
Weeds (U.S.)
World Review of Pest Control

CHAPTER VI:
Water and Our Daily Bread

BEETLE, A. A. (ed.). *Agricultural Problems in Arid and Semiarid Environments*. Laramie, Wyoming, University of Wyoming, 1959, 64 pp.

BÉNÉZECH, C. *L'Eau base structurale et fonctionelle des Etres Vivants*. Paris, Masson et Cie, 1962, 171 pp.

HAGAN, R. M., *et al.* (eds.). *Irrigation of Agricultural Lands*. Madison, Wis., American Society of Agronomy, 1967, 1180 pp.

MOHRMANN, J. C. J., and KESSLER, J. *Water Deficiencies in European Agriculture—A Climatological Survey*. Wageningen, International Institute of Land Reclamation and Improvement, Publ. No. 5, 1959, 60 pp.

RODE, A. A. *Das Wasser im Boden*. Berlin, Akademie-Verlag G.m.b.H., 1959, 464 pp.

TSCHAPEK, M. W., *El Agua en El Suelo*. Vol. I, Buenos Aires, Collección Científica, 1959, 402 pp.

USDA. *Yearbook of Agriculture—Water*. Washington, D.C., USDA, 1955, 751 pp.

Magazines
American Water Works Association Journal
Eau
Ingeniería Hidraulica en México

Irrigation and Power
Revue Générale de l'Hydraulique
Schweizerische Zeitschrift für Hydrologie
Terres et Eaux
Wasserwirtschaft
Vom Wasser (yearbook)

CHAPTER VII:
Is the Developed World Threatened
by a Water Crisis?

CARR, D. E. *Death of the Sweet Waters.* New York, W. W. Norton &
Company, Inc., 1966, 257 pp.
FLEMMING, H. W. *Weltmacht Wasser.* Göttingen (West Germany),
Musterschmidt, 1967, 518 pp.
FURON, R. *The Problem of Water: A World Study.* New York, Ameri-
can Elsevier Publishing Company, Inc., 1967, 208 pp. Trans-
lated from French.
OVERMAN, M. *Water: Solutions to a Problem of Supply and Demand.*
New York, Aldus Books, 1969, 192 pp.
STRECK, O. *Grundlagen der Wasserwirtschaft und Gewässerkunde.*
Berlin, Springer-Verlag, 1953, 466 pp.
WRIGHT, J. *The Coming Water Famine.* New York, Coward-McCann,
Inc., 1966, 255 pp.
WUNDT, W. *Gewässerkunde.* Berlin, Springer-Verlag, 1953, 320 pp.

Magazines
See references under Chapter VI pertinent also to this
chapter.

CHAPTER VIII:
Is Large-scale Irrigation Reaching an End?

HARR, M. E. *Groundwater and Seepage.* New York, McGraw-Hill, Inc.,
1962.
LEOPOLD, L. B. "Rivers," *American Scientist,* L (4), 511–553, 1962.

Magazines
See references under Chapter VI pertinent also to this
chapter.

CHAPTER IX:
Water in International Politics

ADDISON, H. *Land, Water and Food.* 2nd ed. London, Chapman & Hall Ltd., 1961, 284 pp.

CLARK, C. *The Economics of Irrigation.* London, Pergamon Press Ltd., 1967, 116 pp.

COOPER, G. *Along the Great Rivers.* London, Butterworth, 1961, 340 pp.

HART, H. C. *New India's Rivers.* New Delhi, Orient Longmans, 1961, 300 pp.

HURST, H. E. *The Nile.* London, Constable & Co., Ltd., 1952, 326 pp.

MOOREHEAD, A. *The White Nile.* New York, Harper & Brothers, 1960, 385 pp.

————. *The Blue Nile.* London, Hamish Hamilton, 1962, 308 pp.

Magazines
See references under Chapter VI pertinent also to this chapter.

CHAPTER X:
Better Utilization of World Food Resources

BORGSTROM, G. *Japan's Success in World Fishing.* London, Fishing News (Books) Ltd., 1964, 312 pp.

————. *Principles of Food Science.* 2 vols. New York, The Macmillan Company, 1968, 397 + 473 pp.

———— (ed.). *Fish as Food,* Vol. II. New York Academic Press, Inc., 1962, 777 pp.

————, and HEIGHWAY, A. (eds.). *Atlantic Ocean Fisheries.* London, Fishing News (Books) Ltd., 1961, 336 pp.

GOULD, R. F. (ed.). *World Protein Resources.* Washington, D.C., American Chemical Society Publications, 1966, 285 pp.

ORDISH, G. *Untaken Harvests.* London, Constable & Co., Ltd., 1952, 172 pp.

ORGANIZATION FOR ECONOMIC COOPERATION AND DEVELOPMENT (OECD). *Food Aid—Its Role in Economic Development.* Paris, OECD, 1963, 85 pp.

OVINGTON, J. D. (ed.). *The Better Use of the World's Fauna for Food.* Symposia of the Institute of Biology, No. 11. London, The Institute of Biology, 1963, 175 pp.

Magazines
British Food Journal
Canadian Food Journal
Deutsche Lebensmittel-Rundschau
Economic Botany
Food Manufacture (U.K.)
Food Science (Mysore)
Food Technology (U.S.)
Food Technology in Australia
Journal of Food Science (U.S.)
Journal of the Science of Food and Agriculture (U.K.)

CHAPTER XI:
Lakes and Dams for Fish Cultivation

BORGSTROM, G. (ed.). *Fish as Food,* Vol. I. New York, Academic Press, Inc., 1961, 725 pp.

GESSNER, F. *Hydrobotanik II.* Berlin, Deutschen Verlag der Wissenschaft, 1959, 360 pp.

HICKLING, C. F. *Fish Culture.* London, Faber and Faber, Ltd., 1962, 295 pp.

HORN, S. L., and PILLAY, T. V. R. *Handbook on Fish Culture in the Indo-Pacific Region.* FAO Techn. Paper, No. 14, 1962, 204 pp.

HUTCHINSON, G. E. *A Treatise on Limnology,* Vol. I: *Geography, Physics, and Chemistry.* New York, John Wiley & Sons, Inc., 1957, 1015 pp.

JACKSON, D. F. *Algae and Man.* New York, Plenum, 1964, 434 pp.

VIBERT, R., and LAGER, K. F. *Pêches Continentales, Biologie et Amenagement.* Paris, Dunod, 1961, 720 pp.

VIVIER, P. *La Pisciculture.* Paris, Presses Universitaries de France, 1954, 126 pp.

Magazines
Australian Journal of Marine and Freshwater Research
Ecology
Journal of Protozoology
Limnology and Oceanography
Rybolovstvo y Rybodelie (U.S.S.R.)

CHAPTER XII:
Tomorrow's Dinner

ALTSCHUL, A. M. *Protein, Its Chemistry and Politics.* Garden City, N.Y., Basic Books, Inc., 1965, 270 pp.

BODENHEIMER, F. S. *Insects as Human Food*. The Hague, Junk, 1951, 352 pp.

PARSONS, J. J. *The Green Turtle and Man*. Gainesville, University of Florida Press, 1962, 126 pp.

WYLIE, J. C. *Fertility from Town Wastes*. London, Faber and Faber Ltd., 1955, 224 pp.

Magazines
See references under Chapters IV and X pertinent also to this chapter.

CHAPTER XIII:
New Heavens and New Earths

CLARK, C. *Population Growth and Land Use*. New York, St. Martin's Press, 1967, 406 pp.

CLAWSON, M., HELD, R. B., and STODDARD, C. H. *Land for the Future*. Baltimore, The Johns Hopkins Press, 1960, 570 pp.

DEWHURST, J. F., COPPOCK, J. O., YATES, P. L., *et al. Europe's Needs and Resources—Trends and Prospects in Eighteen Countries*. London, Macmillan & Co., Ltd., 1961, 1,198 pp.

GILL, T. *Land Hunger in Mexico*. Washington, D.C., Ch. Lathrop Foundation, 1951, 86 pp.

HILLS, E. S. (ed.). *Arid Lands: A Geographical Appraisal*. London, Methuen and Co. Ltd.; Paris, UNESCO, 1966, 461 pp.

STAMP, L. D. *Our Developing World*. London, Faber and Faber Ltd., 1956, 280 pp.

SUSLOV, S. P. *Physical Geography of Asiatic Russia*. San Francisco and London, W. H. Freeman and Company, 1961, 594 pp.

YATES, P. L. *Food, Land and Manpower in Western Europe*. New York, The Macmillan Company, 1960, 294 pp.

Magazines
Crops and Soils
International Society of Soil Science Bulletin
Journal of Soil and Water Conservation
Mother Earth (U.K.)
Plant Food Review
Pochvodenie
Soil Science and Plant Nutrition (Japan)

General References

ANONYMOUS. *Food and Civilization; A Symposium.* Voice of America Forum Lectures, Springfield, Ill., Charles C. Thomas, Publisher, 1966, 310 pp.

APPLEMAN, P. *The Silent Explosion.* Boston, The Beacon Press, 1965, 161 pp.

AYRES, E., and SCARLOTT, C. A. *Energy Sources—The Wealth of the World.* New York, McGraw-Hill, Inc., 1952, 344 pp.

BAADE, F. *The Race to the Year 2000; Our Future: A Paradise or the Suicide of Mankind.* New York, Doubleday & Company, Inc., 1963, 246 pp. Translated from German.

BANSIL, P. C. *India's Food Resources and Population.* Bombay, Vora, 1958, 252 pp.

BARDACH, J. *Harvest of the Sea.* New York, Harper and Row, Publishers, 1968, 301 pp.

BASSIR, O. *Biochemical Aspects of Human Malnutrition in the Tropics.* The Hague, Junk, 1962, 122 pp.

BEAUJEU-GARNIER, J. *Trois milliards d'hommes, Traité de Démogéographie.* Paris, Librairie Hachette, 1965, 402 pp.

BENHAM, F., and HOLLEY, H. A. *A Short Introduction to the Economy of Latin America.* New York, Oxford University Press, 1960, 169 pp.

BERELSON, B., *et al.* (eds.). *Family Planning and Population Programs: A Review of World Developments.* Chicago, University of Chicago Press, 1966, 848 pp.

BONNEFOUS, G. *La Terre et la faim des hommes.* Paris, Fayard, 1960, 260 pp.

BORGSTROM, G. *The Hungry Planet: The Modern World at the Edge of Famine.* New York, The Macmillan Company, 1965, 480 pp. Paperback edition, Collier Books, 1967.

BRACHER, M. L. *SRO Overpopulation and You.* Philadelphia, Fortress Press, 1966, 216 pp.

BRINTON, C. *The Fate of Man.* New York, George Braziller, Inc., 1961, 532 pp.

BROWN, H. *The Challenge of Man's Future.* New York, The Viking Press, Inc., 1954, 290 pp.

CALDER, N. *The Environment Game.* London, Martin Secker & Warburg, Ltd., 1967, 240 pp.

CASTRO, J. DE. *Death in the Northeast.* New York, Random House, Inc., 1966, 207 pp.

CÉPÈDE, M., HOUTART, F., and GROND, L. *Population and Food.* New York, Sheed & Ward, Inc., 1964, 461 pp. Translated from French.

CHANDRASEKHAR, S. (ed.). *Asia's Population Problems.* With a Discussion of Population and Immigration in Australia. London, George Allen and Unwin Ltd., 1967, 311 pp.

CLAWSON, M. *Natural Resources and International Development.* Baltimore, The Johns Hopkins Press, 1964, 462 pp.

COMMONER, B. *Science and Survival.* New York, The Viking Press, Inc., 1966, 150 pp.

DARLING, F. F., and MILTON, J. P. (eds.). *Future Environments of North America.* Garden City, N.Y., The Natural History Press, 1966, 767 pp.

DATTA, B. *The Economics of Industrialization.* Calcutta, World Press, 1960, 331 pp.

DORE, R. P. *Land Reform in Japan.* London, Oxford University Press, 1959, 530 pp.

DORST, J. *Avant que nature meure.* Neuchâtel, Switzerland, Delachaux et Niestlé, 1965, 424 pp.

EHRLICH, P. R. *The Population Bomb: Population Control or Race to Oblivion?* New York, Ballantine Books, Inc., 1968, 223 pp.

FREEDMAN, F. *Population: The Vital Revolution.* New York, Doubleday & Company, Inc., 1964, 274 pp.

GALBRAITH, J. K. *Economic Development in Perspective.* Cambridge, Massachusetts, Harvard University Press, 1963, 76 pp.

GAYLOR, J. E. *Universal Wisdom.* New York, Vantage Press, 1961, 262 pp.

GLASS, D. V., and EVERSLEY, D. E. C. *Population in History; Essays in Historical Demography.* London, Edward Arnold & Co., 1965, 692 pp.

GOUROU, P. *The Tropical World.* 3rd ed. London, Longmans, Green & Co. Ltd., 1965, 196 pp. Translated from French.

GROENVELD, D. *Investment for Food.* Amsterdam, North-Holland, 1961, 146 pp.

GRUBER, R. (ed.). *Science and the New Nations.* New York, Basic Books, Inc., 1961, 314 pp.

HAMM, H. *China—Empire of the 700 Million.* Garden City, N.Y., Doubleday & Company, Inc., 1966, 310 pp. Translated from German.

HAUSER, P. M. *Population and World Politics.* Glencoe, Ill., The Free Press, 1959, 297 pp.

————. *Population Perspective.* New Brunswick, N.J., Rutgers University Press, 1960, 188 pp.

———— (ed.). *Population Dilemma.* Englewood Cliffs, N.J., Prentice-Hall, Inc., 1963, 188 pp.

HEARST, S. *2000 Million Poor.* London, George G. Harrap & Co. Ltd., 1965, 176 pp.

HEILBRONER, R. L. *The Future as History.* New York, Harper & Row, Publishers, 1960, 217 pp.

————. *The Great Ascent: The Struggle for Economic Development in Our Time.* New York, Harper & Row, Publishers, 1963, 183 pp.

HILLABY, J. *Nature and Man.* London, Phoenix House, 1960, 64 pp.

HOFFMAN, P. G. *World without Want.* New York, Harper & Row, Publishers, 1962, 144 pp.

HOPCRAFT, A. *Born to Hunger.* Boston, Houghton Mifflin Company, 1968, 258 pp.

IOWA STATE UNIVERSITY CENTER FOR AGRICULTURAL AND ECONOMIC ADJUSTMENT. *Food—One Tool in International Economic Development.* Ames, Iowa, Iowa State University Press, 1962, 419 pp.

IOWA STATE UNIVERSITY CENTER FOR AGRICULTURAL AND ECONOMIC DEVELOPMENT. *Alternatives for Balancing World Food Production and Needs.* Ames, Iowa, Iowa State University Press, 1967, 273 pp.

JESUS, C. M. DE. *Child of the Dark.* New York, E. P. Dutton & Co., Inc., 1962, 190 pp. Translated from Portuguese.

JONES, M. *In Famine's Shadow: A Private War on Hunger.* Boston, Beacon Press, 1965, 229 pp. Originally published in Great Britain, under the title *Two Ears of Corn: Oxfam in Action,* by Hodder and Stoughton Ltd., 1965.

KRISTENSEN, T., *et al. The Economic World Balance.* Copenhagen, Munksgaard, 1960, 377 pp.

LAFFIN, J. *The Hunger to Come.* London, New York, Toronto, Abelard-Schuman Ltd., 1966, 208 pp.

LEBRET, L. J. *Suicide ou survie de l'Occident?* Paris, Les Éditions Ouvrières, 1958, 402 pp.

LITTLE, I. M. D., and CLIFFORD, J. M. *International Aid.* London, George Allen & Unwin Ltd., 1965, 338 pp.

MASEFIELD, G. B. *Famine—Its Prevention and Relief.* New York, Oxford University Press, 1963, 240 pp.

MASOIN, M. *L'Energie en révolution.* Paris, Les Éditions Universitaires, 1961, 211 pp.

MCCORMACK, A. *The Population Explosion and World Hunger.* London, Burns, Oates & Washbourne, Ltd., 1963, 165 pp.

MELMAN, S. *The Peace Race.* New York, Ballantine Books, Inc., 1961, 152 pp.

MERTZ, E. T., and NELSON, O. E. (eds.). *Proceedings of the High Lysine Corn Conference, June 21–22, 1966* (Purdue University, Lafayette, Indiana). Washington, D.C., Corn Industries Research Foundation, a division of Corn Refiners Association, Inc., 1966, 186 pp.

MOOMAW, I. W. *The Challenge of Hunger.* New York, Frederic A. Praeger, Inc., 1966, 222 pp.

MUDD, S. *The Population Crisis and the Use of World Resources.* The Hague, Junk, 1964, 563 pp.

MYRDAL, G. *Rich Lands and Poor.* New Haven, Conn., Yale University Press, 1964, 168 pp.

————.*Asian Drama.* 3 vols. New York, Pantheon Books, Inc., 1968.

NESTLÉ, A. *Humanity and Subsistence.* Basel, Nestlé, 1961, 237 pp.

NG, L. K. Y., and MUDD, S. (eds.). *The Population Crisis: Implications and Plans for Action.* Bloomington, Ind., and London, Indiana University Press, 1966, 364 pp. Originally published as *The Population Crisis and the Use of World Resources,* with S. Mudd as editor, The Hague, Dr. W. Junk, 1964.

NICOL, H. *The Limits of Man: An Enquiry into the Scientific Bases of Human Population.* London, Constable & Company Ltd., 1967, 283 pp.

OSBORN, F. (ed.). *Our Crowded Planet: Essays on the Pressures of Population.* Garden City, Doubleday & Company, Inc., 1962, 240 pp.

OVINGTON, M. *Better Use of Plants and Animals.* London, Institute of Biology, 1964, 175 pp.

PADDOCK, W., and P. *Hungry Nations.* Boston, Little, Brown & Company, 1964, 344 pp.

———. *Famine 1975! America's Decision: Who Will Survive?* Boston, Little, Brown & Company, 1967, 276 pp.

PIDDINGTON, R. A. *The Limits of Mankind—A Philosophy of Population.* Bristol, Wright & Sons, 1956, 153 pp.

PINCUS, J. *Trade, Aid, and Development; The Rich and Poor Nations.* New York, McGraw-Hill, Inc., 1967, 400 pp.

RUBIN, J. A. *Your Hundred Billion .Dollars, the Complete Story of American Foreign Aid.* Philadelphia, Chilton & Company, 1964, 299 pp.

SAUVY, A. *Fertility and Survival.* New York, Crowell-Collier and Macmillan, Inc., 1963, 287 pp.

SCHULTZ, T. W. *Economic Crisis in World Agriculture.* Ann Arbor, Mich., University of Michigan Press, 1965, 114 pp.

SCHULTZ, T. W. *Transforming Traditional Agriculture.* New Haven, Conn., Yale University Press, 1964, 146 pp.

SERVENTY, V. *A Continent in Danger.* London, Reynal & Company, Inc., 1966, 240 pp.

SINGER, H. W., KUN, N. DE, and ORDOOBADI, A. *International Development 1966.* Dobbs Ferry, N.Y., Oceana Publications, Inc., 1967, 341 pp.

SINGH, C. *India's Poverty and Its Solution.* Bombay, etc., Asia Publishing House, 1964, 527 pp.

SHIMM, M. G., and EVERETT, R. O. (eds.). *Population Control—The Imminent World Crisis.* London, Oceana, 1961, 253 pp.

SLATER, SIR WM. *Man Must Eat.* Chicago, Chicago University Press, 1964, 112 pp.

SLICHTER, S. H. *Economic Growth in the United States—Its History, Problems and Prospects.* New York, Crowell-Collier and Macmillan, Inc., 1961, 189 pp.

STENHOUSE, D. *Crisis in Abundance.* London and Sydney, William Heinemann, Ltd., 1966, 97 pp.

STILL, H. *Will the Human Race Survive?* New York, Hawthorn Books, Inc., 1966, 272 pp.

STILLMAN, E., and PFAFF, W. *The New Politics—America and the End of the Postwar World.* New York, Coward McCann, Inc., 1961, 191 pp.

STYCOS, J. M., and ARLAS, J. *Population Dilemma in Latin America*. Washington, D.C., Potomac Books, 1966, 249 pp.

THEOBALD, R. *The Challenge of Abundance*. New York, New American Library of World Literature, Inc., 1962, 192 pp.

THOMLINSON, R. *Population Dynamics; Causes and Consequences of World Demographic Change*. New York, Random House, Inc., 1965, 577 pp.

THOMPSON, W. S. *Population and Progress in the Far East*. Chicago, University of Chicago Press, 1959, 443 pp.

TOYNBEE, A. J. *Change and Habit; The Challenge of Our Time*. New York and London, Oxford University Press, 1966, 240 pp.

VOGT, W. *People! Challenge to Survival*. New York, William Sloane Associates, 1960, 257 pp.

VOICE OF AMERICA FORUM LECTURES. *Food and Civilization, A Symposium*. Springfield, Ill., Charles C. Thomas, Publisher, 1966, 308 pp.

WAGNER, PH. *The Human Use of the Earth*. New York, Free Press of Glencoe, 1960, 270 pp.

WELBOURNE, N. *Nutrition in Tropical Countries*. New York, Oxford University Press, 1963, 119 pp.

WHYTE, R. O. *Milk Production in Developing Countries*. London, Faber and Faber Ltd., 1967, 240 pp.

WOODHAVEN-SMITH, C. *The Great Hunger*. New York, Signet, 1964, 434 pp.

WORSLEY, P. *The Third World*. Chicago, University of Chicago Press, 1964, 320 pp.

ZIMMERMANN, E. W., and HUNKER, H. L. *Introduction to World Resources*. New York, Harper and Row, Publishers, 1964, 220 pp.

Magazines

The following scientific, technical, and general magazines regularly contain articles about issues discussed in this book.

Advances of Agronomy
Advances of Food Science
Advances of Microbiology
Advances of Veterinary Science
Cahiers d'outre mer
Current Science (India)
Discovery
Eau
Economic Geography

The Economist
Empire Journal of Experimental Agriculture
Far Eastern Economic Review and Yearbook
Fishing News International
Geographical Journal
Geographical Review
Journal of Applied Biology (U.K.)
Journal of Economic Entomology
Journal of World Phosphorus and Potassium
La Nature
Nature (U.K.)
Naturwissenschaftliche Rundschau
New Scientist
La Pêche Maritime
Pochvodenie
La Population
Population Bulletin (U.S.)
Population Review (India)
Priroda
Science (U.S.)
Science and Culture (India)
Science Journal (U.K.)
Soil Science
Tropical Agriculture
Umschau
Visión
WHO
World Agriculture
World Crops
World Farming
World Fishing

In addition, FAO issues a monthly statistical magazine, *Monthly Review,* as well as statistical yearbooks and a number of informative publications.

Index

Index

(Figures in italics indicate pages upon which illustrations occur.)